Issued under the authority of t'

Manual o
Firemans

A survey of the science of firefighting

Book 12
Practical Firemanship II

London
Her Majesty's Stationery Office

First published 1983

The previous publishing history of
this volume is shown on pages 253-6

ISBN 0 11 340592 8

Preface

This second book on practical firemanship considers five general areas: methods of rescue; decontamination; ventilation; salvage; and, after a fire.

The primary function of a fireman is to save life and Part 1 looks at the various methods of rescue which can be used to achieve this aim. Such rescues are, of course, carried out not only at fires but also during the many types of special service which firemen perform. The endless variety of predicaments in which people and animals find themselves is such that not all can be dealt with here, but the section offers particular advice on some of the more common types and general advice on the remainder. Rescues at fires are, of course, covered in depth.

Part 2 looks at decontamination. The likelihood of firemen encountering chemicals or other dangerous substances during the course of an incident has increased dramatically over recent years. It continues to rise as new materials are introduced and as increasing use is made of both old and new materials in a wide variety of applications. Naturally, firemen take special precautions when dealing with these dangerous substances but they, their clothing and their equipment, still often run the risk of contamination. To avoid damage to firemen's health they must be freed from this contamination without delay and they, their clothing and their equipment must be thoroughly cleansed. Part 2 looks at the special decontamination procedures devised to achieve this end.

Part 3 considers ventilation. The large volume of smoke which a fire can soon produce has always been one of the greatest menaces to firemen and a principal cause of damage to property. Modern materials with their extremely rapid production of great amounts of particularly acrid and damaging smoke have made the problem worse. The removal of smoke and heat by proper ventilation during a fire has therefore become increasingly important.

Part 4 looks at salvage, the lessening or prevention of damage to property which might otherwise result from firefighting operations. The insurance companies which organised the Glasgow, Liverpool and London Salvage Corps were well aware that an effective salvage operation by well-trained men could materially affect the final loss from a fire. Firemen, who must be responsible for the greater part of salvage work, must bear that in mind in their operations. This section concentrates on the work they should carry out, the equipment in general use, and also some specialised items carried by the Corps.

The preceding paragraph indicates that the Fire Service's responsibilities are not restricted solely to the extinguishment of fire and do not end when the fire is extinguished. The last section of this Book, Part 5, surveys the period from when a fire is being brought under control to the time when all men and appliances have left the scene and after. It discusses the considerations which firemen, and in particular the officer in charge, should bear in mind and describes the various duties they must undertake and the actions they should perform. The section pays particular attention to the difficult and highly skilled task of investigating the causes of fire.

Reference in this Book to the male person should be construed as applying, as appropriate, to the female person also. The ranks of junior firewoman, firewoman and leading firewoman have been introduced by the *Fire Services [Appointments and Promotion] [Amendment] Regulations 1976* to equate with the ranks of junior fireman, fireman and leading fireman. References to the latter should, where appropriate, be construed as references to the former also.

The Home Office is indebted to all those who have helped in the preparation of this work.

Home Office
1983

Metrication

List of SI units for use in the Fire Service

Quantity and basic or derived SI unit and symbol	Approved unit of measurement	Conversion factor
Length metre (m)	kilometre (km) metre (m) millimetre (mm)	1km = 0.621 mile 1m = 1.093 yards = 3.279 feet 1mm = 0.039 inch
Area square metre (m^2)	square kilometre (km^2) square metre (m^2) square millimetre (mm^2)	$1km^2 = 0.386$ mile^2 $1m^2 = 1.196$ yards^2 $= 10.764$ feet^2 $1mm^2 = 0.002$ inch^2
Volume cubic metre (m^3)	cubic metre (m^3) litre (l) [$= 10^{-3}m^3$]	$1m^3 = 35.7$ feet^3 1 litre = 0.22 gallon
Volume, flow cubic metre per second (m^3/s)	cubic metre per second (m^3/s) litres per minute (l/min)	$1m^3/s = 35.7$ feet^3/s 1l/min = 0.22 gall/min
Mass kilogram (kg)	kilogram (kg) tonne (t)	1kg = 2.205 lbs 1t = 0.984 ton
Velocity metre per second (m/s)	metre per second (m/s) international knot (kn) [= 1.852km/h] kilometre per hour (km/h)	1m/s = 3.281 feet/second 1km/h = 0.621 mile/hour
Acceleration metre per second^2 (m/s^2)	metre/second^2 (m/s^2)	$1m/s^2 = 3.281$ feet/second^2 = 0.102 'g'

Quantity and basic or derived SI unit and symbol	Approved unit of measurement	Conversion factor
Force		
newton (N)	kilonewton (kN) newton (n)	1kN = 0.1 ton force 1N = 0.225 lb force
Energy, work		
joule (J) [= 1Nm]	joule (J) kilojoule (kJ) kilowatt/hour (kW/h)	1kJ = 0.953 British Thermal Unit 1J = 0.738 foot lb force
Power		
watt (W) [= 1J/s = 1Nm/s]	kilowatt (kW) watt (W)	1kW = 1.34 horsepower 1W = 0.735 foot lb force/second
Pressure		
newton/metre^2(N/m^2)	bar [= 10^{5}N/m^2] millibar (mbar) [= 10^{2}N/m^2] metrehead [= 0.0981 bar]	1bar = 0.991 atmosphere = 14.5 lb force/in^2 1mbar = 0.0288 inch Hg 1metrehead = 3.28 foot head
Heat, quantity of heat		
joule (J)	joule (J) kilojoule (kJ)	1kJ = 0.953 British Thermal Unit
Heat flow rate		
watt	watt (W) kilowatt (kW)	1W = 3.41 British Thermal Units/hour 1kW = 0.953 British Thermal Unit/second
Specific energy, calorific value, specific latent heat		
joule/kilogram (J/kg) joule/m^3 (J/m^3)	kilojoule/kilogram (kJ/kg) kilojoule/m^3 (kJ/m^3) megajoule/m^3 (MJ/m^3)	1kJ/kg = 0.43 British Thermal Unit/lb 1kJ/m^3 = 0.0268 British Thermal Unit/ft^3
Temperature		
degree Celsius (°C)	degree Celsius (°C)	1 degree Celsius = 1 degree Centigrade

Contents

Part 1
Fire Service rescues

Chapter 3 Accidents on motorways and major roads

Chapter 4 Major disasters

Chapter 5 Miscellaneous rescues

Chapter 6 First aid and casualty handling

Part 2

Decontamination

Chapter 7 The identification of dangerous substances

Chapter 8 Chemical decontamination

Chapter 9 Other decontamination

Part 3

Ventilation at fires

Part 4

Salvage

Chapter 12 Salvage equipment

Part 5

After the incident

List of plates

10 An unusual special service involving the rescue of a trainee pilot from a glider which has become entangled in electric power lines.
Photo: West Sussex Fire Brigade.

11 Cliff rescue equipment, including a winch with 150 m. of 7 mm. diameter cable, stretcher, cable guide protector, strops and rescue slings.
Photo: Kent Fire Brigade.

12 Cliff rescue equipment [see Plate 11], with two firemen ready to be lowered with a rescue stretcher. The canvas bag at the head of the stretcher contains first aid kit, two padded rescue slings, and harness for the cliff crew.
Photo: Kent Fire Brigade.

13 Decontamination team at work with full equipment, including air-lines.
Photo: Essex Fire Brigade.

14 Wet decontamination procedure being carried out.
Photo: Essex Fire Brigade.

15 Tarpaulins used to cover a roof should well overlap and be securely fastened. This roof was covered by a Salvage Corps, but firemen should follow the same principles as far as possible.
Photo: London Salvage Corps.

16 This wire mesh guard is protecting a drain from blockage by debris. Manholes should have similar protection.
Photo: London Salvage Corps.

17 The Salvage Corps use hoppers like this to help remove water, usually in buildings with special drainage plugs.
Photo: Liverpool Salvage Corps.

18 The goods on these shelves are being protected by lightweight plastic sheeting. This is easier to support than salvage sheets and keeps the goods visible.
Photo: Liverpool Salvage Corps.

19 Goods in this warehouse are being protected by sheeting. The thorough covering and over-lapping of sheets are particularly important.
Photo: London Salvage Corps.

20 An example of the difficulty in identifying bodies after a fire. There are at least six bodies involved here.
Photo: Commissioner of Police, Metropolis.

21 The different degrees to which these chairs are burnt suggests that the one on the right was the seat of the fire.

22 The pattern of damage to this roof clearly suggests that the fire started at the left hand end. An eye-witness confirmed this.

23 The pattern of damage strongly suggested that an oil heater had flared up without warning. The presence of glass fragments implied a shattering of the drip-feed heater's glass container.

24 The presence of an oil heater, paraffin cans and a funnel at the site of this fatal fire suggested that the heater was being filled, but there was insufficient evidence for the coroner to record this.

25 Evidence of illegal entry before a fire. Note the two unbroken louvre panes carefully removed and placed one under and one on the window-sill.
Photo: Commissioner of Police, Gibraltar.

26 An incendiary device using an old clock mechanism, mains supply, and electric fire.
Photo: Chief Constable, Hertfordshire.

27 The device shown in Plate 26, as found at the scene.
Photo: Chief Constable, Hertfordshire.

28 The removal of debris and furniture has revealed the distinctive flow pattern of an accelerant used in setting this fire.
Photo: Commissioner of Police, Metropolis.

29 Clear evidence of arson in the attempt to create a fire path from mop heads soaked in an accelerant.
Photo: Commissioner of Police, Metropolis.

Part 1
Fire Service rescues

Introduction

The primary function of a fireman is to save life. In many cases this will be his first duty on arrival at an incident, and it will take all his skill, confidence, speed and tenacity.

He may have to manoeuvre and pitch ladders at speed in the most congested, difficult, and hazardous conditions; don breathing apparatus and search smoke-filled premises; find and remove people who are unconscious, disabled, or injured; calm and reassure the hysterical, over-excited, or nervous. He must decide how to effect the rescue and finally he must carry it out. He may be working in darkness or thick smoke, he may have no assistance. Often he will be faced with a complex and exacting situation within two or three minutes of turning out from rest or some routine job at the station. His response must be immediate and there will be little time for adjustment.

A fireman must therefore be trained not only in basic principles but also in more advanced manoeuvres so that he will have some experience of the sort of hazards and environment he will find on the fireground. He must be able to calculate and react almost automatically; he must be capable of using his initiative, ingenuity, experience and equipment in the best possible way. The well-trained fireman should have full confidence in his own ability to rescue people and should be able to inspire the same confidence in them. This in itself heightens the chance of success.

Chapter 1
Rescue at fires

1 General

Many rescues are accomplished each year simply by firemen reaching and reassuring those waiting for help. They can then either lead those people to safety or, if that is not immediately possible, remain with them until other firemen bring rescue apparatus to bear. If the fire is being brought under control, and is sufficiently distant, a fireman could simply remain with people until the smoke cleared and then lead them out by normal means. He must at all times take into account that conditions he regards as bearable may not be so for other people. Usually, however, his calming presence is sufficient to instil confidence and help people to bear discomfort until they are made safe.

There are no hard and fast rules on rescue work. Every incident is different and only the experience and training of a fireman will tell him which method to use. Speed is essential, coupled with agility, persistence, initiative and calculation. Every fireman, from experience, has a list, almost subconsciously acquired, of things which his mind automatically runs through as he arrives at any incident. This will differ from individual to individual but here are some points which he could consider:

(i) on reliable information he should pitch a ladder to where a person was last seen, enter and search;

(ii) people cannot always get to the front of a building. He should therefore make a rapid check of the rear, passing through adjacent premises if necessary;

(iii) if possible, firemen should attack the fire immediately to cover the rescues. Even one fireman with a hose-reel or 45 mm. hose from the appliance tank can hold the fire or give a protective spray to the ladder. Too much delay in attacking the fire could prevent later rescues or cut off those already involved;

(iv) if nobody can be seen but the building is smoke-logged, an officer should have it searched thoroughly by men wearing B.A.;

(v) although a 'persons reported' message from an officer need not, necessarily, be accompanied by a request for assistance, he should bear in mind the possibility of requiring more ladders, personnel or B.A. In buildings where many people are endangered, e.g. hotels, hostels, even minor smoke-logging can cause panic and the possible need for extra personnel and equipment just to handle the public;

(vi) in most Brigades a 'persons reported' message is an automatic request for the attendance of an ambulance. Where this is not the mobilising procedure the officer must remember to order one. Even if people are not burned or otherwise physically injured, smoke inhalation and shock can require hospital treatment;

(vii) darkness can induce fear and confusion. If there is time to floodlight the building firemen should do so, as soon as possible, taking care that lights are diffused and do not dazzle rescuers or those in need of rescue;

(viii) normal appliances should be kept clear of the face of the building to leave room for ladders, turntable ladders or hydraulic platforms to be used.

That list is not intended to be complete or, necessarily, even in order of priority.

2 Rescues by ordinary means

a. Searching

On arrival, the officer in charge should try to find out how many people were in the building and whether they have all been accounted for. At a hotel he can best do this by a comparison of the register with the assembled guests and a check with the staff manager. In commercial premises he should consult the manager or foreman. Unfortunately, too often people are overlooked, e.g. visitors, delivery drivers, contractors, maintenance workers. A fireman should always act on the smallest doubt and initiate a search.

Searching should be carried out methodically. An officer in charge should explain the method he thinks best to his crews and, if necessary, ask for further assistance from his Control. If there is no other indication or evidence, firemen should start the search at the point of greatest danger, so that they progress towards safety. They should always work at least in pairs although large areas, e.g. open-plan offices, auditoriums, will need larger teams eventually. Old multi-storey buildings are always a problem because any fire on an intermediate floor can force people, especially those unfamiliar with the premises, into all sorts of odd corners, e.g. toilets, storerooms, even lifts, or onto the roof. People, particularly children, trapped by fire or smoke often take refuge under beds, in cupboards, under piles of clothes and elsewhere. At one multi-death fire a three year old child managed to get into a 150 mm. space under a settee. *It is obvious that the search must be thorough.*

On entering a room a fireman should first check behind the door. He should make a complete circuit of the wall [see Fig. 1.1] searching under, in and on all articles of furniture. He should not miss doors to bathrooms or toilets by searching too low; he should open all cupboards and wardrobes and remember divans that open for storage, freezers and even large refrigerators. Finally, if the room is big enough and the circuit complete he should try to cross the room diagonally, and back to cover the central area. Halls often have cupboards under the stairs or entrances to cellars. Landings, even small ones, have cupboards or even doors to complete mezzanine floors. A pile of boxes, a ladder or a chair at the head of the stairs may point to people who have escaped onto the roof.

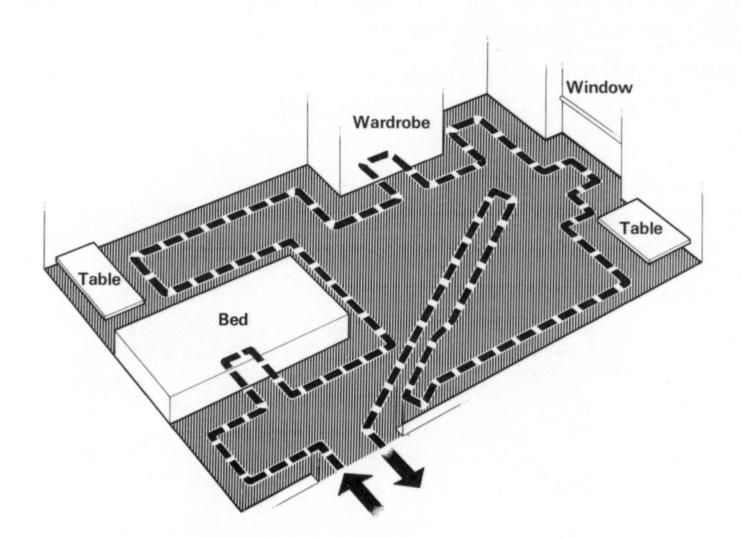

Fig. 1.1 Correct method of searching a room.

If possible, firemen should always assist people out to final safety. Smoke and fumes have a disorientating effect on people, causing lack of judgement. Not knowing they are suffering from ill-effects they may insist that they can get out themselves and then collapse before reaching safety.

b. Secondary means of escape

Personal knowledge of his station's ground is the hallmark of a good fireman. Observation of buildings, both inside and out, should become automatic and a fireman should develop an 'eye' for particular types of buildings. Knowledge of the secondary means of escape [or entry] from a reconnaisance of a building can become invaluable when it is smoke-logged in the early hours of the morning. Even such small details as window-fastenings, positions of fanlights, types of outbuilding roofs and, of course, placing of external staircases can be noticed when visiting or walking about the area. A fireman should explore down alleys, along rear service roads, and into yards. A view from a tall building onto the surrounding lower premises will reveal a useful amount of information on the possibilities for escape. [See Plate 1.]

The methods by which people have escaped from buildings on fire are too numerous to mention. Balconies, parapets, stackpipes, windowledges, knotted sheets, etc. have all been used. Dropping onto outhouses or projecting lower floors is another method and one which firemen should bear in mind for self-rescue, if it ever becomes necessary. There are several points to remember about this particular method. A person using it should:

(i) reduce the height of the drop by lowering the body to the full extent of the arms [see Fig. 1.2];

Fig. 1.2 Method of dropping from a first floor window.

(ii) keep the feet turned outwards to avoid projections;

(iii) try to note the lie of the surface below, e.g. flat or sloping, and its composition, tiles, asbestos, cement, wood, corrugated iron, etc.;

(iv) allow the knees to bend on impact to absorb the shock;

(v) be ready to spreadeagle to avoid sliding off a slope.

A fireman attending an incident should always, almost automatically, be noting alternative means of escape both for himself and his companion(s) and for anyone requiring rescue. If he has previous knowledge of an alternative he will have that much more confidence.

c. Fireman's lift

An unconscious or injured person may have to be carried or lowered out of a building. The usual maximum crew of two men can carry out 'picking-up drill' as laid down in the *Fire Service Drill Book*. They should remember that when wearing C.A.B.A. it is difficult to put a body across the shoulders in the usual 'carry' position. If possible, it would be better to carry the person between them to safety or to where he or she can be removed by other means.

It is not unlikely that more than one casualty will be found by a crew and they each have to move a body. The method will depend on the size and weight of the casualties. If they are unconscious in smoke speed is essential to get them to fresh air and safety. Dragging by the shoulders is probably the easiest way for a fireman to move a relatively heavy person. Another method is illustrated in Fig. 1.3, utilising a neckerchief or similar item to

Fig. 1.3 Method of dragging an unconscious person on the level.

Fig. 1.4 Method of dragging an unconscious person downstairs.

tie the hands of the casualty together. In negotiating stairs firemen must ensure the body is on its back, supported by the armpits, and drawn down head first [Fig. 1.4].

d. Removal of patients from hospitals, nursing homes etc.

When a fire occurs in, or near, a hospital or similar institution it may be necessary to evacuate wards. Normally, hospital staff will remove the patients but fires have a habit of occurring when the least number of staff are available and firemen are likely to be involved in the evacuation as soon as they arrive. Officers in charge must allow for this if they request assistance. Mass evacuation requires a lot of hands especially in geriatric or psychiatric establishments where, perhaps, only the minority of patients can walk. Even they take time to get moving, whatever the circumstances, and their progress can be very slow.

The degree of evacuation will depend largely on the type of premises. If the building is equipped with sufficient compartmentation against fire and smoke spread it may only be necessary to move the patients into a safer area adjacent. In other cases it may be necessary to take them down stairs or external escape stairways to the open air or another building. Health Authority fire officers will have their own contingency plans and will have trained their nursing staff in these. Again, firemen should be aware of these plans by exercises, visits and liaison.

Notwithstanding this co-operation and pre-planning, a fireman must remember that a real fire will be disturbing for the patients and, possibly, the nursing staff. It is his duty to calm and reassure and control the evacuation. Nursing staff will know the degree of illness of their patients so he must listen to their advice.

Methods of evacuation

How the evacuation is carried out will depend upon the circumstances e.g. fitness of patients, urgency of circumstances, whether the move is horizontal or downstairs. The methods taught, and the equipment used, vary greatly but some are explained and illustrated here, namely:

two, three or four handed seats;

carry chairs;

blanket removal;

blanket, mattress and line or sling;

rescue sheets.

(1) Two-handed seat

Two firemen face each other on either side of the patient. Stooping they each place their inside arm under the patient's back just below the shoulders, raise him and put their outside arms under his thighs, clasping hands with a hook grip [Fig. 1.5]. The patient can place his arms round their shoulders to steady himself. The firemen rise together and step off with short normal steps.

(2) Three-handed seat

This is used when one of the firemen needs to have a hand free to support an injured leg or, perhaps, some item of medical equipment which must go with the patient. The grip will vary according to whether the left or right leg is supported. If it is the right leg the bearer on the patient's left grasps his own right wrist with his left hand and the other bearer's left wrist with his right hand [Fig.1.6]. The other bearer then grasps the first bearer's left wrist leaving his own right hand free to support the injured leg. The patient can place his arms round the bearers' necks and steady himself.

(3) Four-handed seat

This provides a firm support for a heavy patient who can use his arms to support himself. In this case each fireman grasps his own left wrist with his right hand, using his free left hand to grasp the right wrist of his companion [Fig. 1.7].

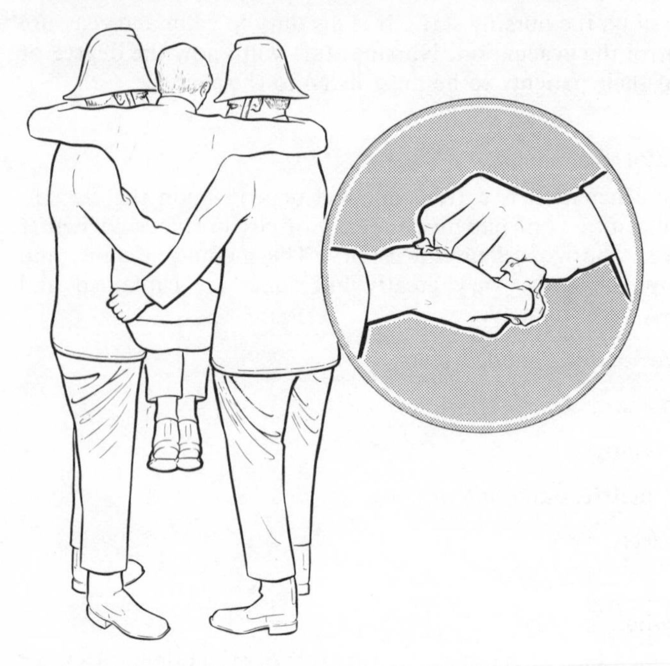

Fig. 1.5 Two handed seat.

Fig. 1.6 Three handed seat.

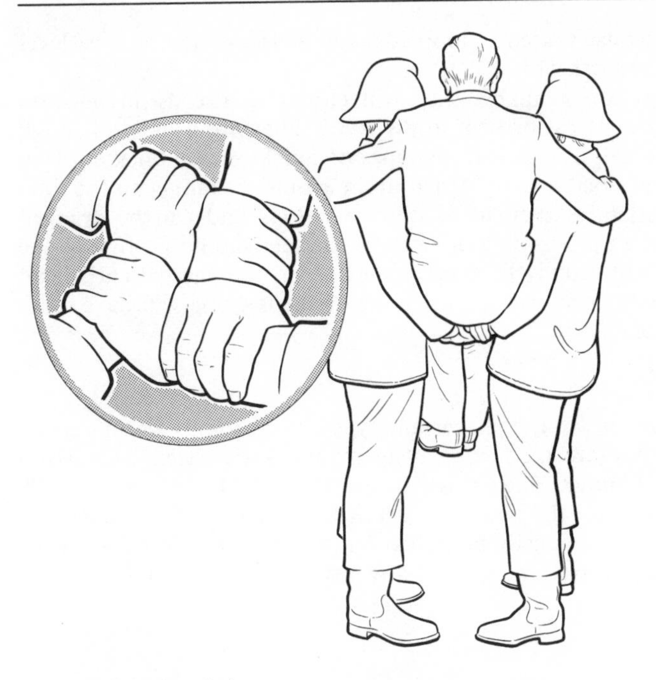

Fig. 1.7 Four handed seat.

(4) Carry chairs

These are purpose-designed light support chairs into which the patient is placed and can be strapped. Two firemen can then carry the patient to a safe area.

(5) Blanket removal

Two firemen stand on the same side of the bed, remove the bedclothes and pass a blanket under the patient. They then lift up the edges of the blanket until the patient is in a sling. The two edges are then folded and the slack rolled up until the patient is firmly secured. They then press their knees against the side of the bed and drag the patient towards them to the edge of the bed. Both lift together and gently slide the patient onto the floor removing him by pulling on one end of the blanket.

(6) Mattress and line [or sling]

Two firemen stand one on either side of the bed. If a line is used this will have a loop spliced in one end. This loop is passed under the mattress, at about the patient's shoulder level, and the running end passed through the loop. The line is then tightened to bring the mattress up on either side of the patient. The line is held in position whilst a second loop is made at the patient's knee level and finished off with a slip knot.

If slings are available they will either be already in position under the mattress or kept in the ward. They are usually of tough canvas or nylon with various types of quick release buckles. Two are used per bed and tightened up in a similar manner to the line.

The patient is then lifted onto the floor and can be dragged along. When proceeding downstairs the feet should go first as the mattress will usually be deep enough to protect the patient's head and a patient who can see where he or she is going will have more confidence.

(7) Rescue sheet

These may be found in certain types of hospitals or in certain wards. They are made of strong nylon fabric fitted with nylon webbing handles and cross straps [Fig. 1.8] and are usually permanently on the bed. The straps are designed to lie under the mattress but can easily be pulled out and buckled and the towing straps used to pull the patient down stairs or on the horizontal.

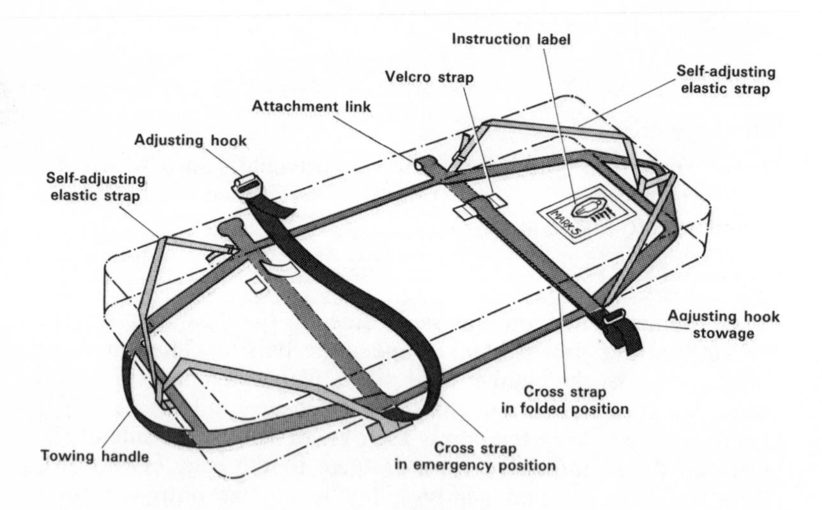

Fig. 1.8 Typical rescue sheet for hospital use.

3 Rescues using ladders and hydraulic platforms

If hydraulic platforms are included under the title of 'ladders'—in that they are extendible mechanisms—rescues can be said to fall into two categories:

(i) where a ladder is used as a means of access to a building but the rescue is accomplished by other means, e.g. lowering by line;

(ii) where a ladder is used both as access to the building and as a means of leading, carrying or assisting people down or across to safety.

a. General

Several classes of ladders are in use in the Fire Service and, although each has its particular function, they all complement one another. Figure 1.9 shows examples of ladders and their appropriate 'reach'. Fireman must remember that a lot of factors will affect 'reach' at an incident. For example:

(i) the design of the building, including mezzanines, podiums, step backs etc.;

(ii) access to the building e.g. open basement areas, gardens, trees, car parking;

(iii) the intensity of the fire and smoke on the lower floors.

Firemen have got to know the limitations of their equipment, especially as they often have to work at, or near, those limits.

The use of ladders is described in the *Manual of Firemanship* Parts 1 and 2 and the various basic drills in the *Fire Service Drill Book*. It is obvious that firemen are seldom going to find perfect conditions for pitching ladders on the fireground and, when basic drills are mastered, must go on to practise more advanced training in order to be ready when other conditions arise. The important factor at incidents is speed. Firemen must, therefore, learn to slip, manoeuvre and pitch ladders at speed, at all angles and all heights. Conditions at fires deteriorate rapidly and any delay in getting to work can lead to loss of life because conditions rapidly become almost impossible. The various methods of rescue whether by lowering, carrying, assisting, or a combination of all or any two, have to be practised until they are second nature. Firemen should, and in fact often will have to, be able to adapt and improvise on their basic drills. A rescue carried out 'by the book' is the exception rather than the rule. It should be borne in mind that when people are being assisted down from a building a fireman should stay close beneath them on the ladder. This is to ensure that, if they collapse on the ladder, they can immediately be pinned against it until the fireman is able, usually with help, to carry them to safety.

The notes on extension, escape, T.L. and hydraulic platform drills in the *Fire Service Drill Book* are instructions which should be learnt and applied, where possible, by all firemen. In addition,

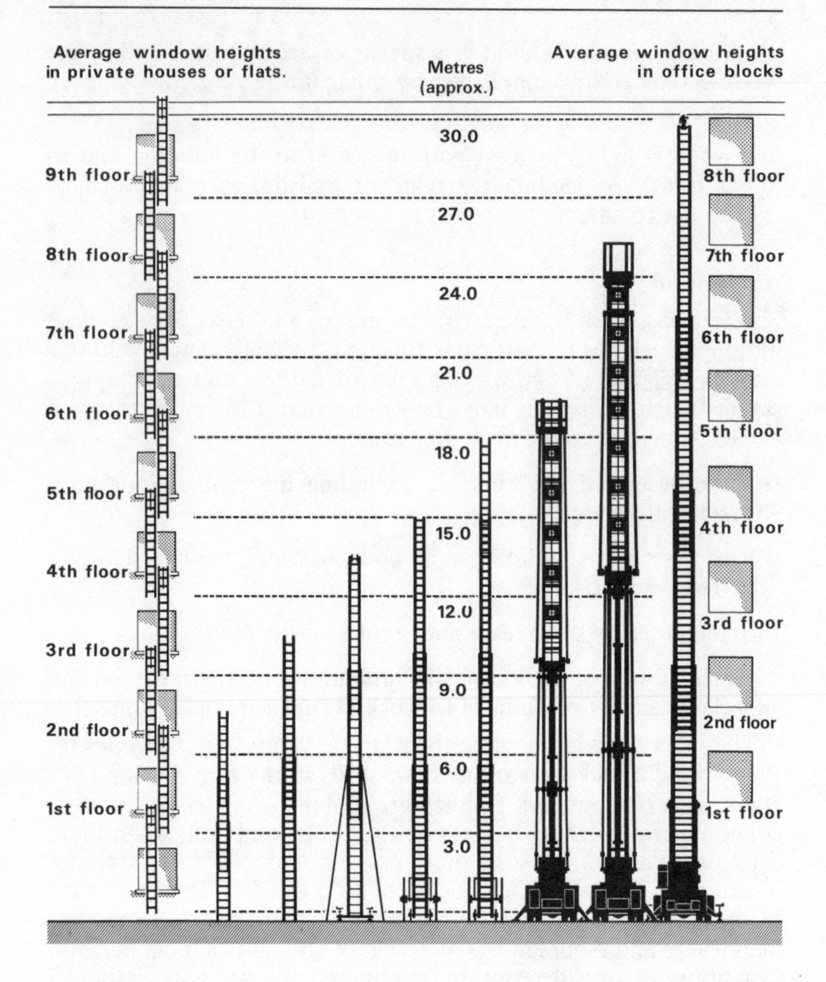

Fig. 1.9 Heights and floors reached by various ladders. N.B. Floor heights vary considerably; those on the left are typical of flats, those on the right, of offices.

they should remember to try and pitch ladders to the windward side of a window. This should mean that smoke and flame are blown away from the rescue. In all probability, this location would also be where firemen would find the people to be rescued.

If the rescue is taking place over the fire, and there are sufficient personnel available, a covering spray, to keep the worst of the smoke and flame away, will help. Firemen must, however, take care not to make the ladder too slippery or to obscure entry into the building. The number of people who can safely be allowed onto a ladder at the same time depends on the type of ladder, the angle of pitch and, in the case of a T.L., whether the head is resting or not. The cage of a hydraulic platform is also subject to weight restrictions. Firemen must keep this in mind and control and calm people, if necessary staying with them until they are safe.

b. Windows and window fittings

Modern building methods mixed with the old mean another important aspect that firemen should note on their ground—that of windows and window fittings. In private houses it is very common to have large areas of unopenable glass with, perhaps, small glass louvres at the top or sides. Double glazing in both private and commercial premises is becoming prevalent. There are a variety of types shown in the *Manual* Book 8, Chapter 5, but many other designs are to be found. Pre-knowledge of these types and some thought to the problems that could occur will save time and, possibly, a few lives.

c. Ladders

(1) Extension ladders

Various sizes of extension ladders are used by Brigades in this country, ranging from maximum extensions of 13.5 m. through 10.5 m., 10 m. and 9 m. to the double or triple short extension ladders which can be quickly dismantled.

The 13.5 m. ladders are fitted with props and can be used to good effect in restricted spaces, reaching a normal fourth floor window and providing a stable platform for rescues. The various shorter extension ladders are without props and have, obviously, less reach but more manoeuvrability. They can be used for bridging or inside premises and parts of the short extension ladders can be used in lieu of stretchers for lowering or raising casualties.

(2) Hook ladders

There are still a large number of properties in towns and cities which have faces inaccessible to escapes, extension or turntable ladders, or hydraulic platforms. Long rows of virtually monolithic five to seven storey houses, hotels etc. are to be found in these areas. The only ladder which can be taken through the premises, or adjacent premises, to effect a rescue at the back is a 'hook ladder'.

Most rescues using this ladder entail lowering a person by line, and firemen should never scale a building with a hook ladder without carrying a special sling or line carrier containing a lowering line [see the *Manual* Book 2, Chapter 12]. However, some rescues have been carried out by people climbing down these ladders, guided by firemen, sometimes to by-pass a fire on an intermediate floor.

These ladders can be used from the head of any other ladder, carried up inside a building and used on any side from an upper floor, and carried across roofs, and other building projections of the type to be found in the tangle of buildings very prevalent in inner city areas.

(3) Escape ladders

Wheeled escape ladders are usually of the 15 m. type. They are still carried by a few Brigades but are steadily being replaced by 13.5 m. ladders. Provided there are no obstacles to surmount or circumvent they can be brought into action very quickly, often, in a dire emergency, by two men. They can be bridged and provide a robust steady platform for rescue. The points to be considered when using an escape are laid out in the *Fire Service Drill Book* 'Notes for ladder drills'.

(4) Turntable ladders

Where it can be sited, extended, and trained, a turntable ladder is of particular value in reaching people trapped above the fourth floor to as high as the tenth floor [depending on storey heights] of a building. When resting on the building it can provide a substantial staircase for a number of people to use. It can be retrained and re-pitched quickly without moving the appliance and can bridge considerable distances [see Fig. 1.10]. There are, of course, limitations which are automatically indicated to the operator but care is still necessary [see the *Manual of Firemanship* Part 2, Chapter 4]. Some modern T.L.s have cages attached under the head which are used in a similar way to a hydraulic platform.

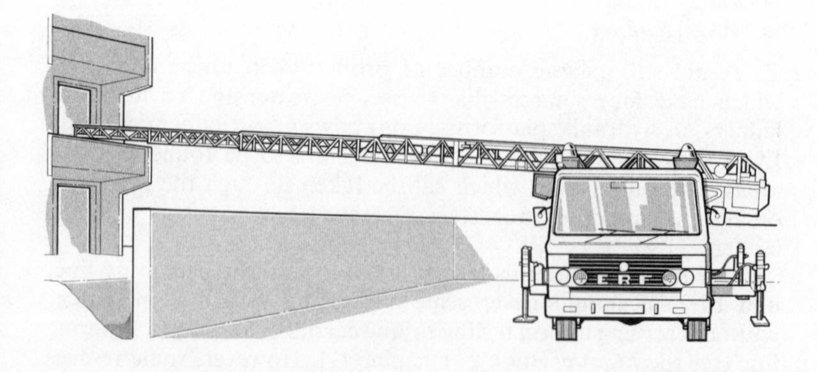

Fig. 1.10 Method of effecting a rescue by bridging with a turntable ladder.

(5) Hydraulic platforms

This apparatus can be used in similar circumstances to a T.L. However, its articulation, cage accommodation and ability to be controlled from the cage or the ground give it some advantages. Its capability of reaching over and down behind obstacles is one, but it has not [up to the present in this country] the height or projection of the modern T.L. It can provide accommodation for a small number of people in the cage, picking them off at different windows and levels if necessary, but must deposit the load before returning for more. Some are equipped to carry a stretcher alongside the cage and to provide resuscitation from, or in, the cage.

(6) Non-Service ladders

On arrival at a fire involving rescues firemen may find the general public attempting rescues by all manner of means, e.g. building ladders, window cleaning ladders. Their design and condition are usually just not up to the stresses being placed on them. Every effort should be made to get Brigade equipment into operation as quickly as possible to replace these before accidents happen.

d. Bridging with ladders

Depending on the distance to be spanned over obstacles, various ladders can be used to bridge distances. These can be between two buildings or parts of the same building, across gardens or basement areas, or possibly across a canal where the absence of a towpath precludes gaining access by other means. Circumstances will obviously dictate which type of ladder will be most suitable. The *Fire Service Drill Book* in Drill E10 lays out the method of bridging an escape and Drill L7 does the same for the 10 m. or 10.5 m. extension ladders. Particular attention should be paid to the reference to bridging in the relevant Notes. Reference to bridging by T.Ls has already been made on page 16. Firemen should remember that a ladder used for bridging is being used in a way for which it was not primarily designed. The ladder must not be over-loaded and greater care must be taken when crossing it to avoid any whipping or twisting. This applies to all ladders from short extension to T.L.

e. Lowering by line

There are occasions during rescue operations when it may be impractical or impossible to carry or assist a person down a ladder or help him out by normal means. This quite often applies when the rescuers have reached the person by hook ladders, and other ladders and normal means of escape are out of the question. Firemen will then have to resort to effecting a rescue by lowering line.

If a rescue needs a hook ladder approach then the conditions for lowering could be difficult and will require a high degree of expertise. The position from which the lowering is done is seldom straightforward: in cold and wet weather hands may not be as nimble as usual; smoke may impair the vision and the breathing of the rescuers; there may be little room for deploying the lowering line, and there could be obstructions to a 'clean lower'. Firemen have got to be well-trained, quick, cool, calm and meticulous.

The following points should be considered:

(i) the lowering line should be fitted with running eyes on the two legs of the line. The standing part of the shorter leg [indicated by a Turk's Head knot—see *Manual*, Book 2, Chapter 13] should be placed under the casualty's armpits around the chest and the longer leg round the knees [see Fig. 1.11]:

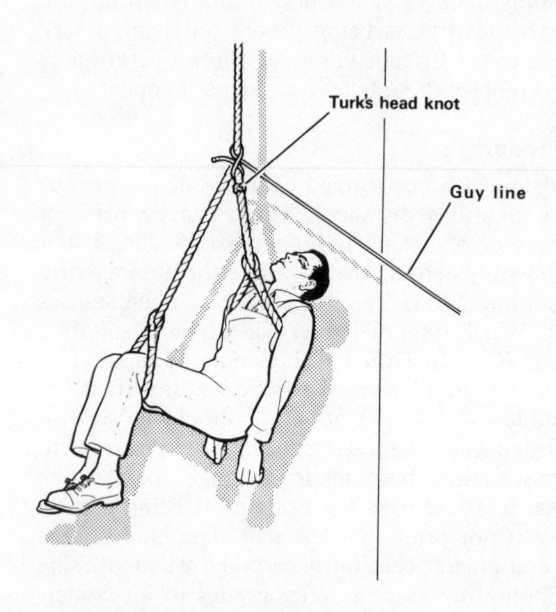

Fig. 1.11 Method of lowering by line.

the shorter leg must be used in this position:

(a) to keep the head upright; and

(b) to ensure that if the splice 'draws' the person will still be held securely by the standing part.

The guy line, which should be attached by a clove hitch to the standing part [one half of the hitch above the splice, the other below], should then be held out of the window at arm's length and dropped. The fireman, or firemen, below can keep the body away from the building by hauling on the guy line;

(ii) if a lowering line is unavailable, a long line can be used and a chair knot tied in it. If the distance to lower is less than about 12 m. the knot can be tied in the centre and one end of the line thrown down to be used as a guy line. If it is more than 12 m. the chair knot should be tied at one end and a second line bent on to it by a round turn and two half-hitches above the knot to act as the guy line;

(iii) if possible when selecting a position from which to lower, firemen should remember that a line gets less wear running over wood than over stone or metal. Time permitting, a sack or cloth under the point of contact will help;

(iv) the lowering should be carried out as far as possible as laid down by Drill M2 of the *Fire Service Drill Book*. If, for various reasons, this is not possible, firemen must try to use some object around which the line can be led and controlled. The line should be passed hand to hand and not allowed to run through the hands in these circumstances. A steady rate should be maintained and the man lowering should be well braced back. His companion, after ensuring the casualty is clear of the opening, should assist, either as is laid down for No 2 in Drill M2, or by backing up on the line behind No 1, in order among other things to ensure that the line runs freely. If there is any convenient area to lay out the line, e.g. down a stairwell or along a passage, this will help to effect a smooth lowering;

(v) if the lowering can be done in conjunction with a ladder, it must be carried out in accordance with the appropriate Drill from the *Fire Service Drill Book*. The proper safety measures should be taken at all times;

(vi) occasionally, lowering lines are fitted at one end with a spring hook or a thimble and are used in conjunction with a sling. Figs. 1.12 and 1.13 show two methods.

f. Rescue of injured persons

Occasionally firemen will need to raise or lower injured persons on a ladder or stretcher because there are no other ways of getting them to the level from where they can be carried to an ambulance. To lower or raise them in a sling or lowering line would aggravate the shock and injuries. This could have to be done with the casualty in either a vertical or a horizontal position, depending on the circumstances.

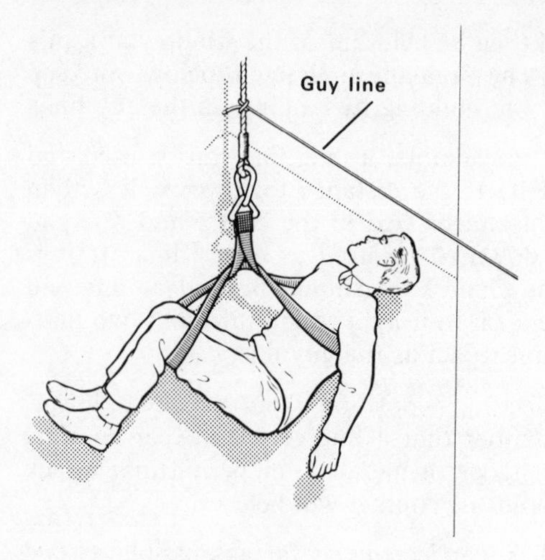

Fig. 1.12 Use of a sling for lowering.

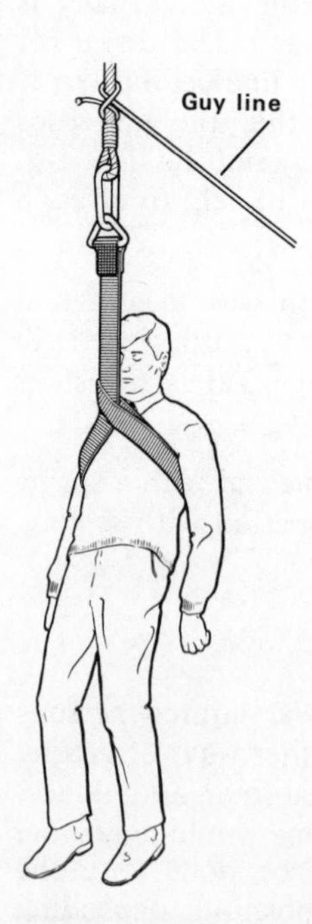

Fig. 1.13 Alternative method of using a sling for lowering.

It is obvious, depending on the type of injuries, that effective first aid methods to immobilise limbs, support the head or back etc. [see Chapter 6] will have to be used and the patient made as comfortable as possible before securing him or her in or on the ladder or stretcher. Plenty of padding [especially in a lowering by ladder] will be needed, with blankets and, often, fire tunics being used.

(1) Horizontal lowering or raising

Drill E8 in the *Fire Service Drill Book* shows how this should be done utilising an escape ladder and short extension ladder section, or a 13.5 m. ladder. In order to keep the casualty clear of the building and other obstructions a guy line should be attached at the points indicated in the Drill. Firemen should remember that an excessive sideways pull on the guy line could hazard the escape or 135 ladder by pulling it across the face of the building. Slings can be used as shown in Fig. 1.14. It should also be borne in mind that it is always better for the casualty if the head is a little higher than the feet when lowered and, when the ladder or stretcher is being eased out of the opening, the feet should go out first.

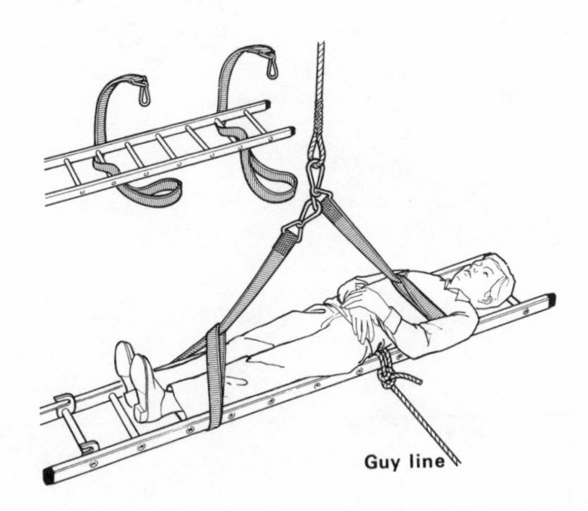

Fig. 1.14 Method of lowering or raising an injured person horizontally.

(2) Vertical lowering or raising

Usually lowering or hoisting a casualty vertically requires a special type of stretcher in which the casualty can be firmly strapped and which is also of reasonably small cross-section to enable it to be manoeuvred through narrow openings and round obstructions. All types have facilities whereby either lines or slings can be attached at points along the stretcher for a horizontal lowering but they have also a large metal ring at one, or both, ends for a line to be attached for a vertical lift:

(i) a common type is the 'Neil Robertson' [see Fig. 1.15] which is made of canvas and bamboo and literally wraps round the casualty, who is strapped in. There are carrying loops at the side;

(ii) a second type is the 'Paraguard' [see Fig. 1.16] which has a tubular frame jointed to be folded for easy storage and for the transport of a sitting patient. The whole packs into a valise which can be carried aloft on the back of a fireman;

(iii) a third is the 'Chance' [see Fig. 1.17] which is very similar to (ii) in that it has a tubular jointed frame and is carried folded in a valise. It has folding legs and a special sling with four legs ending in karabiners.

Fig. 1.15 Neil Robertson stretcher.

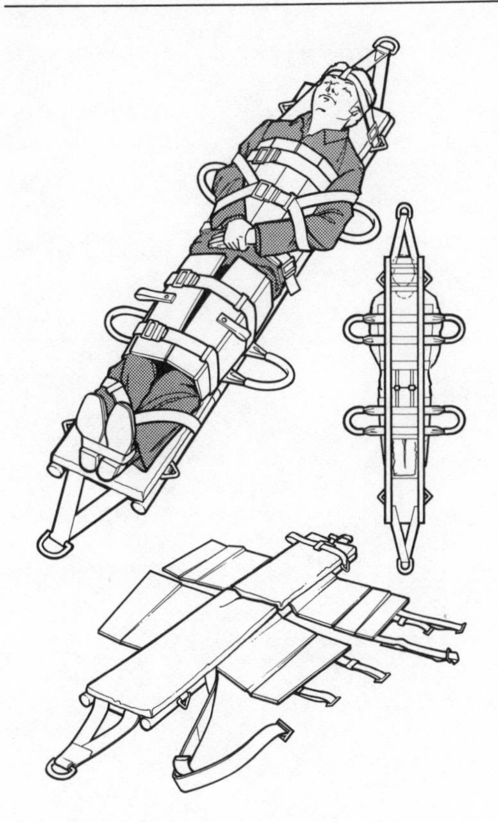

Fig. 1.16 Paraguard stretcher.

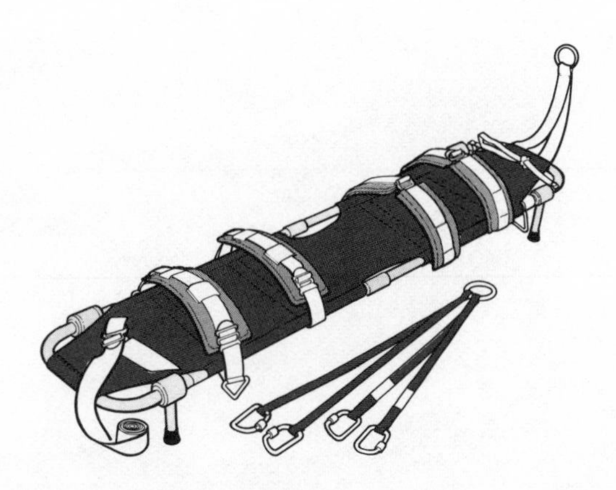

Fig. 1.17 Chance stretcher.

Chapter 2
Rescues from lifts and escalators

1 General

Apart from effecting rescues at fires, firemen are often involved in other 'special service' rescues. A number of such calls are to incidents involving lifts, either where people are shut in a lift car because of a malfunction, or where someone has been trapped in the lift mechanism. In some large modern buildings with complex lift systems there are resident mechanics. This is not common however and firemen therefore need some familiarity with the main types of lift, their basic methods of operation, the safety devices they incorporate, and the action to take at incidents.

2 Electric lifts

a. Description

An electric lift [see Fig. 2.1] consists essentially of a platform or car suspended by steel ropes from a winding machine. The car runs on guides so that it is free to move only in a vertical direction. A person in the car or at a landing can start, stop, or reverse the machine by some form of automatic push-button control. There is nearly always a counterweight which also runs in vertical guides and balances the car plus 50% of its load. This reduces the energy used in driving the lift. The guides are usually T shaped or circular in section and made of steel; the control is electrically operated. Some old lifts, however, run in timber guides and a few of these have mechanical control.

There is, additionally, often a control panel on top of the car from where a maintenance mechanic can move the lift.

Within this broad framework, the details of lift design vary considerably. Two particularly distinctive types are the wall climber and the double decker lift. The wall climber is not encased in a lift well and may operate on the outside of a building; the double decker lift serves two floors at once and consists of two cars coupled one above another with a small space between them: it is as yet uncommon in Britain. Two British Standards apply to lifts: BS 2655 and the later BS 5655.

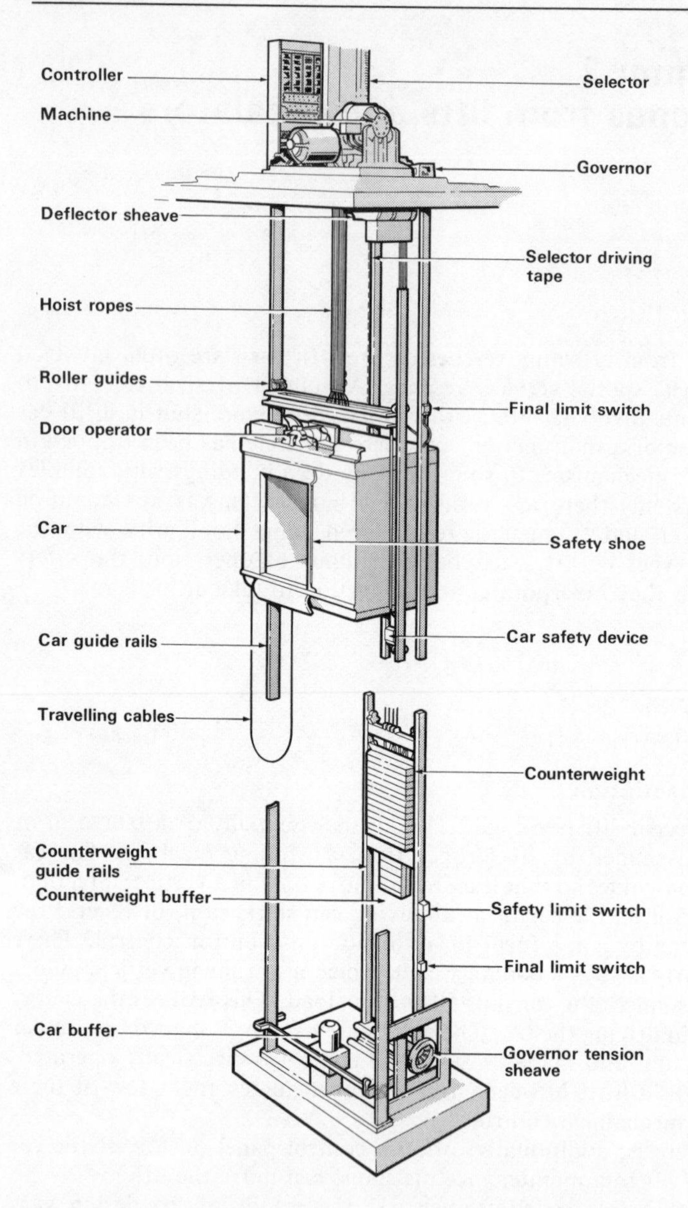

Fig. 2.1 Typical electric lift installation.

b. Driving mechanism

The winding mechanism [see Fig. 2.2] comprises a motor, worm gear and brake. It is usually mounted on a common bedplate. The rotation of the motor (1) is transmitted to the lift car by a worm reduction gear and steel wire ropes. The ropes are either wound on a drum or run through V shaped grooves in a traction sheave (2) mounted on the wormwheel shaft of the gear. With traction drive, a counterweight is essential in order to provide the necessary tension in the ropes to make them grip in the traction grooves. The machine is fitted with a brake (3) operating on the coupling (4) which connects the motor shaft and the worm shaft. The coupling serves as both coupling and brake drum. The brake is fitted with friction shoes which act on the drums by means of springs or weights. An electric solenoid holds them off when the motor is operating. The motor shaft at the free end is extended and made square (5) to accept a handle, removable smooth wheel or fixed smooth wheel by which the winding gear can be hand operated.

High speed lifts are fitted with a specially designed slow speed D.C. motor [Fig. 2.3(1)], the shaft (2) of which is coupled direct to the driving sheave without gearing. There are special winding facilities for these machines. [See Section 3.e, below].

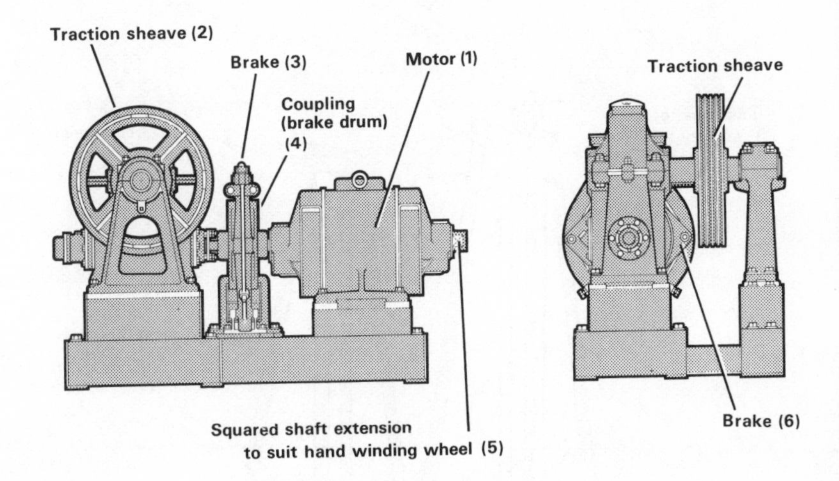

Fig. 2.2 Driving mechanism of an electric lift.

c. Lift car

The lift car [see Fig. 2.4] usually consists of two separate units, the framework and the car body. Some modern lifts do not, however, have a separate frame and firemen would have to bear this in mind if it was necessary to cut into the walls of the car.

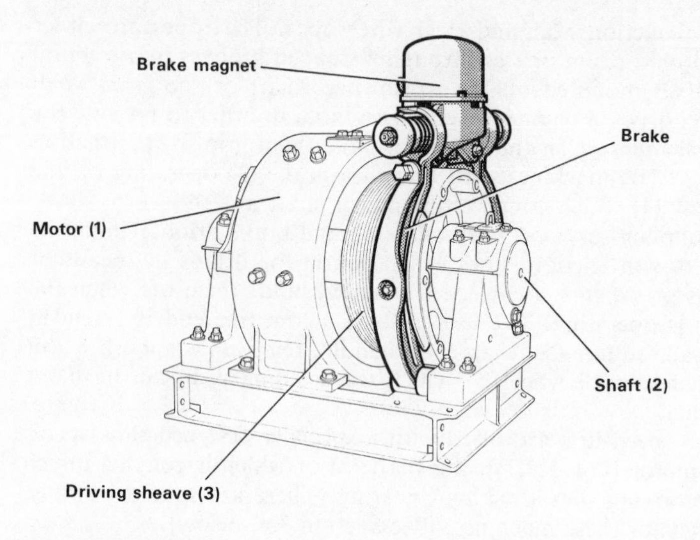

Fig. 2.3 Driving mechanism of an electric lift [gearless].

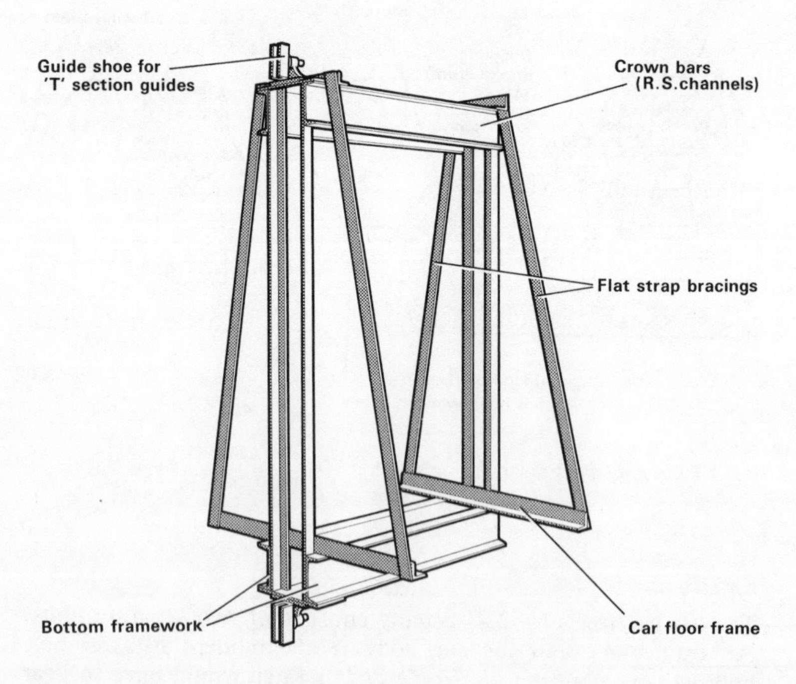

Fig. 2.4 Lift car.

The car frame is formed from steel channel sections and rolled steel angles bolted or welded together. It is made sufficiently rigid to withstand the operation of the safety gear without permanent distortion. The side frames are built of steel angles and gusset plates riveted at each corner. Vertical or diagonal stays give extra strength and stiffness. The main suspension channels, generally termed the crownbars, are fixed to the top frame, to which is bolted the housing for the two top guide shoes. The bottom sections carry the safety gear and the two bottom guide shoes. The lifting ropes are either attached direct to the top crownbars or pass over guide pulleys attached to them. The guide shoes are shaped to fit the guides. On modern high speed passenger lifts roller shoes [see Fig. 2.10] are now common. These consist of three rubber tyred rollers, one operating on the face of the guide, the other two on the sides. The arms on which the rollers are mounted are spring-loaded to maintain even pressure on the guides.

The car bodywork is in panels assembled within the framework and fixed to the encircling steelwork. There may be an access trap in the car roof. An electric interlock prevents the lift being started whilst this is open.

d. Safety devices

To prevent any uncontrolled descent of the car, a safety gear is invariably fitted. This clamps the car to the guides if the ropes break or if the speed of descent exceeds a pre-determined value. As an additional precaution the safety gear is sometimes arranged to operate if the ropes stretch unequally.

It is sometimes also necessary to fit a safety gear on the counterweight. This only applies, however, where there is any accessible space under the lift well.

(1) Instantaneous safety gear

The instantaneous safety gear is designed to stop the lift car within a short distance. It is not used on lifts with speeds greater than one metre per second as a sudden stop from higher speeds would cause severe shock to passengers.

Fig. 2.5 shows one form of such a gear.

This is the serrated cam type which is obsolescent but still found on some older lifts. The cams (1) operate on opposite sides of the same guide (2) so that equal pressure is applied to each in opposite directions. There is therefore no tendency for the guide to be forced out of the vertical plane. The gear has two connecting shafts each with a serrated cam keyed at either end. The shafts rotate in opposite directions when the safety rope is pulled. The safety rope may be fastened to one of the cams or to the cam shaft; it then passes up the lift well, over pulleys or a governor in

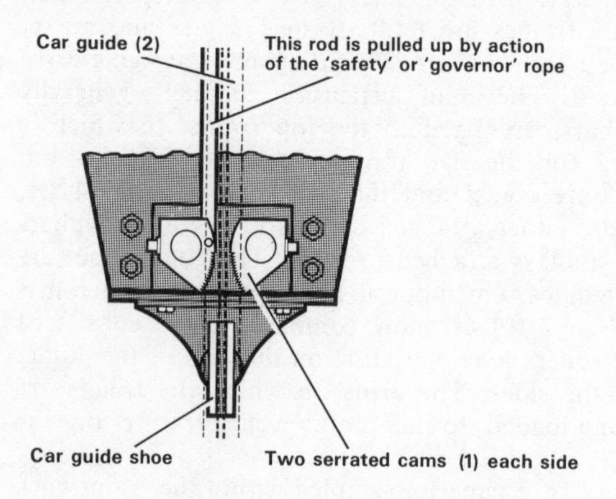

Fig. 2.5 Instantaneous safety gear: serrated cam type.

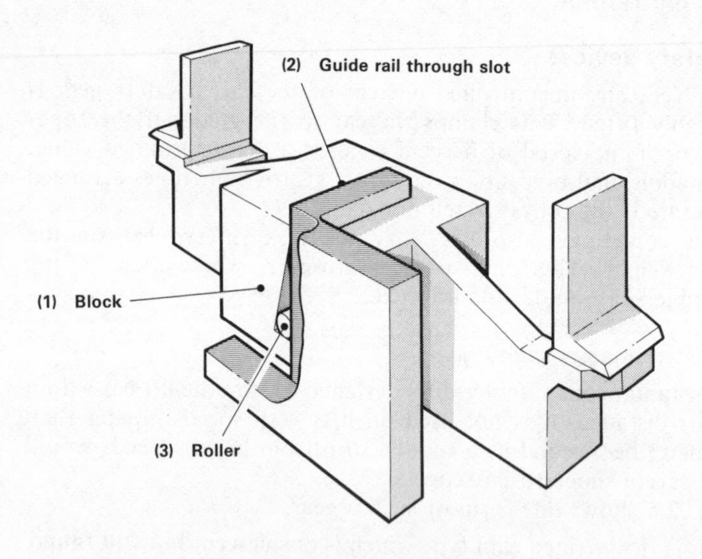

Fig. 2.6 Instantaneous safety gear: roll type.

the machine room, then down to the counterweight, where it is anchored. A direct pull on this rope, such as breaking or slackening of the suspension rope would cause, would rotate both shafts, bringing the leading edges of the cams into contact with the guides.

The falling car would automatically provide the remaining motion of the cams necessary to clamp the car to the guides. The rotation of the cam shafts also operates an electric contact which cuts off the current and applies the brake.

A second type of instantaneous gear is the roll type [see Fig. 2.6]. This consists of two safety clamps—one per guide—which are bolted to the bottom of the lift car frame. On each clamp there is a block (1) with an open slot through which the guide rail (2) passes. One side of the slot is parallel to the rail, the other side is inclined towards it and contains a hardened steel roller (3). When the downward speed of the lift becomes excessive, the roller is raised to wedge itself between the rail and the inclined surface of the slot and thus stops the car. The gear is actuated by means of a governor [Fig. 2.7(a)]. This is driven by means of a governor rope (1) which passes over the governor sheave (2), as in Fig. 2.7(b). If the downward speed of the car rises above a pre-determined level or the ropes break, the cast iron dogs (3), driven outwards by centrifugal force, lock against the normally stationary ratchet wheel (4) and cause it to rotate with the governor sheave. This moves the gripping yoke (5) so that it causes the gripping shoe (6) to clamp the governor rope against the sheave. This pulls on the rope and so operates the safety gear.

Firemen should never attempt to reset safety gear which has operated.

(2) Progressive safety gear

The progressive safety gear [see Fig. 2.8], sometimes known as the flexible guide clamp gear, is used on lifts faster than one metre per second and is designed to bring an over-speeding car to a

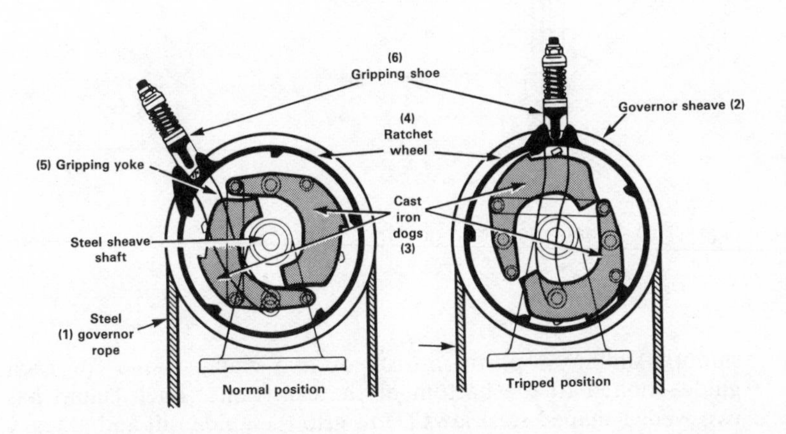

Fig. 2.7(a) Governor gear.

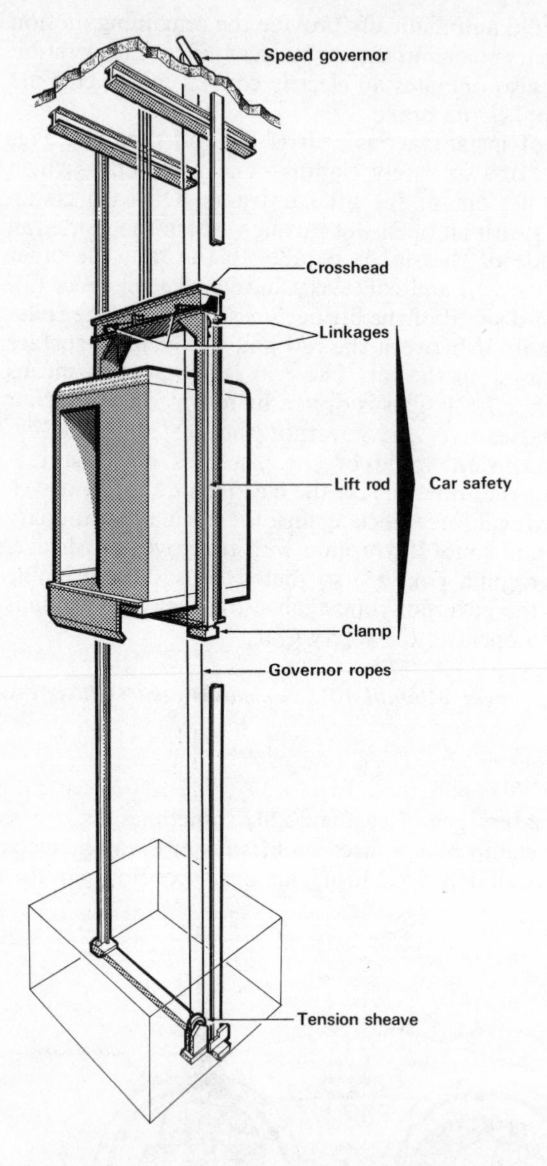

Fig. 2.7(b) Arrangement of a governor gear.

smooth sliding stop. It consists of two clamps—one for each guide—bolted to the bottom of the car frame. Each clamp has two wedge-shaped steel jaws (1) to grip the guide rail and a heavy flexible spring (2) to regulate the pressure the jaws exert. The gear

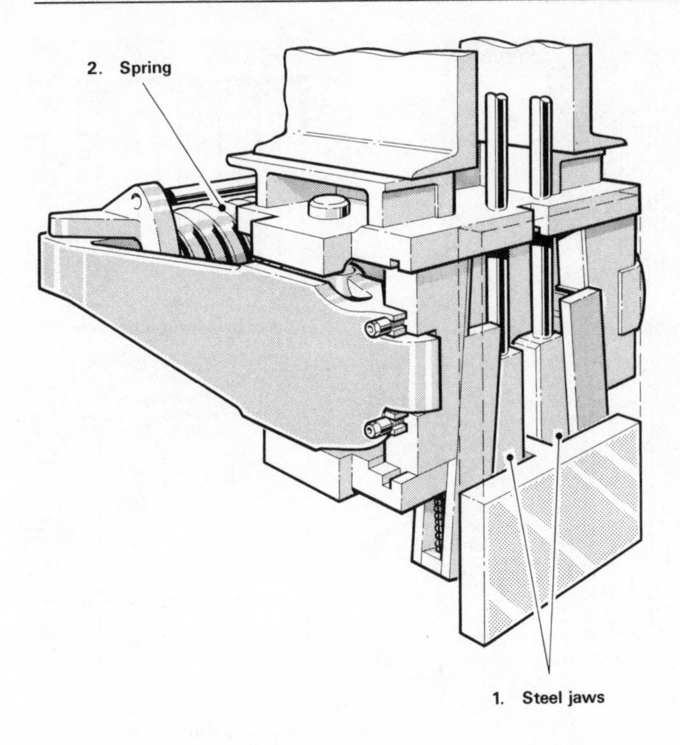

Fig. 2.8 Progressive [flexible guide clamp] safety gear.

is actuated by a governor. When the downward speed of the lift car exceeds a pre-determined limit, fly-wheels within the governor are driven outwards by centrifugal force and operate a safety switch to cut off the power and apply the brake. If this does not stop the car, further motion of the fly-wheels trips a latching device which in turn releases a swing jaw to clamp the governor rope against a fixed jaw. The resultant pull on the rope operates the safety gear, causing the movable jaws of the clamp to wedge themselves between the guide rail and side of the clamp with pressure gradually increased by the spring until the car is stopped.

e. Lift gates and doors

(1) Description

One form of protection for lift cars and landing entrances is the collapsible gate of the over-hung type [see Fig. 2.9(1)]. Ball-bearing rollers running on an overhead track support the gate and a specially shaped bottom track guides the pickets or vertical bars. Entrances to goods lifts usually have a collapsible type shutter

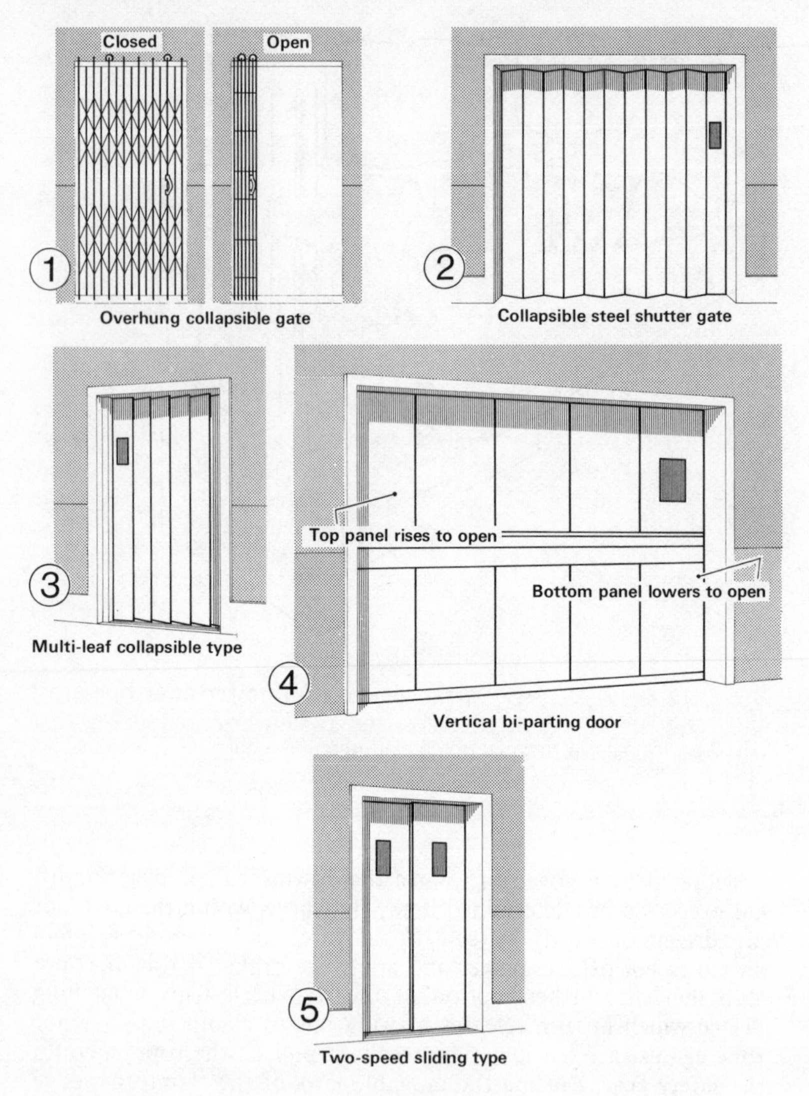

Fig. 2.9 Various types of lift gates and doors.

gate [see Fig. 2.9(2)]. This is similar but has vertical pickets of heavier section. The front face has hinged steel plates arranged in concertina fashion to allow the gate to be opened.

Occasionally, the landing protection consists of multi-leaf collapsible doors [see Fig. 2.9(3)]. These consist of several narrow vertical panels attached to an ordinary collapsible gate, allowing the unit to bunch into a comparatively small space.

Vertical bi-parting doors [see Fig. 2.9(4)] are sometimes used on heavy duty goods lifts. They are arranged in two halves, the top half rising and the bottom half lowering when the doors are opened. The car opening is usually protected by a single mesh rising gate, the movement of which is in conjunction with that of the landing doors.

On most modern passenger lifts, doors of various types have superseded gates. These are usually sliding doors of the over-hung type [see Fig. 2.9(5)]. The bottom edges are provided with rectangular guides that travel in the machined grooves of the landing sills. The doors, of metal or occasionally wood, are suitably framed and reinforced where necessary to carry the operating mechanism. The door hangers are made with ball-bearing steel rollers mounted on brackets fitted on the top of each door panel. The rollers run on specially shaped steel top tracks fixed to the entrance frame. There is a small check roller below each suspension roller on the same bracket. This engages the underside of the track and so prevents the doors from being lifted upwards.

(2) Power operation of doors

Fig. 2.10 shows a simple arrangement of a power door operator. This consists of a motor connected to a worm reduction gear which is attached to the car door by a crank and a system of arms and levers. The operating arm (1) is fulcrumed at (2) and connects to the doors as shown. An adjustable connecting rod (3) is fixed to the top arm (1) and then to the crank (4) on the worm gear (5). When the crank is driven in a clockwise direction, movement of the arm round its fulcrum opens the door. The reverse movement closes it.

Fig. 2.11 shows the method of connecting centre opening doors so that one geared unit operates them. Connection between the car doors and landing doors is by a ramp and skate. When the car is at a landing the skate is between the ramps and the action of the power driven car doors opens or closes the landing doors simultaneously.

Control of the door operator is automatic with that of the lift. When the car stops at a floor, it completes a circuit which causes the mechanism to open the doors. Touching a button to call the lift in either direction likewise completes a circuit and closes the doors. The car doors usually have a sensitive edge, so that if, when closing, they encounter an obstruction, such as a person entering or leaving, they will immediately re-open. Sometimes a light is focused across the lift entrance to photo-electric cells connected into the door control circuit: the doors can only close when this circuit is not interrupted.

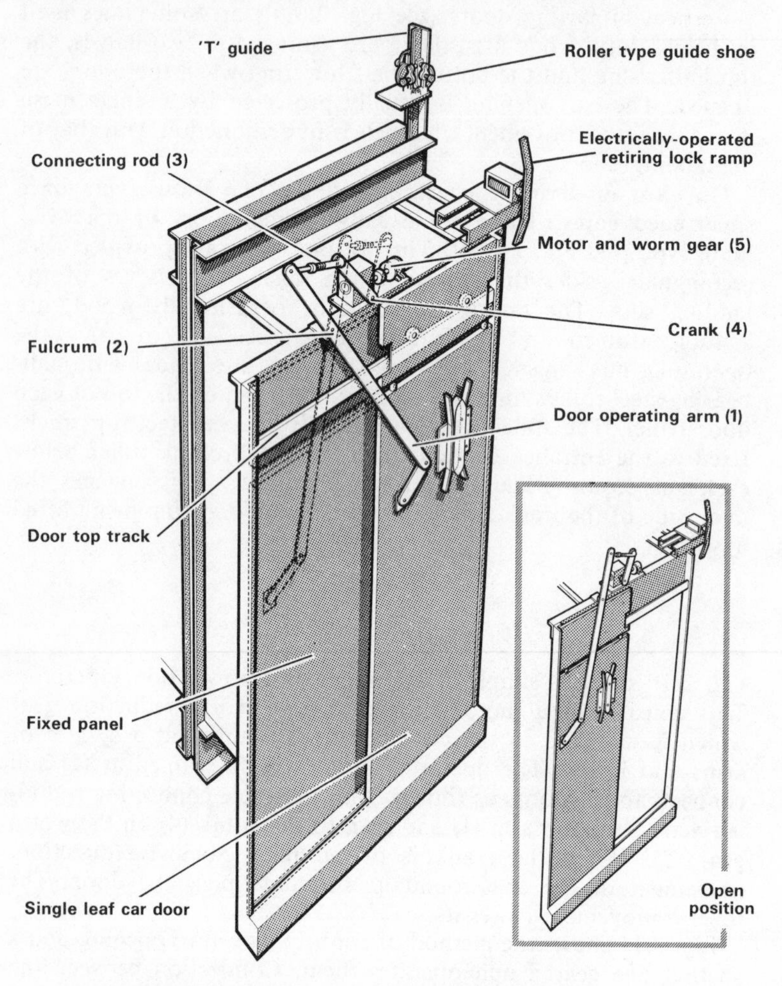

Fig. 2.10 Arrangement of a power door operator.

All power-operated landing doors have a key slot into which a special key may be inserted for emergency release [see Fig. 2.13]. There should always be a spare key in the lift machine room.

f. Locking devices

(I) Lift gates and doors

Legally all lift gates and doors must have an efficient locking device [see Fig. 2.12]. This prevents the movement of the car by cutting the supply to the control circuit unless the gate or door is

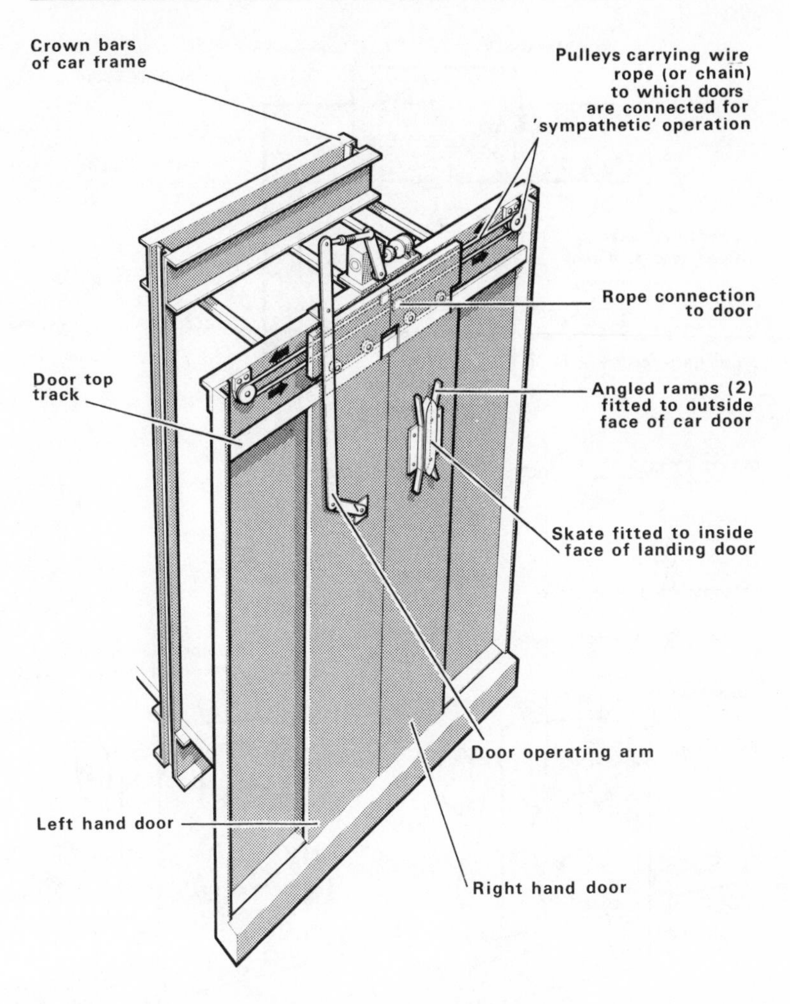

Fig. 2.11 Method of connecting centre opening doors.

properly closed. The interlock is fitted above the car door top track in such a position that a striker fitted to one of the leading pickets raises the lock contact arm and short-circuits the contacts when the gate is closed. When it opens, the contact arm drops through the combined effect of gravity and a spring, and the control feed is cut off.

(2) Landing gates and doors

The commonest form of locking system for landing gates and doors [see Fig. 2.13] consists of a lock box on the gate or door

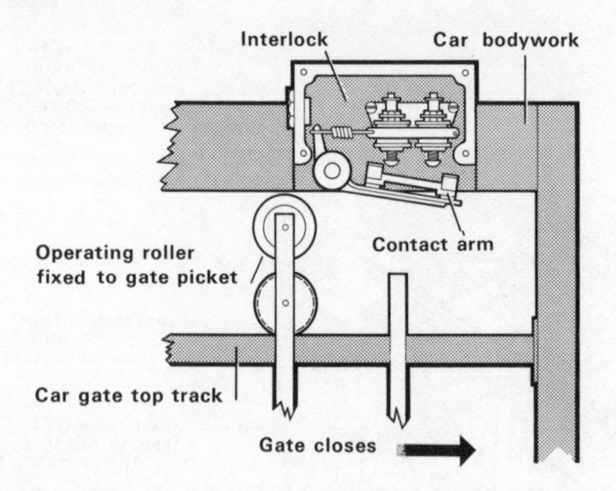

Fig. 2.12 Electric interlock for a lift car gate.

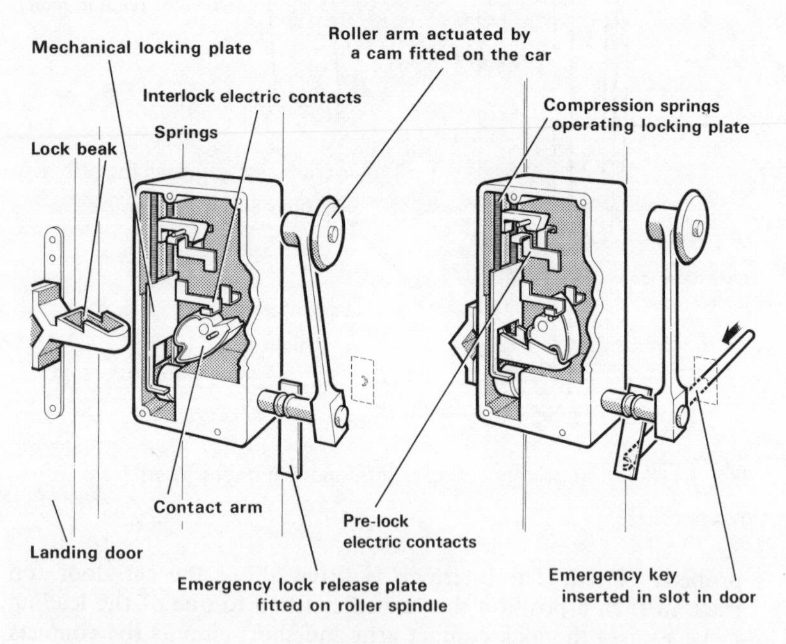

Fig. 2.13 Locking device for a lift landing gate or door.

framing into which a lock beak on the landing door engages. The device consists of a mechanical lock combined with an electric interlock. Except for pressure on a car or landing button or operation of the car switch, the control circuit is completed when the interlock is operated. The door is mechanically locked before the interlock makes contact. Accordingly, before the mechanical lock can be released to open the door, the electric interlock must be broken to disconnect the control circuit. The lock is operated by a cam fitted to the car. This hits the lock-operating roller ram when the car reaches a landing.

3 Rescues from electric lifts

a. Types of rescue

There are two broad classes of incidents involving lifts which firemen might attend: those where people are shut in the car as the result of a malfunction and those where a person is trapped in the lift mechanism. The latter class is clearly the more serious and these incidents usually occur through carelessness or over-familiarity on the part of someone servicing the lift or through vandalism. In the first class of incident, the people are usually in little danger except through their own panic. It is therefore important to calm and reassure them.

b. Action on entering a building

On entering a building firemen should take with them the basic gear they will require. If someone has been injured, this should include first aid equipment. The officer in charge should also check that an ambulance or doctor has been called where necessary; a surgical team may also be required. The officer should see that the lift company responsible for maintenance of the equipment is called to give help and advice and to carry out any subsequent repairs and restoration of service. He will usually find the relevant details on the lift or in the machine room.

c. Starting operations

After locating the machine room, firemen should first isolate the lift from its source of supply by using the main switch or circuit breaker. [This does not switch off the light in the car.] They should then locate the car. They should check that the suspension ropes of both the car and the counterweight are taut. If they are slack, the firemen should secure the car against uncontrolled movement by passing lines under the crownbars of the car sling and fastening them to the guides above the next highest guide fitting. It will be advisable to use more than one line or to multiply the number of falls to ensure the car is held securely. Slack ropes are more common with the earlier drum drive mechanism than with the modern traction drive. Firemen can identify the type of drive by looking at the winding mechanism

Firemen should make no attempt to release an operated safety gear: they must call the lift engineer.

d. Hand-winding of geared lifts.

Electric lifts have provision for hand-winding. Normally, this is by means of a hand wheel, or sometimes a fly-wheel, painted yellow in parts. In some old lift motor rooms, however, there may be cranked handles. All winding handles should be kept in the machine room, near the motor. In an emergency, and in the remote possibility of there being no other provision for hand-winding, firemen may use a Stillson wrench or adjustable spanner on the motor shaft if the car has to be moved against its free running direction.

The hand-winding spindle is invariably a squared extension of the motor armature shaft; its position should also be clearly marked on the lift motor. Sometimes it has a cover held by wing nuts but it is also advisable to have a screwdriver available to remove it if necessary. Painted arrows, or occasionally a plate on the motor casing, usually show the direction to turn the handle to raise or lower the lift.

To operate the lift by hand, firemen should fit the handle to the squared shaft extension of the motor. One fireman then turns it while another hand-operates the brake. Fig. 2.14 shows various types of brake. One [Fig. 2.14 (1)] has an emergency release lever; on another [Fig. 2.14(2)] pressure has to be exerted on the link rods; and for another [Fig. 2.14(3)] an emergency brake release lever is provided in the machine room. After hand-winding, firemen should immediately reset the brake if it has not reset automatically. The reduction gear is almost invariably reversible. The brake must therefore only be released after the winding handle has been securely held, and it must be applied before the fireman who is winding lets go again. While the lift is being moved, there should be a fireman at the landing opening from where he can observe the movement and only he should give orders. It is best to do this by radio to avoid the possible need for relaying messages between a number of people.

e. Hand-winding of gearless lifts

High speed gearless lifts have a different method of hand operation from that described above. Provided the lift was manufactured before 1981, there will be a secondary system of gearing known as 'barring gear' [see Fig. 2.15]. This is usually a square threaded rod connected from the motor bed plate to the sheave or brake drum and operated by a nut rotated by means of a tommy bar. In a motor room with more than one gearless machine there will be just one set of barring gear.

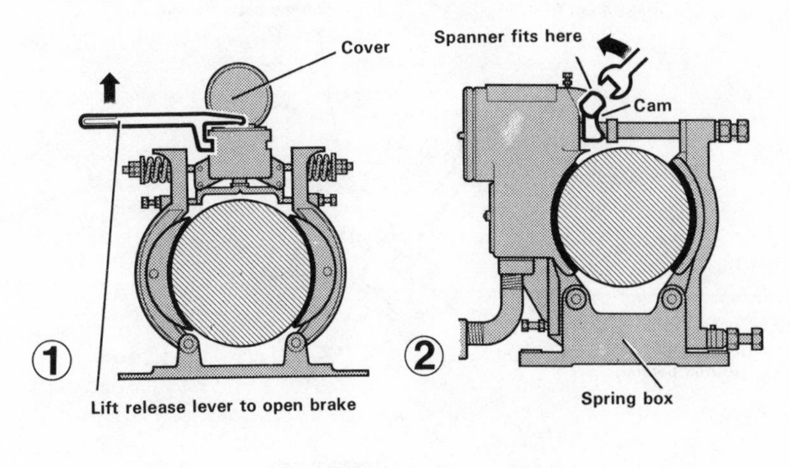

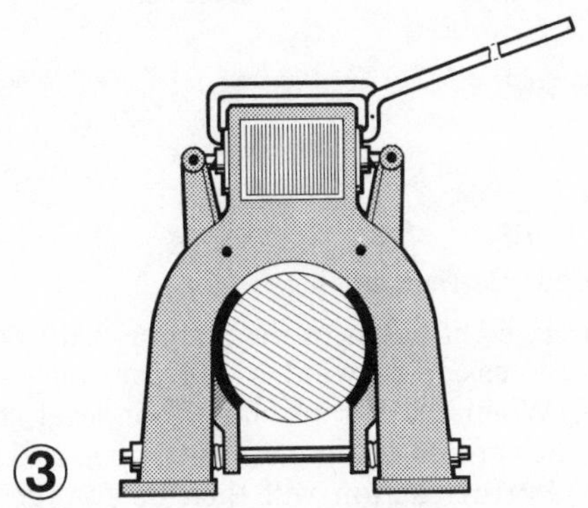

Fig. 2.14 Various types of brake.

f. Future trends

BS 5655 lays down that when the effort to move a car is in excess of 400N there should be a means of electrical operation controlled from the machine room. Instructions should be provided in the machine room or machine enclosure. This will apply to all gearless and some geared machines and it will not be possible to hand-wind them. They will not usually have a trap door in the car roof. This Standard comes fully into effect after 31 May 1984.

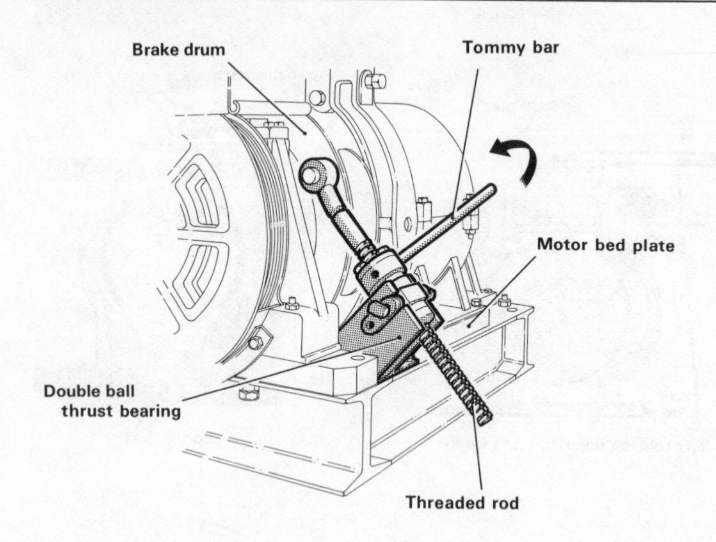

Fig. 2.15 Barring gear.

g. Moving the lift

(1) To release people shut in

Since the counterweight balances the car plus half its safe working load, it is always easier to wind a full car down and a lightly loaded car up. When the car reaches floor level, the automatic lock will allow the car and landing doors to open and the occupants to be released. Further action will then be for the lift engineer, but fireman should leave the lift safe by ensuring it cannot be operated until the defect is remedied. They can best do this by leaving the main power switch open. They should also secure landing gates carefully before leaving.

(2) To release a person trapped

Firemen should first examine the way the person is lying to determine the best method of effecting a release. In general, it is best to move the car in the opposite direction to that in which it had been travelling when the person was caught. Firemen must of course first establish the correct direction for hand-winding. A casualty suspended in any way from the lift must be supported before firemen move it. It may be possible to lever the car horizontally far enough to free a trapped person. Removing the top guide shoes gives considerable movement but it is often more difficult to reach and remove those on the underside. Even where the shoes have been removed, the proximity of the safety gear cams limits further movement. On some installations, however, it may be possible to move the car sideways enough to clear the cams from the guides. If this method does not give additional clearance, firemen should remove the clips holding the guides to the fixings adjacent to the car. This will allow the guides to spring from the vertical plane when the car is levered back. If the car has stopped adjacent to a guide fixing, it may not be possible to gain the necessary access. The only course available will then be to cut away the guide immediately above and below the safety gear cams. The lift will still be safe as the ropes will continue to hold it.

If they cannot move the car or counterweight by levering, firemen must operate the lift. They must do so by hand to cause the minimum disturbance to the casualty.

h. Moving the counterweight

Occasionally, the counterweight traps someone such as a maintenance fitter. Counterweights also have guide shoes and the quickest way to release a trapped person is to remove the shoes, and perhaps a guide fixing, then swing the weight clear. If it is necessary to move the weight manually, firemen should recall that the direction of winding will be the reverse of that shown for the car.

i. Lifts which cannot be moved

Sometimes the lift will jam and be impossible to move by hand. In such circumstances, the first course is usually to effect an entry through the landing door adjacent to the point where the lift has stopped. Firemen assisting people out in this way should take care that the people do not fall down the well [see Fig. 2.16]. When such an exit is not possible, firemen should lower a ladder to the top of the car. On some lifts there is a trap door here through which those within can escape.

Firemen should be aware of blind wells. These are where the lift does not stop at all floors and there is consequently a long run of lift well without a landing door. There will be emergency doors to give access to the shaft, but these can be up to 11 m. apart.

4 Hydraulic lifts

Hydraulic lifts occur in a variety of buildings up to four floors high or, occasionally, somewhat higher. Figs. 2.17, 2.18 show the two most common types: the direct acting, that has a jack or jacks fixed direct to the side or underside of the car; and the indirect acting, roped, that has a jack or jacks connected to the

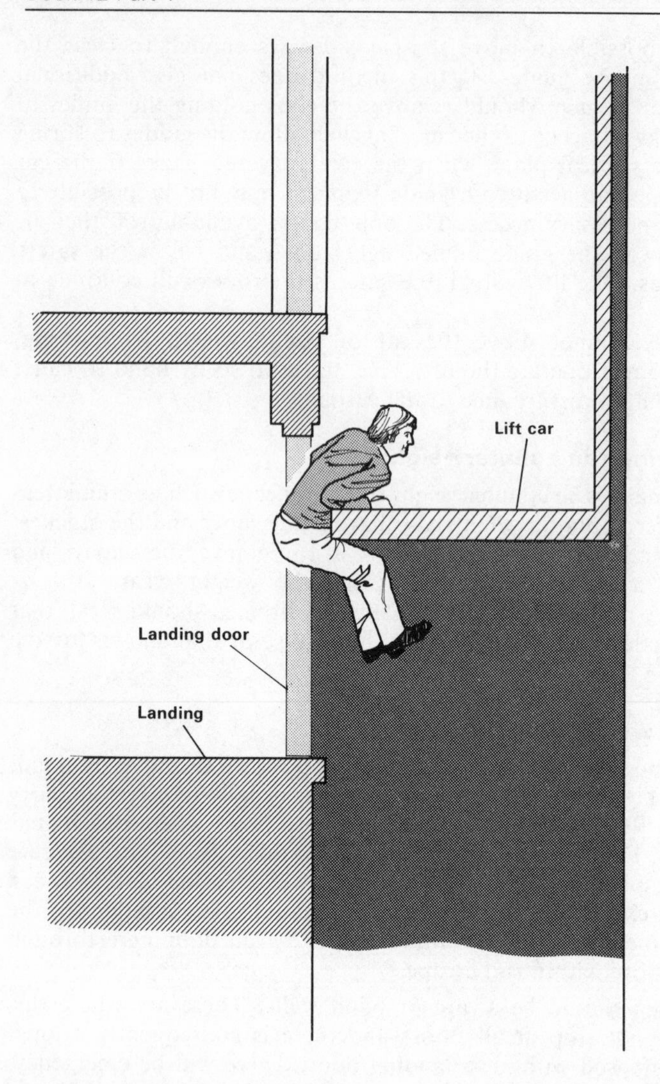

Fig. 2.16 Rescue from a lift which cannot be moved by hand. The danger of a fall into the shaft is indicated.

lift car via chains or ropes. When attending an incident, firemen must first establish whether they are dealing with an electric lift or one of these hydraulic types.

A hydraulic oil pump and motor power the lift. To raise the car, the motor drives the pump, which pumps oil at pressure into the jack, which then lifts the car. Almost invariably the car is

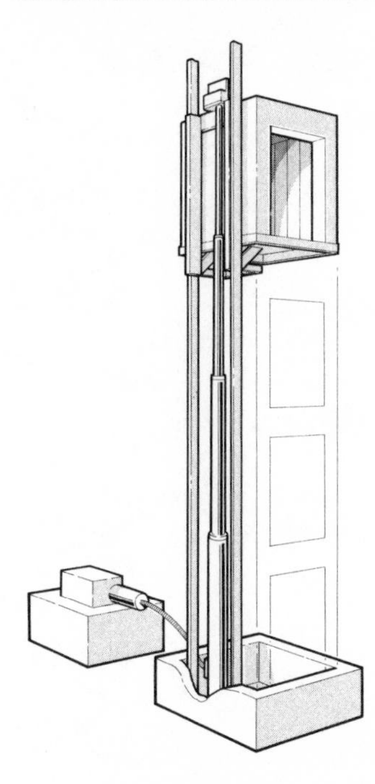

Fig. 2.17 Direct acting hydraulic lift.

raised by power and lowered by gravity. Firemen must appreciate that with hydraulic lifts the machine room may be remote from the installation itself. They should familiarise themselves with machine room locations in advance. Otherwise, they must ask the building occupant or search for such clues as the direction of the hydraulic pipeline run.

Safety devices interlock with the hydraulic control gear so that their operation immediately stops the car. Landing doors are mechanically and electrically interlocked; lift doors are always electrically interlocked and often mechanically. An indirect acting lift has conventional safety gear. To release it, the car must be moved upwards by power, hand pump, or lifting tackle. The gear is electrically interlocked, so that when it is engaged the main motor drive cannot function. A service engineer will be necessary to over-ride this interlock if the gear is to be released by main motor power.

Many hydraulic lifts have one or more pipe rupture valves integral with, or screwed direct to, the oil inlet of the jacks. Their purpose is to protect against a rupture of the hydraulic pipeline. When this occurs, the valve immediately locks shut and prevents further oil escaping from the jack. This prevents the car lowering.

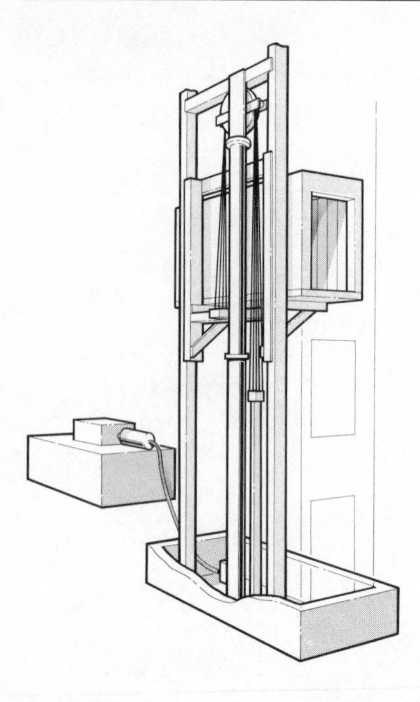

Fig. 2.18 Indirect acting [roped] hydraulic lift.

These valves can only be released by raising the car. Some do have an emergency bleed-off connection. Letting oil leak through this allows the slow lowering of the lift, but the operation must be carried out with caution.

Firemen can lower the lifts by a special hand lowering valve sited at the hydraulic power unit. The control is usually of the dead man type, either a knob or lever which is pulled or pressed to release the oil from the jack and so allow the lift to lower by gravity. The control will probably be marked as such and probably painted red; hand lowering instructions are usually posted by the hydraulic power unit.

Before hand lowering an indirect acting lift, firemen should check for a slack chain if the car is jammed in the well [there is sometimes a protection against this]. There is a danger otherwise that when the obstruction, e.g. a distorted door caught on a sill, is released, the car will fall down the well out of control. They should also turn off the isolator before lowering the lift. This prevents operation of the automatic re-levelling system, which normally keeps the car level at a floor even with a slight jack leak. There should be a noise of oil returning to the tank when

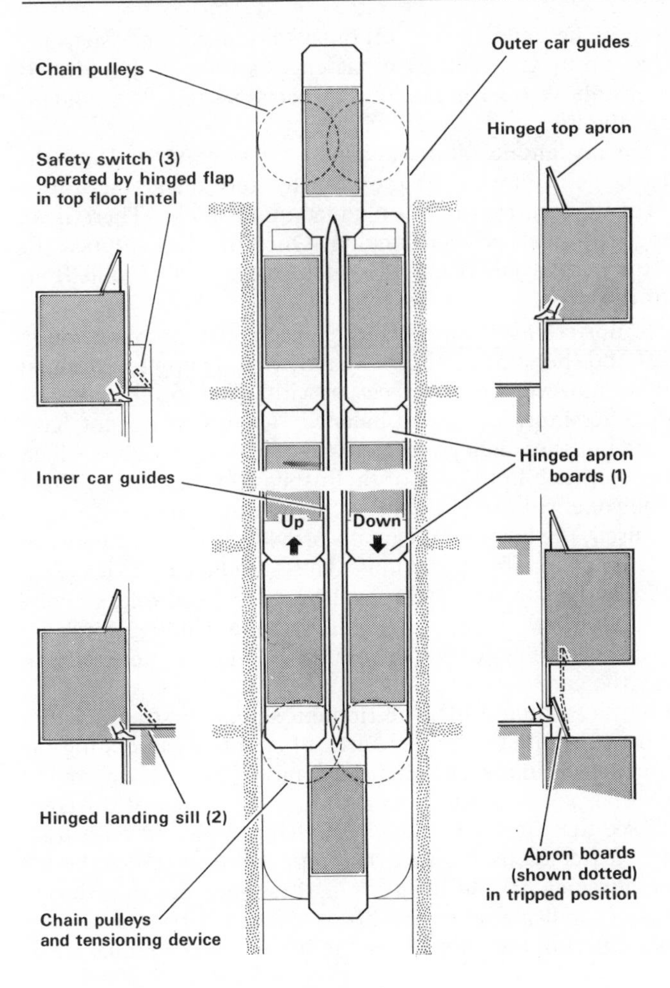

Fig. 2.19 Paternoster continuous lift.

the hand lowering control is operated. Fireman should check that the car is actually moving.

5 Paternosters

The paternoster consists of a series of cars carried on endless chains, moving in a clockwise direction [see Fig. 2.19]. Each car holds two people and the lift gives a simultaneous up and down service. The vertical space between the cars is filled in by special apron boards (1) which are hinged to move if they meet an obstruction. The landing sill (2) is also hinged and specially designed to tip up if struck by a passenger's foot or shoulder. If this happens above the top landing, a special switch (3) automatically stops the lift.

There are no landing doors and passengers enter or leave the lift whilst it is in motion. If they fail to step out at the top or bottom, they are carried over or under quite safely. There is an emergency stop push at each landing. Once this has stopped the lift only the special key-operated switch, usually at ground floor level, can re-start it.

The paternoster has the same winding mechanism as an orthodox electric lift and the same method of hand-winding applies. Manual operation is however generally easier with paternosters, as they are at all times more or less in balance. These lifts do not have safety gears but there is a continuous steel wire safety rope which passes through each link roller of the suspension chains. If a chain breaks, the rope will safely hold the cars in position.

When raised, the landing or car sills provide a clearance between car and landing of about 250 mm. This should be sufficient to safeguard any person who falls from being trapped and severely crushed. If, however, it is not possible by hand-winding to release without further injury a trapped person, it may be necessary to lever away the car.

When hand-winding a lift, the fireman should first ensure that the machine is isolated from its source of supply by operating the circuit breaker or main switch in the motor room. He should remember that passengers may be shut in at a number of different levels and see that they are told what is happening and reassured. There are barrier cords for each landing, to hook across the lift entrances. Firemen should always put these into position during operations to indicate that the lift is out of service and stop passengers entering the cars whilst the lift is under manual operation.

6 Escalators

Incidents involving escalators are not common and those which firemen might have to attend even more rare. In case of accidents, however, firemen should familiarise themselves with any escalators on their own ground. Fig. 2.20 shows a typical escalator system. When called to an escalator incident firemen should first close off upper and lower landings with suitable barriers, open the machine room floor plate at the upper landing, then locate and turn off the main switch [see Plates 2a, b]. Having removed from the motor shaft its metal, or more commonly, plastic cover, they should then locate and place on it the hand-winding wheel which will usually be painted yellow. Next they should locate the brake

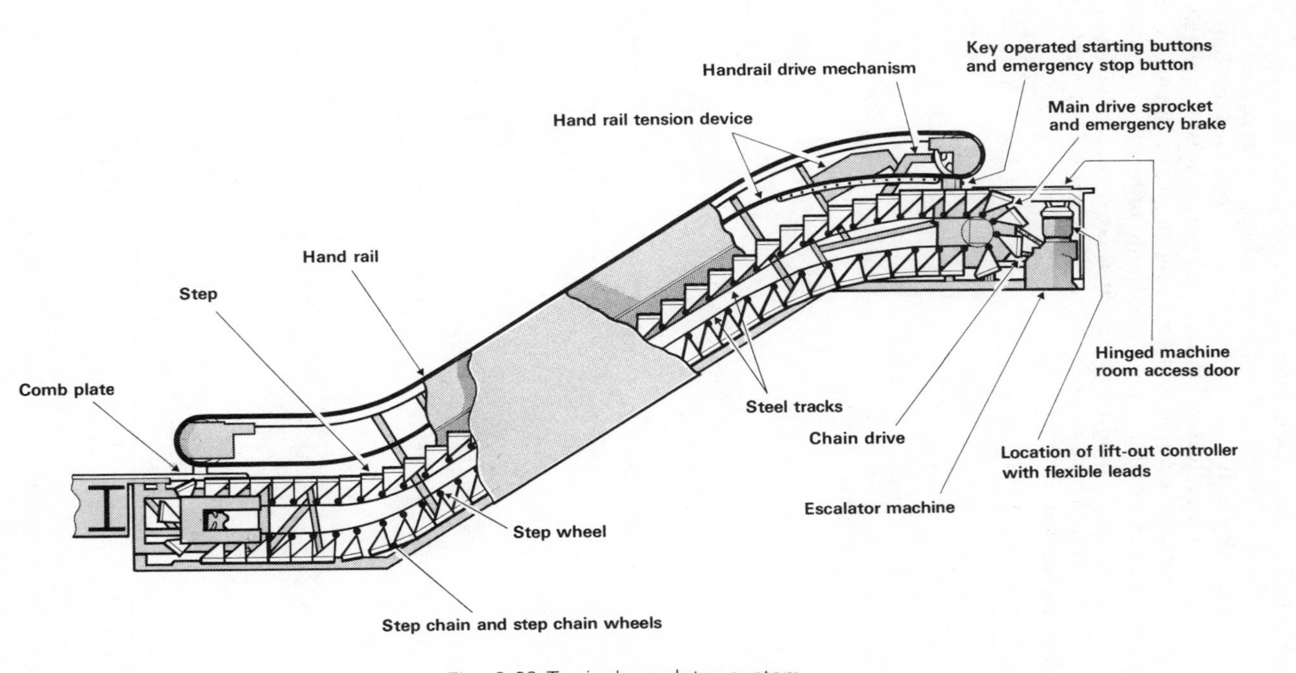
Key operated starting buttons and emergency stop button
Main drive sprocket and emergency brake
Hinged machine room access door
Location of lift-out controller with flexible leads
Handrail drive mechanism
Hand rail tension device
Steel tracks
Chain drive
Escalator machine
Step chain and step chain wheels
Step wheel
Hand rail
Step
Comb plate

Fig. 2.20 Typical escalator system.

release lever, place it on the brake if it is not permanently fitted, and use it to lift the brake. They should then turn the wheel in the desired direction which will be indicated on the machine. They should release the brake when the wheel is removed or hand-winding stops for any reason. When the operation is completed, they should replace the cover, switch on the main switch and close and secure the floor plate. They should only restart the escalator when it is clear and should not return it to service unless it is known to be safe. Where there is any doubt they should refer to the maintenance engineers.

Chapter 3
Accidents on motorways and major roads

1 General

Fire Brigades are often called to assist in extricating persons trapped in motor vehicles. Many of these accidents take place on motorways or other major and trunk roads where firemen performing rescue operations may be subjected to personal hazard from high speed traffic which is often difficult to control. The problem is increased when such accidents occur at night, when visibility is poor owing to fog or when icy road conditions prevail, so that multiple crashes are not uncommon.

It is essential that all Fire Brigade drivers should ensure that they are fully conversant with the provisions of the highway code relating to motorways and major roads.

Most Fire Brigades, in collaboration with police forces, have agreed procedures for crews attending such incidents, so that they may be afforded some degree of protection against injury from other road users. Local circumstances will dictate to some extent the most suitable procedure for each particular area, as the factors which have to be taken into account include the type of road [motorway or trunk road], the location of fire stations and the distance which appliances with specialised equipment may have to travel to reach the scene of the accident.

Because of the special construction of motorways with their limited number of access and exit points and the dangers of crossing from one carriageway to the other, this Chapter will deal primarily with motorways, but many of the principles may also be applicable to other major roads and dual carriageways with fast moving traffic.

2 Design of motorways

Motorways in Great Britain are designed to enable vehicles to travel at sustained high speeds without the hindrance of cross roads, roundabouts, 'give way' signs, right, left or 'U' turns. Certain stretches of motorways mainly in urban areas—are built above ground level and are known as 'elevated sections'.

All motorways have dual carriageways with a clearly defined central reservation. On most motorways each carriageway has three lanes but on some there are only two lanes. It is possible that some motorways in the future may have more than three lanes. On the nearside of most motorways is a section known as the 'hard shoulder' on which vehicles may stop in an emergency. Most motorways have safety barriers on the central reservation and, at intervals of about three to four kilometres, there are emergency crossover openings fitted with drive over bollards for use by the emergency services. Figure 3.1 shows in diagrammatic form some of the typical features of motorway design.

The features of motorways in Scotland may vary slightly from those in England and Wales. Where the differing features are significant, they are mentioned at the end of the following paragraphs.

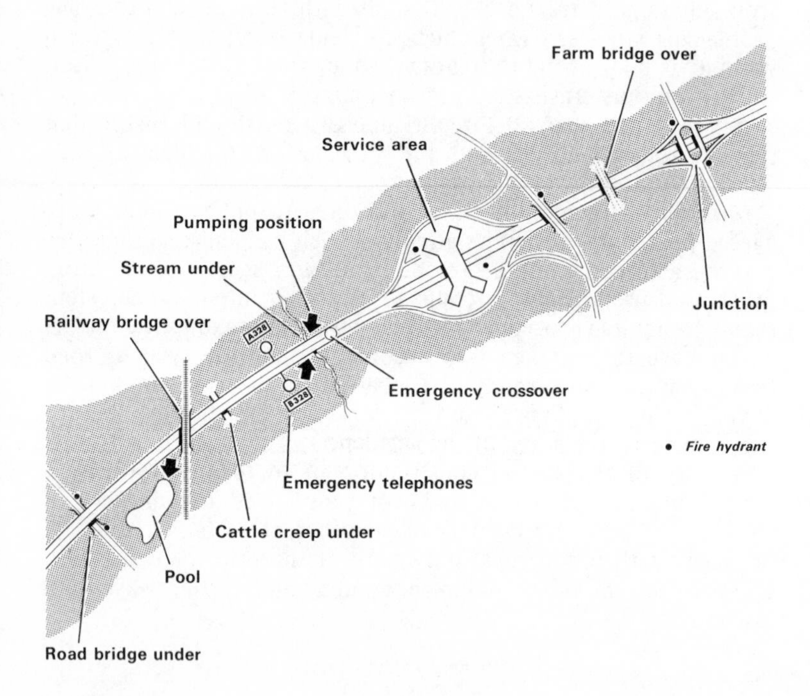

Fig. 3.1 Typical features of motorway design.

a. Carriageway indentification

On motorways in England and Wales, the carriageway on which junctions are marked with increasing numbers [starting from

Junction No 1] is referred to as the 'A' carriageway while the opposite carriageway, on which junctions are marked with decreasing numbers is known as the 'B' carriageway. Thus, on the M4 motorway, the westbound carriageway—leading away from London—bears the prefix '4/A' and the eastbound the prefix '4/B', the carriageway letter being preceded by the number of the motorway. In Scotland, carriageways are indicated according to the direction of travel, i.e. northbound, eastbound, westbound and southbound.

b. Emergency telephones

Emergency telephones linked to Police Control Rooms, are provided at approximately 1.6 km. intervals along each carriageway and are usually sited on opposite positions on each carriageway. On elevated sections emergency telephones are at more frequent intervals, generally about 400 metres apart. Each emergency telephone has a unique reference number, displayed on the approach side of the box, which includes the carriageway letter A or B but *not* the route number of the motorway. Brigades should keep a record of these reference numbers and the appropriate location of the emergency telephones as they provide a positive location of the whereabouts of the caller and calls to incidents on motorways will usually emanate from them. In Scotland, emergency telephones are indicated according to whether they are sited N.S.E.W. of the central reservation. Prior to locating the actual telephone, motorists will first see a notice [which is reflective] on which is printed SOS, a telephone symbol and the number of that telephone.

c. Marker posts

Between emergency telephones are marker posts, spaced at intervals of approximately 100 metres, which carry an indication of the direction of the nearest emergency telephone. As each marker post is uniquely numbered, it may be used to pin-point an incident on a motorway with considerable accuracy.

d. Motorway junctions

Access to and exit from motorways is limited to access and exit points via slip roads running parallel with the traffic flow [Figure 3.2].

Each junction is given a specific number, which is displayed on the directional signs at the exit points on the motorway and which is also shown on maps of the motorway. Most service areas [supplying petrol and refreshments] and maintenance units [repair units, gritters and snowploughs], have private access roads with locked gates. Arrangements are usually made for emergency services to hold keys.

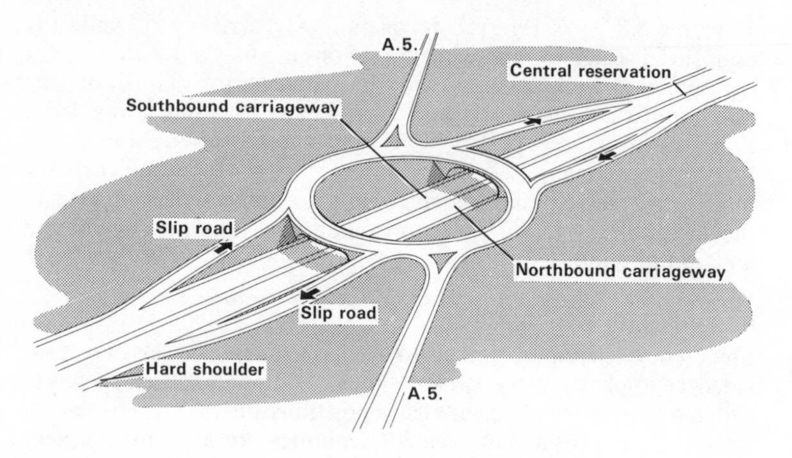

Fig. 3.2 Typical motorway junction showing the means of access and exit.

e. Motorway warning signals

Most motorways are now equipped with matrix type signals switched remotely from Police Control Rooms. Amber lights flashing alternately above and below the legend shown by the signals draw drivers' attention to the warning messages which they convey—e.g. lane closure, advised maximum speed. On the remaining stretches of motorway where there are no matrix signals, flashing amber lights without a legend mean drivers should not exceed 30 m.p.h.

Where the signals are mounted on posts [beside the carriageway or slip road] they concern drivers in all lanes, but where they are on gantries over the road each signal applies to drivers in the lane below that signal. On rural motorways the signals are normally placed at intervals of about three kilometres with additional signals at junctions. On urban motorways they are usually less than one kilometre apart and mounted on overhead gantries.

Pairs of red lights flashing alternately from side to side mean drivers must stop. However, this prohibition does not apply to vehicles being used for Fire Brigade, ambulance or police purposes as specified in Regulation 34(1)(b) of the *Traffic Signs Regulations and General Directions 1981*.

f. Emergency crossovers

Although a member of a Fire Brigade in the exercise of his duty is excepted from the regulations which make it an offence to make a 'U' turn on a motorway, such a manoeuvre is extremely dangerous even when the motorway is apparently clear. Thus, once a fire appliance has entered the carriageway of a motorway it is normally committed to remain on that carriageway until a junction is reached. In cases of extreme emergency where it may be necessary to transfer to the oposite carriageway, an emergency crossover may be used. This manoeuvre should only be carried out in extreme cases and then only under the direction and supervision of the police. Detailed procedures for crossing carriageways in such circumstances should be predetermined by individual Brigades in consultation with the local police.

There may be exceptional circumstances where the officer in charge of an appliance approaching an incident from the opposite carriageway arrives at the scene and considers that there is an urgent need to send firemen across to the incident. In such circumstances an early decision is necessary to enable the driver to pull up on the hard shoulder opposite the incident. If the officer in charge decides that immediate assistance is necessary, he should normally despatch two men [leaving a minimum of two men, including the driver, on the appliance] to cross the carriageway on foot carrying a flashing lamp, to be placed to warn approaching traffic of the incident, together with first aid equipment and any other small items as may be necessary. Because of the serious risk to life, firemen should not attempt to cross the carriageway on foot with any heavy equipment. Subject to Brigade procedures or other overriding circumstances the fire appliance should continue to the next junction in order to return to the incident on the correct carriageway.

g. Water supplies

The supply of adequate water for firefighting at incidents on motorways can be a problem. Arrangements for overcoming this problem need to be preplanned and might include the provision of water tenders and water carriers. Typical positions of hydrants near to motorways are shown in Figure 3.1. Some motorways have hydrants but these are usually restricted to a few areas. Indicator plates to identify the location of hydrants and other emergency water supplies on or near a motorway may be displayed on certain stretches of motorway, usually on the buttresses of bridges. Such plates will be to Class B or Class C of BS 3251 [see the *Manual* Book 7, Chapter 8]. The Department of Transport has undertaken to consider any proposals which are made by Fire Brigades for laying spur mains and installing hydrants at positions where water mains cross motorways or at places where special difficulties in providing water supplies exist and for the provision of hydrant indicator plates.

3 Patrol of motorways

Police motorway patrols are responsible for the operational policing of motorways and special motorway patrol vehicles are used. Amongst other equipment, these vehicles carry 'POLICE ACCIDENT' [see Figure 3.5] and 'POLICE SLOW' signs often supplemented with blue flashing lights. These signs are positioned on each side of the carriageway to warn approaching traffic of any hazard ahead. In addition, the police use traffic cones to divert traffic from one lane to another when there is an obstruction. The cars used are generally painted white with 'POLICE' signs on them, and these signs can often be illuminated when necessary.

4 Calls to incidents

In the majority of cases, calls for emergency assistance to incidents on motorways are made from the emergency telephones to Police Control Rooms and, if Fire Brigade assistance is required, the police will pass on details to the appropriate Fire Brigade Control. Pre-arranged plans with the local police will ensure that full information is given as to the location of the incident. In urban areas particularly, accidents may be observed and reported other than by the emergency telephones, and if such a call is received direct from such a source, every effort should be made to ascertain the direction of travel of the carriageway involved and if possible other information such as numbers of emergency telephones or marker posts which will help to pinpoint the incident. Details of the information received should be passed to the police.

In respect of incidents on other dual carriageway roads it is also important to identify the direction of travel of the carriageway on which the incident has occurred and the location of the incident.

A typical Fire Brigade first attendance to incidents on motorways would be one pump or water tender and one emergency tender or rescue vehicle on the carriageway on which the incident is reported and one pump or water tender from the opposite direction on the other carriageway. This dual approach will cover the contingency of:

(i) the incorrect carriageway being reported in the initial message;

(ii) vehicles being spread across both carriageways following an accident;

and

(iii) traffic building up over all lanes behind an accident and delaying appliances on the affected carriageway.

5 Police accident procedure

All police forces operating motorway patrol vehicles have definite instructions regarding motorway accidents. Approach is always made from the rear, even if this means approaching on the other carriageway, passing the accident [maybe dropping one man and certain equipment], and then going on finally to cross at a suitable point and approaching the accident from the rear.

The positioning of the 'POLICE ACCIDENT' and 'POLICE SLOW' signs will normally be at the distances shown in Figure 3.3, but the position of the traffic cones will vary according to which lane the accident is in. If the accident is in the left-hand or centre lane, the police car, being white, will serve as a warning to approaching traffic, and would normally be placed on a line with the offside of and about 25 metres to the rear of the incident [Figure 3.3, top]. However if the damaged vehicle nearest the approaching traffic is light in colour, the police car may be placed on the hard shoulder, slightly to the rear of the incident, with the blue roof warning light flashing and the headlights directed on to the light coloured vehicle. The traffic cones would be used to divert traffic into the centre and/or the right-hand lanes.

If the accident is in the right-hand lane, the police car would be placed on the approach to the obstruction and the traffic cones would be placed to divert the traffic into the centre lane [Figure 3.3, lower plate]. The warning signs would be positioned as for the other lanes.

6 Safety precautions

It should be remembered that conditions on a motorway at the time of an accident may increase considerably the risks in a fast approach to the scene of an incident and there is the danger of a further accident, especially in foggy weather or if icy road conditions prevail.

a. Positioning of Fire Brigade appliances

(1) When the police are already in attendance

Because the police patrol motorways and calls are generally made from the emergency telephones direct to the Police Control Rooms, the police will almost invariably be in attendance before the first Fire Brigade appliance and a police vehicle will in that case have been placed in the lane approaching the incident. The Fire Brigade officer in charge of the first appliance would then position his appliance in the best operational position taking into account any advice from the police. If this appliance is sited between the police

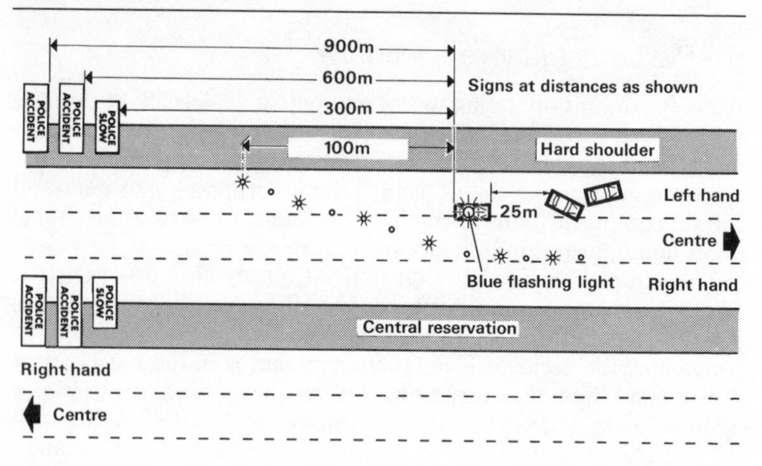

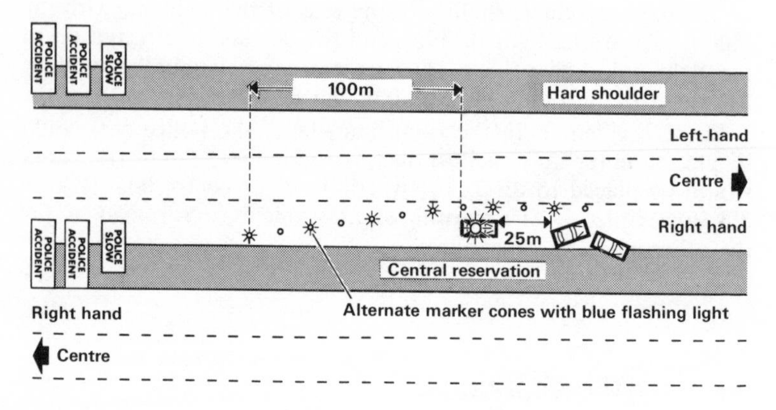

Fig. 3.3 Typical layouts for the position of police warning signs and traffic cones at accidents on motorways. Above: at accidents in the left-hand or centre lanes. Below: in the right-hand lane.

car and the incident, it should be placed in a 'fend-off' position at a shallow angle to approaching traffic. If it is placed beyond the incident, sufficient room should be left between the incident and the appliance to enable an ambulance to draw in and remove casualties. Further appliances should be driven past the incident. Personnel should dismount from the side away from passing traffic.

(2) When the police are not already in attendance

If the police are not in attendance and no warning signs or traffic cones are in position, one, or even two, appliances should be parked to provide some degree of protection for men working at the incident. The police park their motorway patrol vehicles in line with the traffic so that their prominent POLICE sign on the top or back of the car can be clearly visible to oncoming traffic, but a Fire Brigade appliance being used as a 'fend-off' vehicle should be positioned at a shallow angle to approaching traffic so that, should a vehicle strike the appliance, it will be deflected away from the obstructed lane.

At accidents in the left-hand lane of either two or three lane motorways, one Fire Brigade appliance should be positioned at the 'fend-off' angle in the lane approaching the incident and a second appliance, if present, should proceed beyond the incident and stop on the hard-shoulder—both positions are shown in Figure 3.4(1). For an incident in the centre lane of a three lane motorway, or if the obstruction covers both the left-hand and centre lanes, two appliances will be required for 'fend-off' and should be parked in the centre and left-hand lanes as shown in Figure 3.4(2), so that traffic is prevented from coming up on the nearside where crews would be working. For incidents in the right-hand lane of either two or three lane motorways, one appliance should be positioned at the 'fend-off' angle in the lane approaching the incident as shown in Figure 3.4(3) to divert traffic into the centre or left-hand lanes; other Fire Brigade appliances should be parked beyond the incident in the right-hand lane and not on the hard shoulder so that, if equipment is required, it is not necessary to cross the flow of traffic.

If the incident involves both the centre and the right-hand lanes, two appliances will be required to divert traffic into the left-hand lane, and the appliances should be positioned at the 'fend-off' angle in the centre and right-hand lanes as shown in Figure 3.4(4). The blue flashing lights on 'fend-off' appliances should be kept switched on as an additional warning to oncoming drivers. In fog, rear fog lamps, where fitted, provide an additional useful warning sign at an incident. At night time or during fog, a searchlight should be erected on a tripod behind the rearmost appliance in order to illuminate it; in clear weather, a distance of 20 m. would be suitable. There may be circumstances where the use of vehicle hazard warning lights could be useful; in such a case, however, it is important to ensure that their use does not obscure the visibility of the blue flashing light, which alone conveys the essential warning of the presence of emergency service vehicles.

b. Signs and traffic cones

By arrangement with Chief Constables, many Brigades carry 'POLICE ACCIDENT' signs (Diagram No 635 prescribed in the *Traffic Sign Regulations and General Directions, 1981*). If these signs are available, and the police have not already set theirs in

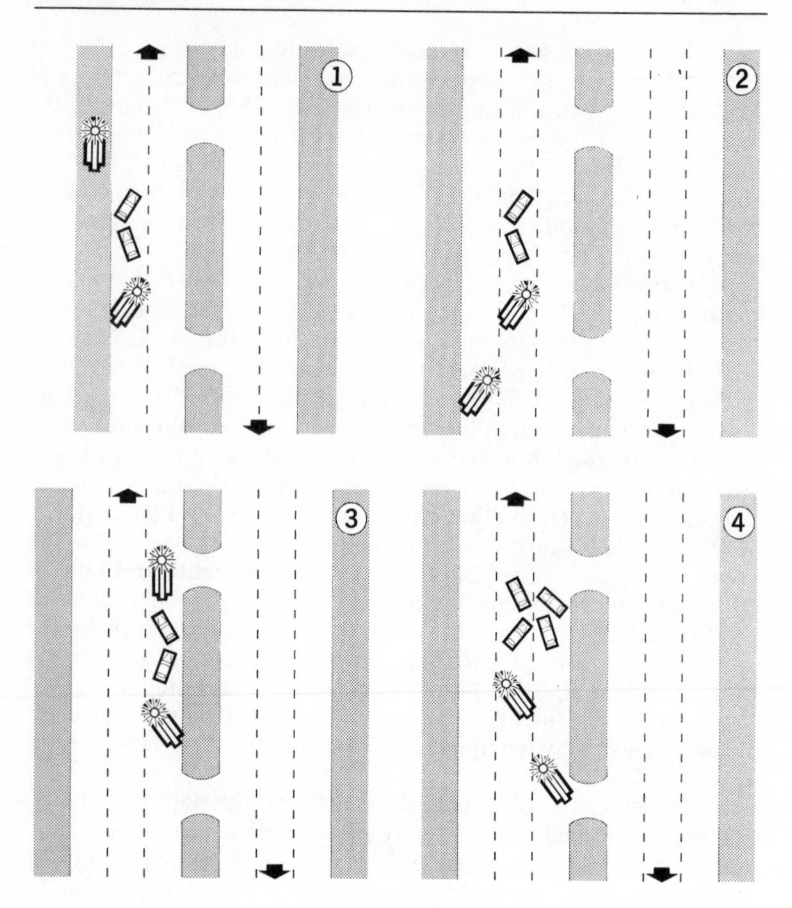

Fig. 3.4 Positioning of Fire Brigade appliances before the arrival of the police so that the appliances provide protection for firemen working at the incident. (1) For incident in the left hand lane of two or three lane motorways. (2) When the obstruction covers the centre lane, or both the left hand and centre lane. (3) For incidents in the right hand lane. (4) For incidents covering both the centre and right hand lanes.

position, a crew member should erect the 'POLICE ACCIDENT' sign [Figure 3.5] on the approach to the incident to warn traffic to slow down. The effectiveness of the sign can be increased by day or night by placing a blue flashing light on a tripod [as used by the police] behind the sign, but if such a light is not available, a lamp [flashing if possible] should be placed at the foot of the sign. Ideally a warning sign should be placed 900 metres from the

Fig. 3.5 Placing a 'POLICE ACCIDENT' sign in position in front of a blue flashing light on a tripod.

incident, but if this is not practicable e.g. because manpower is not available it should be at least 400 metres from the incident.

If traffic cones are also carried they should be set out in the same way as the police would place them as shown in Figure 3.3.

c. High conspicuity clothing

Because there are motorists who disregard warning signs and approach and pass a fire or accident with little or no reduction in speed, the Central Fire Brigades Advisory Council has recommended that Fire Brigade personnel attending such incidents on motorways or other major roads should be provided with high conspicuity clothing. This should, if possible, comprise a high conspicuity, fluorescent surcoat in Saturn yellow with reflective tape as shown in Figure 3.6. The majority of the material used in the surcoat should be plastic-coated fabric with the remainder of the garment consisting of strips or tapes of a retroreflective material—to be fixed to the front, back and sides of the garment—to ensure effective visibility at night.

The high conspicuity clothing should be donned en route to an incident on a motorway by all personnel except the driver, who should dress as soon as possible after arrival, and in any case before venturing on to the carriageway.

Fig. 3.6 Fireman's surcoat for use on motorways and other major roads.

7 Operational procedure

The first officer to arrive at a rescue incident may well find a number of willing helpers endeavouring to assist the trapped persons, each one of the opinion that his method is best. Unless they are achieving satisfactory results, helpers should be requested to stand clear while a calm but careful inspection of the situation is made. Taking into account the rescue equipment available or on the way, a plan of action should be made and put into operation at once. Requests for assistance in the form of appliances and equipment should be made as soon as possible. Where appropriate, alternative methods should be considered and, where practicable, incorporated into the main plan. It is important, however, not to constantly 'chop and change' the plan of action.

In his assessment of the situation, the officer in charge should be concerned with the following tasks:

(i) ensuring the continued safety of his personnel and equipment;

(ii) dealing with any fires in vehicles where persons are trapped;

(iii) dealing with any other fires;

(iv) taking note of special risks, such as vehicles carrying dangerous substances;

(v) making an inspection of the incident to ascertain the number and location of persons who are actually trapped in vehicles, and the number of persons who are not trapped but who will require medical aid;

(vi) considering the order of precedence in dealing with casualties;

(vii) organising and directing personnel and equipment to vehicles where persons are trapped;

(viii) considering whether further special equipment will be required for the extrication of casualties;

(ix) deciding whether to move casualties to a place of safety whilst awaiting the arrival of ambulances;

(x) co-operating with other emergency services in the removal of casualties from the scene.

As soon as possible a thorough search must be made to locate casualties and to assess the extent of injuries. It should be remembered that casualties are not always confined to crashed vehicles; valuable information can often be obtained from witnesses of the accident as to the whereabouts of injured persons, some of whom may have been taken into nearby property.

a. Liaison with other services

An important aspect of the success in actually carrying out rescue operations is that of command and control. The statutory powers laid down in Section 30(3) of the *Fire Services Act* relating to firefighting operations do not extend to rescue operations, unless fire is involved. It must be emphasised that it is essential to have liaison and agreement with the other emergency services together with a broad definition of responsibilities. Without this liaison, particularly at major incidents, there could be a lack of co-ordinated effort to the detriment of those trapped in wrecked vehicles [see also Chapter 4—'Major disasters'].

8 Rescue techniques

a. General considerations

Each accident is different and each will present different factors which firemen will have to bear in mind when attempting to rescue victims. It is therefore impossible to lay down in advance hard and fast rules as to the procedures firemen should follow. Generally speaking, they should have extinguishing media ready in case of fire, should wear protective gloves and high conspicuity clothing, should enter vehicles as quickly as possible to give moral and physical support to those being extricated, and should try to create ample space in which to work. The choice of the most appropriate equipment and rescue techniques will obviously depend on the type of incident and the damage to the vehicle. Firemen should always bear in mind the dangers inherent in a road traffic accident and take appropriate precautions [see 8f. below]. Plates 3—8 show firemen at work at various accidents.

b. Entry with little damage

The main requirement in carrying out a rescue from a crashed vehicle will usually be speed.

Doors are the most obvious means of entry but recent developments make it very difficult to burst open a lock if it has jammed. It may be easier to try a door other than the one giving immediate access or it may be possible instead to prise a door open using a spread ram [see Fig. 3.7 and Plate 3]. A knowledge of car door locks will help in deciding on the means of entry. Unless firemen can make an entry easily and quickly by a door they will do better to try another approach.

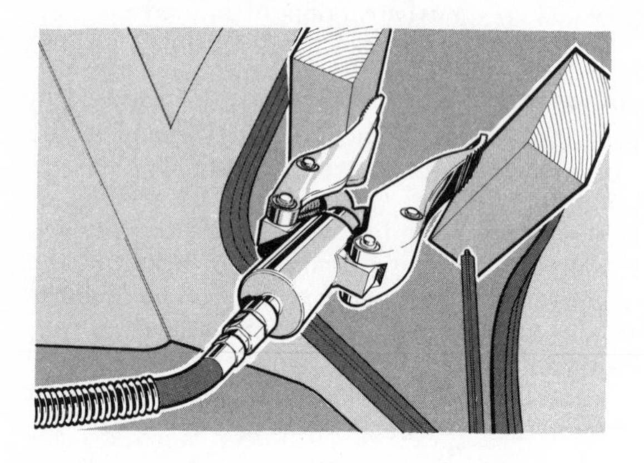

Fig. 3.7 Use of a spread ram to open a door.

They should be able to effect a quick and simple entry by removing the front or rear screen. The best way of doing this is to cut round the screen rubber with a sharp knife, following the edge of the glass, which can then be lifted out without levering. This method is, however, not possible when the glass is glazed direct into the body aperture with a thermo-setting material [more common with the windscreen than with the back window]. Another means of entry is to prise out the glass by inserting a screwdriver between it and the seal [Fig. 3.8].

This could cause the screen to shatter but as most front screens are of zoned toughened glass, this should not cause injury to either the entrapped person or the fireman. Some extra care would have to be taken on a rear window. Many cars are now of a 'hatchback' design with folding rear seats. This can facilitate entry and give working space. In older cars entry via the boot may be possible providing the rear squab can be removed.

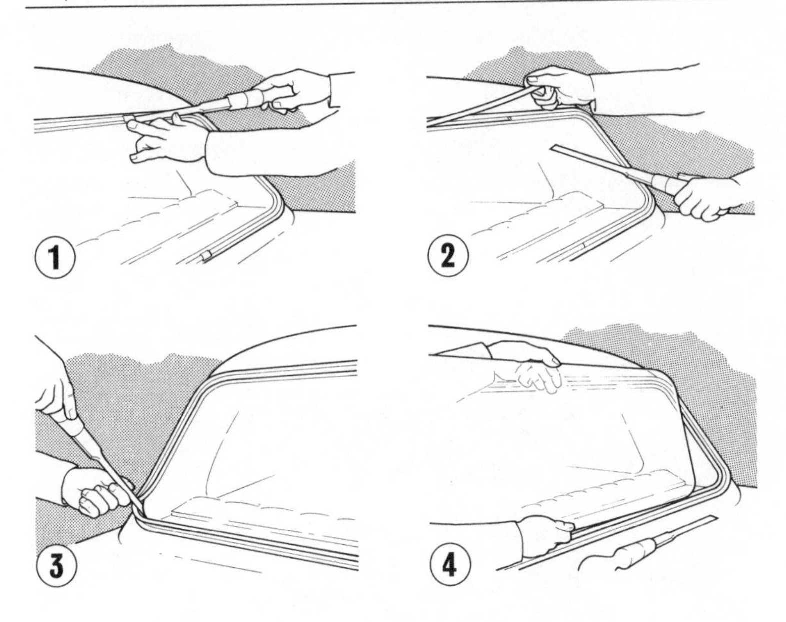

Fig. 3.8 Using a screwdriver to prise out a windscreen.

c. Entry with considerable damage

If the previous methods are not sufficient it will be necessary to cut through panels.

Fig. 3.9 shows the construction of a typical modern car. The roof offers better access than the floor because it is thinner and because it is not impeded by the central tunnel and cross members. By cutting through the A, B/C, D, and possibly E posts as appropriate, firemen can make it possible to remove or lever open the roof or door panels. Fig. 3.10 illustrates a type of 'body cutter' capable of exerting a pressure of 700 bars.

In jacking, firemen must use the strongest base points of a car, e.g. the bottom of the B/C post or the rear door aperture to the junction of the fascia, A post and windscreen pillar, or the seat cross-members. For some accidents air bags may be more suitable than jacks. *Manual,* Part 2 gives more information on jacks etc. [See Fig. 3.11.]

d. Larger vehicles

For larger vehicles the technique used will depend on their construction. Most will have a more rigid chassis and jacking will be possible in a variety of positions. However, some buses and

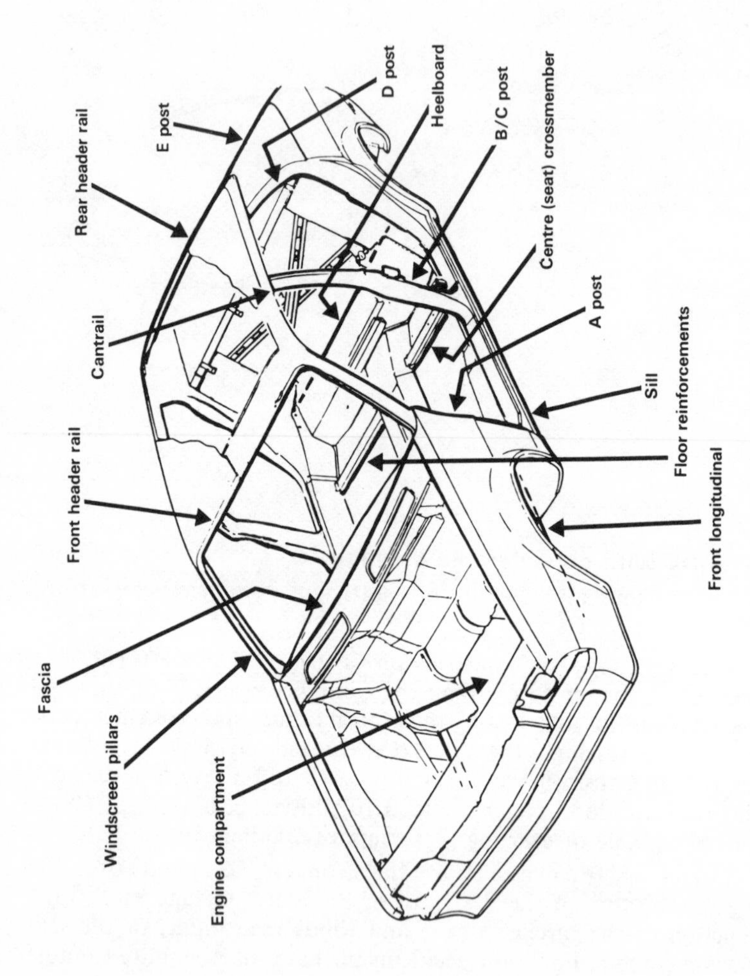

Fig. 3.9 Typical modern car.

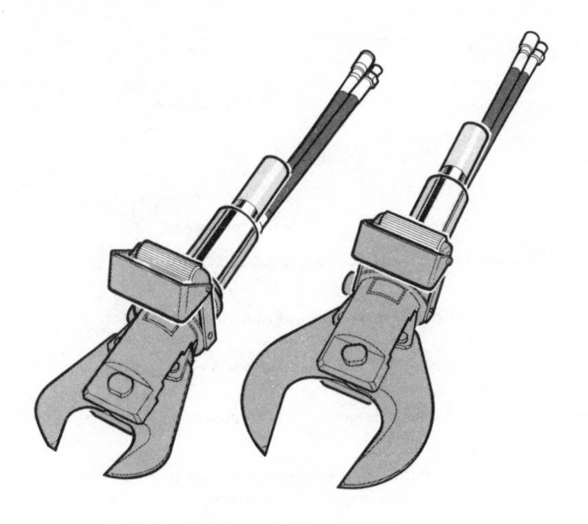

Fig. 3.10 Example of a body cutter.

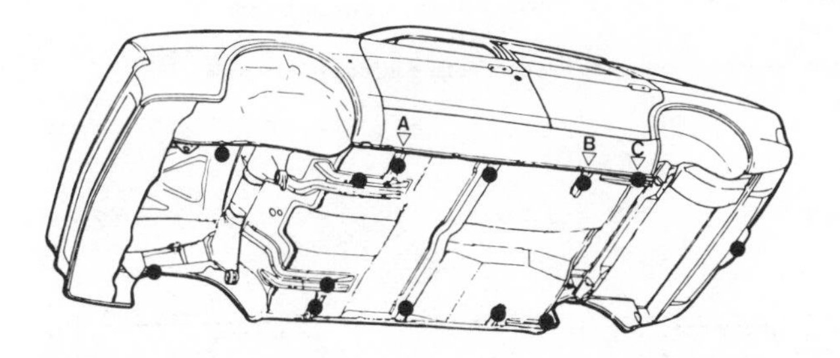

Fig. 3.11 Jacking points on a typical car.

coaches are constructed without a chassis and can only be lifted at certain points. Here again there are many types of lorries and quite a number of types of buses and coaches. Visits by firemen to road transport organisations and passenger vehicle garages will yield a lot of information. Most organisations will be pleased to assist by pointing out jacking positions, lifting points and likely areas of danger [see Fig. 3.12]. Firemen should bear in mind with regard to buses, coaches etc. especially, that they need to know not only their own local types, but also those that may pass through their districts. They should also be aware that bodies may be mounted on chassis in different ways, some of which may preclude the use of some of the jacking points illustrated.

①

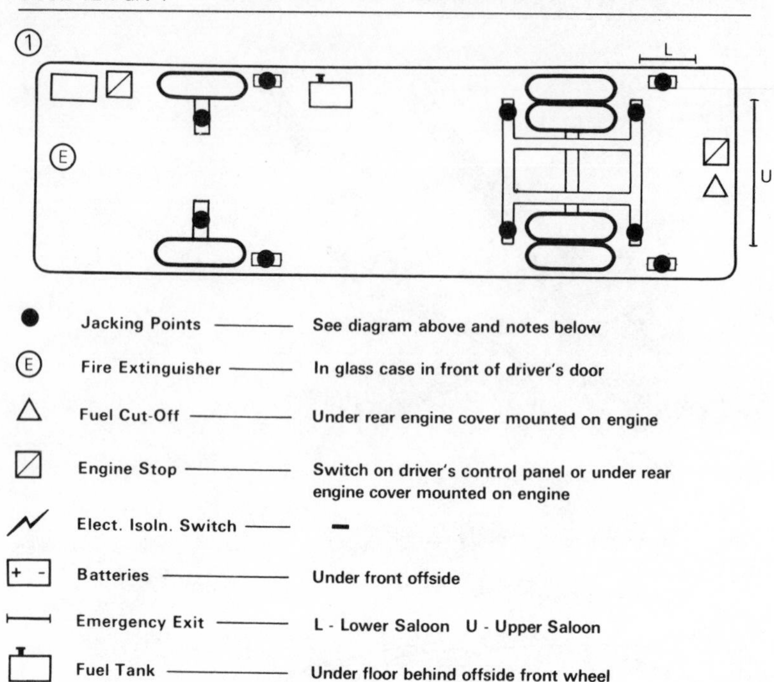

●	Jacking Points	See diagram above and notes below
Ⓔ	Fire Extinguisher	In glass case in front of driver's door
△	Fuel Cut-Off	Under rear engine cover mounted on engine
⧄	Engine Stop	Switch on driver's control panel or under rear engine cover mounted on engine
⚡	Elect. Isoln. Switch	—
+ -	Batteries	Under front offside
├─┤	Emergency Exit	L - Lower Saloon U - Upper Saloon
▭	Fuel Tank	Under floor behind offside front wheel

②

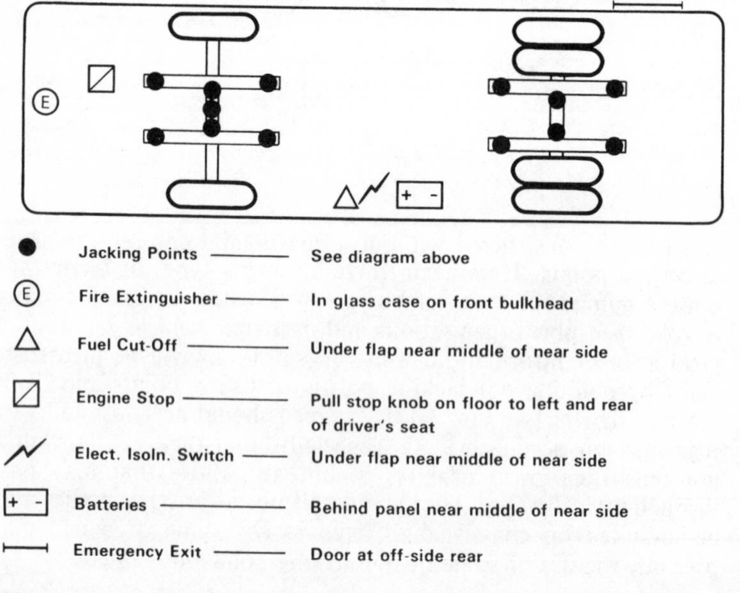

●	Jacking Points	See diagram above
Ⓔ	Fire Extinguisher	In glass case on front bulkhead
△	Fuel Cut-Off	Under flap near middle of near side
⧄	Engine Stop	Pull stop knob on floor to left and rear of driver's seat
⚡	Elect. Isoln. Switch	Under flap near middle of near side
+ -	Batteries	Behind panel near middle of near side
├─┤	Emergency Exit	Door at off-side rear

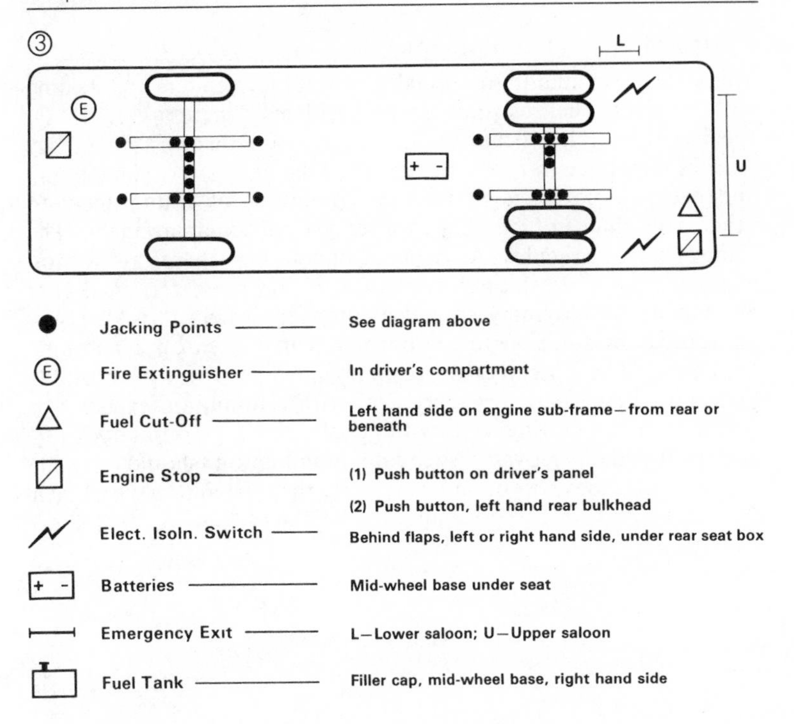

Fig. 3.12 Examples of jacking positions etc. for larger vehicles (1) Leyland Titan. (2) Bristol single decker. (3) Leyland Atlantean.

Lifting large vehicles without a crane is difficult. However, it is often necessary to lift only a very small distance to release people trapped. Firemen must not rely solely on the support of jacks, air-bags, spreaders etc. Both during and after lifting they must securely insert solid blocks of timber or metal to prevent the weight falling back onto a victim or fireman through a sudden failure of the equipment. This will also allow primary equipment to be withdrawn whilst larger secondary, and more powerful equipment, is inserted to extend the lift or the movement.

A vehicle raised on one side by only a few degrees does tend to slide away from the jacking position and it must be wedged or anchored to prevent this. A vehicle being righted must be controlled by lines from the lifting side as there is the obvious tendency for it to bounce on its tyres and roll the other way. With vehicles such as petrol tankers in particular, firemen should bear in mind the possibility of fire and lay out appropriate firefighting equipment ready for instant use.

e. Use of special equipment

Many Brigades maintain specialist emergency tenders for dealing with incidents such as road traffic accidents. There are J.C.D.D. specifications [Nos 8 and 9] for two types. However, emergency tenders may have to travel further than the nearest available pump and because of traffic or weather conditions or commitment to other calls may not be able to attend a particular accident. The Central Fire Brigades Advisory Council has therefore recommended that at least once appliance of the pre-determined first attendance should carry special equipment to help those trapped or injured, in addition to the normal gear carried on a pumping appliance. The special gear recommended is a set of portable hydraulic lifting and spreading gear with a minimum capacity of 4 tonnes, metal cutting tools with goggles [see Figs 3.13 and 3.14], and heavy duty gloves. Adequate illumination should also be ensured. Brigades choose independently the type and make of gear they want, within these requirements. Plates 3, 4, 6, 7, 8 show equipment in use.

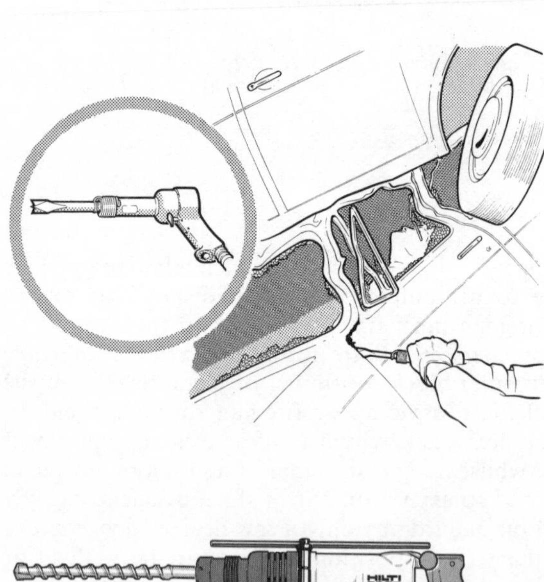

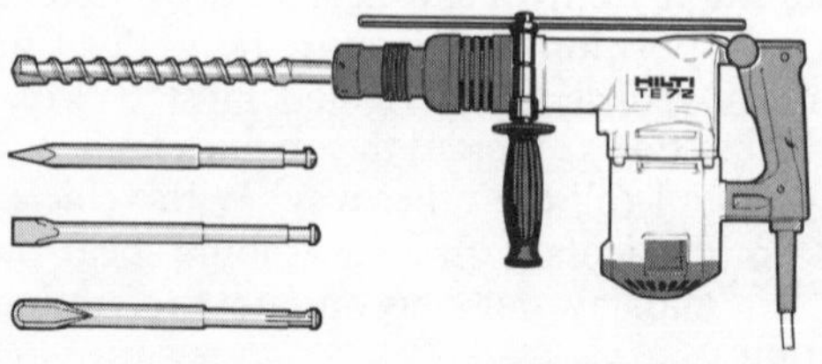

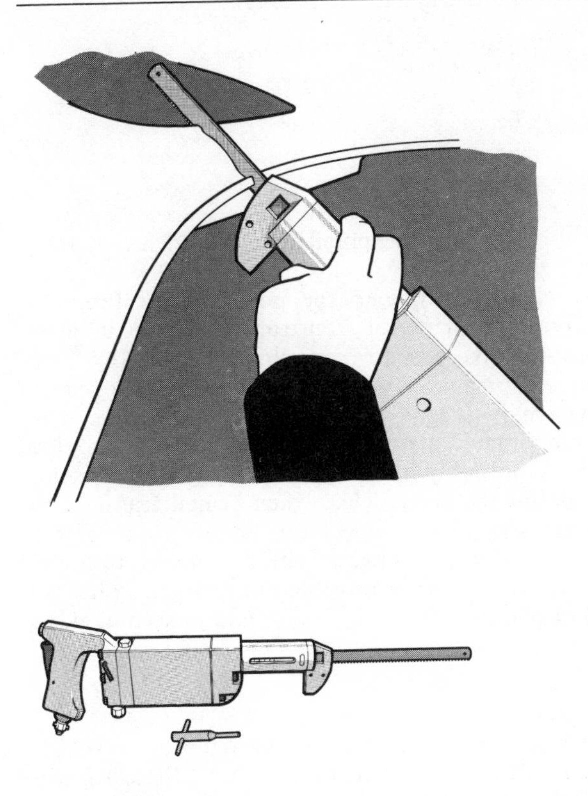

Figs. 3.13 & 3.14 Metal cutting tools.

Firemen who may have to use special equipment will receive instruction on the particular items they will handle. They should also pay strict attention to any manufacturer's instructions. The *Manual*, Part 2, gives further general information on the special equipment that might be used at road traffic accidents.

f. Safety considerations

Firemen should not forget that, even though an accident has happened on a relatively minor road, passing traffic can still be travelling fast. Many Brigades carry 'Police Accident' signs [Fig. 3.5] and in the absence of police, firemen should position and if possible illuminate these so as to give an approaching motorist ample warning. The *Highway Code* publishes *'overall stopping distances'* which combine a driver's *'thinking distance'* and his *'braking distance'*. Examples of *'overall stopping distances'* for *light* vehicles at various speeds are:

Km/h	*O.S.D.* (metres)
30	12
65	36
95	70
120	120

Firemen must also consider the possibility of wet, icy or foggy conditions.

An accident often gives rise to the possibility of fire, due, usually, to the presence of petrol from ruptured tanks or pipes. Firemen will have to take care to cover this possibility by laying out firefighting equipment, especially when using any sort of cutting equipment e.g. Cengar saw, zip-gun, oxy-propane. They must also remember that many modern cars now contain moulded and foam plastics not only in seats but as filling and sound absorbent material in the body. This, when heated, can give off toxic fumes. They should disconnect the battery if possible to avoid short circuiting any electrical wiring whilst cutting and causing sparks or arcing. Other possible dangers are hydrolastic fluid pipes and displacers, hydraulic brake fluid pipes and glass.

9 Making up

The Fire Brigade is not responsible for the removal of vehicles involved in an accident. Its role really ends with the extrication of casualties and the extinguishment of any fire. Unless it is necessary for rescue, vehicles should not be moved as the police will want to note distances, position, skid marks etc. Before departure, however, firemen should clear from the road any dangerous substances such as oil, petrol and broken glass. The officer in charge should hand to the police any valuables or personal effects found at the scene.

Chapter 4
Major disasters

1 Definition

A major disaster is primarily an incident which causes, or threatens, multiple deaths and injuries or severe disruption and which is beyond the normal capacities of the Fire, police and ambulance services. It will require, from the outset, their special mobilisation, organisation and co-ordination, and may also involve other services or undertakings not normally engaged in emergency work. It is likely to arise with little or no warning and to require operations of a more than usually protracted and difficult character.

a. Criteria

It is probable that there will, on such occasions, be many casualties but the number of killed and injured should not by itself necessarily determine whether an incident amounts to a major disaster. Other factors, such as the type and location of the incident, the number of services likely to be involved, and the time to effect rescues, to establish control and to restore normality, will also all be important. So, for example, if an aircraft crashes at an airport and there are 50 casualties, it may be possible to deal with the incident relatively simply and quickly but the same occurrence in a built-up area could well amount to a major disaster because of the over-all disruption and the extensive, complicated operations necessary to deal with it.

b. Examples

Each incident must be judged on its merits but, apart from the foregoing, the following are examples of likely major disasters: a passenger train collision or derailment; a road traffic accident involving many vehicles and/or people on a busy road; an industrial accident, malfunction, or other incident involving dangerous substances; a structural collapse trapping people; a major explosion; a flood, landslide, or subsidence; a heath or forest fire threatening lives and property over a wide area.

2 The disaster plan

In order to cope successfully with major disasters a certain amount of pre-planning is essential. For this purpose each Fire Authority should have its own plan ready for implementation as the need arises. This will normally form part of an over-all major disaster plan drawn up in co-operation with the Brigade, other emergency services, and other organisations likely to be involved. A senior officer of the Authority will normally be responsible for liaison with the bodies concerned about the plan, its co-ordination and its revision as necessary.

a. The role of the Fire Service

The main requirement at a major disaster will be to deal with the immediate situation, prevent it from deteriorating, and restore normal conditions as soon as possible. To help in achieving this end, the plan prepared by the Brigade should be flexible in operation and capable of adaptation to any circumstances. The primary and immediate duties of firemen will be to effect any necessary rescues, to extinguish any fire already in progress, and to prevent or be ready to deal with any threatened fire. They will also assist other services as far as possible, particularly where their specialist skills or equipment can be specifically helpful. They may, for example, assist with first aid, carry out pumping, or provide lighting.

b. Command

The senior Fire Brigade officer present will retain legal responsibility for the control of firefighting operations and firemen will work in crews under the command of their own officers even when assisting other services. Over-all command will be as determined in the local plan. Although not prescribed by law, it will, normally, be in the hands of a senior police officer as Incident Controller; he will act throughout, however, in consultation with senior officers of the other services involved. A Local Authority official, such as the Chief Executive, may have over-all responsibility in the wider context.

c. Co-operation with other services

Co-ordination of effort with other services will also be as determined in the plan. Firemen should ensure they are familiar with the arrangements that have been made. The Fire Service officer in charge at an incident should keep constantly in mind the need for consulting other services and for taking their advice and guidance into account. He should also ensure that the other services and, in particular, the Incident Controller are kept informed of the state and progress of Fire Service operations. Without neglecting his own urgent responsibilities, he should be ready to meet requests for guidance, advice, help and information from the other services.

3 Implementation of the plan

The plan may be implemented following a request from another service, in response to a call or calls from the public which clearly indicate a major disaster, or following Fire Brigade attendance at an incident.

a. Initiation following first attendance

Where it is not clear in advance that an incident amounts to a major disaster the officer in charge of the first appliance to arrive should assess the situation to the best of his ability and inform Brigade Control if, in his opinion, the plan should be put into effect. He must bear in mind that, while an adequate response to the situation is urgent, the decision to implement a major disaster plan is a very serious step to take. Such implementation is very wide in its implications and will involve considerable disruption and diversion of numerous people, facilities and equipment from other important duties. He should therefore frame his message with consideration and include as many details as possible, using any special code or format laid down by his Brigade for such circumstances. His information should include: the exact location of the incident; a description of the situation; an estimate of the numbers believed trapped or injured; the extent of the hazard; weather conditions; any roads blocked; and, the best means of access. When giving details of access he should remember that in some circumstances it may be more effective for appliances not to work directly at the scene, but, for example, from a bridge over it.

b. Mobilisation.

Brigade Control will carry out mobilisation on receipt of a major disaster message. It will also notify the other services and call on neighbouring Brigades for assistance as necessary. Such assistance will be over and above any normal arrangements for mutual aid. Details of mobilisation will be in accordance with local circumstances. There should, however, be provision for the attendance of at least six–ten pumping appliances and any special appliances or equipment likely to be needed. The plan should also prescribe the number and rank of officers to attend, including any with a special function, such as the Brigade Photographer, and any required to help the officer in charge with specific tasks; it should provide for keeping senior officers and other relevant personnel informed of developments.

Closing-in moves for officers and appliances should begin as soon as possible, to maintain fire cover elsewhere in the Brigade area for the duration of the incident.

4 Control and communications

a. Siting

It is important that there should be an effective Fire Service control point as soon as possible. Initially this may be a temporary forward control or contact point near the incident but, when the main Fire Service control is established it will need to be located some distance back. The officer in charge should bear in mind that while the Fire Service might be the first to arrive in force, other services will be in attendance subsequently, also in large numbers. His command and control point lay-out should make allowances for this. He should therefore take into account the likely position of the other services' controls and of the main Incident Control since he will have to work in close co-operation with them. He should, however, remember that there can be radio interference between mobile controls if they are too close, say less than 15m. apart. It may accordingly be necessary to make special arrangements for liaison, e.g. by runner, portable radio, or land line.

b. Subsidiary control points

Where an incident takes place over a wide area, the officer in charge should consider establishing subsidiary control points at relevant places, from where messages can be relayed back. Again, it may be necessary to make special provision for maintaining communications. It will be important that he remains up-to-date on the position in different sectors. He should ensure that any information from the first attendance is transferred to his control point when it is established. A careful record of the incident should be maintained as this could form the basis of any necessary amendments to planning later on.

c. Communications

Apart from ensuring satisfactory communications at the scene of the incident, the officer in charge must also see that there are adequate and effective communications with Brigade Control. Control will need to be aware of the situation as it develops and situation reports must be transmitted at regular intervals.

The officer in charge should make his facilities available to other services, if necessary. Later, however, particularly at widespread incidents, it may be necessary to co-ordinate all communication arrangements. The Incident Controller will decide this after consultation. It may involve the provision of extra equipment or facilities by British Telecom or the Home Office Directorate of Telecommunications.

d. Identification

The location of the control point should be made known to all involved in the incident and clearly indicated. The officer in charge should also ensure that he is readily identifiable as such. Where Brigades provide items specifically to assist with identification [specially labelled jackets, flags, noticeboards, etc.] these should be used.

5 Deployment of resources

a. Holding area

As a large number of appliances are likely to become committed in the course of a major disaster, it is desirable to establish a holding area where they can rendezvous in the first instance and be available for deployment. Such an area will obviate the scattering or haphazard location of Fire Service reserves and reinforcements and prevent unnecessary congestion. The officer in charge should designate such an area if one is not prescribed by the Brigade plan. Alternatively, the Incident Controller may arrange for a general rendezvous and holding area. The police will be responsible for control of this and for traffic management generally; this will include any decision to close the area to all but essential vehicles and exclude the public completely, if that is necessary, to avoid obstruction.

b. Reporting in

When new appliances and crew first arrive at an incident they should at once report in to the control point, by radio if necessary. They should not engage in action before this. On arrival men should park their appliances in such a way not to cause obstruction, and remain with them until re-deployed.

c. Fire Service equipment control

There will need to be careful supervision of specialist Fire Service equipment, especially where there is little available at the incident and it is in wide demand, perhaps in a number of different places. To ensure it is employed to the best advantage and not mislaid or misused, the officer in charge should arrange an area for its distribution *and return*, making sure its location is known, illuminating it if necessary, and appointing a person to be responsible for it. Care will be needed in loaning equipment to non-Fire Service personnel and a Fire Brigade operator should always accompany it. There must be close contact between the equipment area, the Fire Brigade control point, and the Incident Control over deployment, particularly where a question of priorities arises.

d. Specialist officers

In addition to appointing an equipment officer, the officer in charge should also consider the desirability of appointing individual officers to be responsible for other special areas, if this is not laid down in his Brigade plan. Typical such areas are: Control Unit; safety; breathing apparatus; communications; water; foam; staff duties; salvage; transport; decontamination; press; fire investigation; and liaison. Officers assigned to these duties should occupy themselves solely with them and not the general conduct of the incident.

e. Tackling the incident

The first point of contact with an incident is not necessarily the centre of it nor the point where the greatest problem exists. The officer in charge should further bear in mind that his initial resources will be sparse. He should concentrate them where they can be most effective and not disperse them piecemeal throughout the incident. In some circumstances it will be desirable to divert men from firefighting or rescue to assist in other ways. However, where a fire could occur or spread rapidly the officer in charge should give orders to lay out, charge and man hose-lines. Otherwise crews may become dispersed on other work and have to be remustered before jets can be got to work: this delay might have serious consequences.

The officer in charge will, of course, be responsible for ensuring that men and equipment are ordered on as necessary within the framework of the plan. He should particularly bear in mind any special needs determined by the incident, such as the requirement for maximum amounts of foam at an aircraft crash. He should ensure that there is adequate provision for the fuelling and maintenance of appliances and equipment. Other services may need to call on these resources and at a later stage it may be necessary for the Incident Controller to co-ordinate arrangements over the incident as a whole.

The officer in charge should not send a stop message or release his men and resources from the incident before consultation with the Incident Controller.

f. Outside help

The officer in charge may be able to supplement his own resources by help from outside bodies. Organisations such as the Red Cross/ St John Ambulance Brigade may be better placed to help other services but the officer should bear in mind the possible provision of specialist advice or equipment by bodies such as Gas, Electricity and Water Boards, British Rail, H.M. Coastguard, and the Forestry Commission, by contractors, and by chemical manufacturers. In addition the Armed Forces may assist with tasks of reconnaissance, search, rescue and engineering, under the provisions of the Military Aid to the Civil Community Scheme. This is described in the Ministry of Defence pamphlet of that title. Requests for military aid from the Fire Service, after approval by the Chief Fire Officer or his Deputy, should be made through the Incident Controller.

On arrival at an incident firemen are likely to find members of the general public actively engaged in rescue work. It may be difficult to persuade them to leave, particularly if they have friends, relations or colleagues trapped, injured or in danger. Pending the arrival of further personnel, the officer in charge should try to channel their efforts into organised activity to give general assistance where they themselves will not be at risk.

6 Casualties

Any major disaster is likely to involve many casualties: fatalities, severely injured, slightly injured, and shocked. Firemen should bear in mind that some rescues may actually be impossible without medical or surgical help.

a. Handling casualties; the casualty clearance area

The handling of casualties will normally be the responsibility primarily of the ambulance and medical services. The senior Fire Brigade officer will, however, retain responsibility for firefighting and rescue. Firemen may have to take immediate action to help casualties on arrival at an incident and may also be required to give assistance later. In so doing they should follow the procedures described in Chapter 6 of this Book. They should establish priorities, taking care, for example, not to waste effort on extracting the obviously dead when others yet living need urgent treatment. To ensure quick and efficient treatment, firemen should bring the injured to a casualty clearance area. This will be arranged and supervised by police in consultation with medical personnel and will, where possible, be located near a similarly supervised ambulance assembly area.

b. Providing information

Firemen should ensure that relevant information about those with whom they have dealt is conveyed to medical personnel. There may be local arrangements for this purpose, but a simple method is to label the people rescued. Labels should include such details as: whether a tourniquet has been applied and, if so, when; whether morphine has been administered and, if so, the time and dosage; and whether severe haemorrhage has occurred. Priority of removal from the incident should also be indicated.

The senior police officer will arrange for the documentation of casualties and the recording of where they have been taken, in order to deal with queries. Police will also make necessary mortuary arrangements. If firemen have to move corpses or parts of bodies during their operations they should ensure that the details are conveyed to the relevant control.

7 Welfare considerations

A major disaster will lay a particular responsibility on the officer in charge to provide for the well-being of his men, not only for their own sakes but also to ensure that the incident is dealt with as efficiently as possible.

a. Reliefs

Any such incident is likely to be protracted. The officer in charge must therefore consider the possible need for reliefs. He should be able to estimate at an early stage the likely extent and duration of Fire Service involvement and should inform Brigade Control of this as soon as he is able. Control will then arrange the adequate level of relief.

b. Refreshments

The need for feeding and refreshment will also arise during the course of a lengthy incident. If the Brigade does not have its own arrangements or if these need supplementing, the officer in charge should bear in mind the possibility of help from other sources such as the W.R.V.S. or Salvation Army. He should also liaise with the other services and with the Incident Controller, as, particularly at longer incidents, there would be merit in the co-ordination of feeding, refreshment and possible rest areas. If refreshments cannot be provided readily, this may affect the arrangements that have to be made for reliefs.

c. Health and Safety

Health and Safety at Work legislation obliges employers and employees to conduct their work in a safe manner. While a certain amount of danger is bound to be present at a major disaster, all personnel must bear safety considerations in mind throughout. A designated officer should have specific responsibility for safety. He should ensure, in particular, that adequate protective clothing is available and worn by all those operating in areas of likely hazard.

8 Other considerations

a. Handling materials at the scene

It is very important to cause as little disturbance as possible to materials at the scene of a major disaster: debris, wreckage, etc. can help later investigations into the cause of the incident which in their turn can help prevent a recurrence. Firemen should therefore not move items unnecessarily and should take care how they move themselves and their equipment to avoid destroying evidence. This is particularly important at aircraft crashes or incidents involving explosives.

They should also take care in the handling of personal property found at the scene. It is not always possible to identify this as belonging to a particular individual and it should therefore be handed to the police for safe-keeping.

b. Press etc.

At any major disaster there is likely to be pressure for specific or general information from the press, television companies, news agencies and others, including members of the public. Arrangements for answering such queries and for making general statements should be made in conjunction with the other services involved and will usually be the responsibility of the Incident Controller or a person nominated by him.

c. Training

It is important that major disaster plans are kept up-to-date and tested periodically. Therefore, while day-to-day drills will cover the basic skills necessary in such circumstances, firemen should expect to engage with other services in special exercises for this purpose.

Chapter 5
Miscellaneous rescues

In 1981 the Fire Service attended some 54,000 special service calls of an emergency and humanitarian type. This figure does not include calls to road traffic accidents. A list of the different types of call attended by the Service would be endless and only a few of the more common types, plus one with potential, will be dealt with in this Chapter. Firemen must be aware of the potential for special services on their 'patch'. A look at any construction site with its mounds of sand and gravel, excavations, scaffolding, tower cranes etc. should give a fireman food for thought. Children have a knack of getting into the most difficult places and it is the Brigade who will be called upon to extricate them. Possibly it is in this sphere that the ingenuity, persistence and skill of firemen are most required.

1 Sewer rescues

Despite elaborate safety precautions taken by the water authorities men are still occasionally trapped or overcome in sewers. The main cause is the presence of 'sewer gas', a mixture of methane [CH_4] and sulphuretted hydrogen [H_2S]. Both gases are flammable and explosive within certain limits and H_2S is particularly toxic. Another cause could be collapse of old sewer workings during modernisation.

a. Locating the victim

There is always a 'top man' or surface man who remains above ground when sewer men are below. He maintains contact with them and it is from him that a call will come. He should be able to indicate accurately where in the sewer the accident has happened and the number of people involved. Firemen should remember that if there is a considerable flow in the sewer an unconscious person may be washed down stream.

b. Operational procedure

At least two or three manholes should already be open for ventilation and usually the casualty will be found in the vicinity of one of these. If possible firemen should bring him to the nearest shaft to the surface, provided it is large enough to take him. It is fairly obvious that they should wear B.A. and use sparkproof illumination. They may be able to take in a resuscitation set but provided the victim is uninjured and can be moved would do best just to get him to the surface as quickly as possible.

c. Moving the victim

The Service has developed the use of various harnesses, stretchers and other methods of raising a man in the confines of a sewer. One type of harness and one example of the use of lines is shown in Figs 5.1 and 5.2. Sewer men usually wear a belt fitted with shackles onto which their own rescue harness can be snapped.

2 Potholes and disused mineshafts

These present very similar problems to those of sewers although on a larger and potentially more dangerous scale. Breathing apparatus will often be necessary when lowering firemen down shafts but will just as obviously be an encumbrance and also probably unnecessary in a pothole. Both types of incident require thorough organisation, specialised equipment, and expertise, and can take a long time.

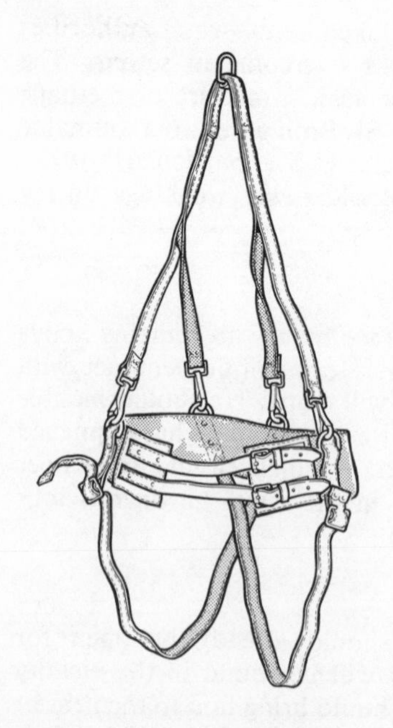

Fig. 5.1 Type of harness used in effecting a rescue from a sewer.

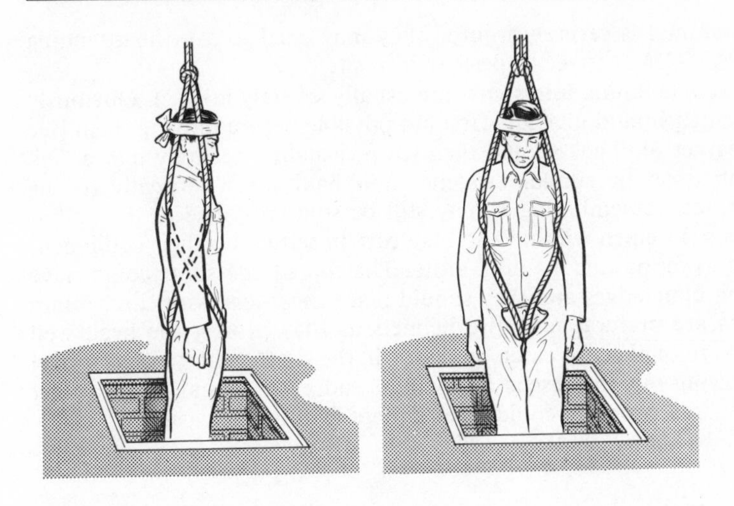

Fig. 5.2 Use of lines in a rescue from a sewer.

a. Pothole rescues

In a potholing area there will usually be a number of experienced teams and their expertise should be used. They will probably know where the casualty could be lying, the best route in and out and how to set up lines, communications and rescue equipment. The job of the Service would normally be to supply equipment and manpower on top. Lightweight pumps may be necessary to relieve flooded areas, and small generators for lighting. Firemen should take precautions to ensure that exhaust fumes are not drawn underground. Other items of equipment which may be needed are lines, winches, sheer-legs, crowbars, resuscitation gear, gloves and, possibly, short ladders. Local Brigades will have their contingency plans for such incidents which will involve the other emergency services. Communications in these areas can be a particular problem and firemen should know the 'dead' spots for radio.

b. Mines and wells

Mineshafts and old wells are particularly hazardous because of the general decay and, often, their proximity to other shafts. Great care not to disturb the sides is necessary when manoeuvring in the shaft. At night especially firemen near a shaft should keep to safe illuminated paths. Animals becoming wedged in the shaft or found swimming in the flooded bottom are the most frequent rescues. Trying to fix a rescue sling on an animal can in itself be difficult and firemen must bear in mind their own safety. Where an animal is severely injured they may need to ask the attending R.S.P.C.A. officer to destroy it in situ.

People falling into shafts are usually severely injured. Obviously firemen should give any first aid possible before moving them [see Chapter 6]. They should then strap casualties securely into a Neil Robertson or similar stretcher and haul them vertically to the surface, remembering it may still be some distance to the ambulance. Firemen will have to take care in setting up their equipment for lowering and hauling aloft. The top of the shaft could have crumbling edges and they should place sheer-legs with care. Bump hats are preferable to fire helmets as they protect the head well but are unlikely to catch on debris in the shaft. Safety of personnel carrying out the rescue is essential and even a small delay to get prepared properly could ensure there is only one casualty.

3 Trench collapse

The introduction to this Chapter mentions the potential for special services on, for example, building sites. A similar incident is where a trench collapses and traps someone. This can result from excessive rainfall affecting the stability of the terrain, vibration from nearby heavy plant, insufficient piling and bracing of the trench sides, etc.

The incident may require just the removal of a quantity of soil but more usually also involves metal piling, timber shoring, props, corrugated iron sheets, ladders, etc.: see Plate 9

Firemen must be aware, primarily, of the danger of further collapse. As contact is being made with the victim, the officer in charge must carefully consider:

(i) how he is going to clear the trench of the general debris without causing a further collapse;

(ii) what manpower he may need, remembering this sort of task is arduous and requires frequent reliefs;

(iii) what special equipment he may require, e.g. sheer-legs, tackle, floodlights, air-lines, special stretcher.

The first fireman down must have a line on himself not only for hauling out but also for quick tracing if there is a further collapse. If there is room he should also take a resuscitation set, if one is available. Quite often, by clearing a small area to the victim's face, the fireman can apply the mask and restore consciousness.

Another method of ensuring the trapped man's survival, especially if the incident is likely to be prolonged, is to put a compressed air breathing apparatus mask on him, leaving the remainder of the apparatus [out of the frame and harness] as close as possible. If there is a further collapse the man will at least have an air supply. The officer in charge should also consider the use of air-lines for both the victim and the firemen digging him out [*Manual*, Book 6, Chapter 13].

He should get expert advice on how best to re-shore the trench from the site contractors. A mechanical excavator, not necessarily for excavating but for holding or even pushing back the piling, might be helpful.

The officer in charge must also remember finally to:

(i) keep the number of firemen in the trench to the minimum necessary;

(ii) maintain good access and egress for them;

(iii) designate at least one officer to watch for any signs of further collapse;

(iv) control strictly the movements of relief crews, other emergency personnel and civilians involved, especially round the edges of the trench;

(v) plan reliefs and refreshments well in advance and bearing in mind (i) and (iv) ensure the changeover is smooth.

4 Cliffs and quarries

Some Brigades carry out rescues of people who have fallen down a cliff or quarry, been cut off by the tide, or have been for some other reason trapped in an inaccessible position. Cliff sides are often nearly vertical and in some places may overhang at the top. There is danger from falling debris, particularly with limestone formations.

The obvious method of effecting a rescue in these circumstances is for firemen to be lowered to the trapped person, who can then be helped up or, if injured, brought up in a harness or stretcher. In some cases it may be better to lower the person to ground or beach level instead.

Particular care must be taken over safety measures:

(i) all equipment must be tested thoroughly, regularly and after use;

(ii) helmets should be worn at all times [crash helmets are usually more convenient than standard fire helmets];

(iii) an officer should be stationed if possible where he can see the whole of the manoeuvre;

(iv) there must be adequate communication between the man in charge of the lowering and raising, the rescuers, and the watching officer. This would preferably be radio backed up by a system of whistle signals;

(v) adequate and regular training should be carried out.

Brigades which are likely to carry out such rescues sometimes carry special equipment for the purpose. Plate 11 shows such equipment laid out and Plate 12 shows it ready for use.

5 Machinery

The Service is often called to people with limbs trapped in machinery. Since this type of incident can be time-consuming and the victim will usually be in pain, a doctor should be summoned immediately to give relief and perhaps advise on the best method of extrication. Occasionally surgical teams will be necessary. Depending on the type of machinery, it may be possible to dismantle all or part of it and free the limb or enable the casualty to be taken to hospital while still trapped. There greater medical help can be given while the Brigade finishes the job. Firemen should support any casualty suspended by a trapped limb and attempt to stop any bleeding [see Chapter 6] but avoid the application of a tourniquet if possible.

They should remember that vibration can deepen shock or distress and if using oxy-propane cutting equipment should protect the casualty from the sparks, fumes and heat. The advice of the firm's engineer should be sought, if he is available, but the ultimate responsibility for dismantling or cutting remains with the officer in charge.

6 Collapse of a building

Occasionally during demolition or when a heavy lorry crashes into it or following a gas explosion, a building collapses and traps people. Depending on the amount of debris to be moved, man-power is usually the main requirement. The officer in charge should use to the best advantage local people who have already begun rescue operations, but if there is any chance of further collapse he should withdraw them, reduce his own men's involvement to the minimum, and designate an officer solely to watch the remaining structure. It may be difficult to find those who are trapped and they themselves may be unconscious or too heavily buried to move. Firemen should ask neighbours the possible number of casualties and their probable location. Sometimes a call for complete silence will help to locate people. Firemen should request the attendance of a local authority building surveyor as soon as possible and should always consider the possibility of using local heavy equipment.

7 Suicide attempts

The rescue of people threatening to jump from bridges, buildings, scaffolding, etc. is usually a matter for the police but the Service, because of its expertise and equipment, is at times called in to help. A fireman's ability to calm, reassure and persuade a potential suicide to return to safety will, if he can reach the person, depend largely on his own demeanour, words and actions. A ladder or hydraulic platform might enable him to reach and bring down the person. On bridges and suitable metalwork especially, the use of a T.L. hook belt sometimes helps by freeing both hands. In any dangerous position, however, the fireman must always wear a safety line properly anchored by another fireman. He must always remember that a potential suicide can become violent at any time, even when actually on a ladder. Ultimately, achieving two casualties instead of one is pointless.

8 Children

The Service is well aware of the unusual predicaments into which children get themselves. However, once a child is the centre of rescue operations and can see or, in some cases, feel a fireman near who can talk, encourage and explain what is going on, he or she will usually behave well, better, probably, than the parents. Some children may however prefer to have their eyes covered if they have to be carried down. Firemen should remember that if they have to apply resuscitation to a child they must take care to use less pressure and/or ventilation to avoid causing injury. Also, they should bear in mind that if they have to cut away metal or brickwork, a child is more susceptible to vibration, fumes and heat.

9 Animals

Provided that the lives of firemen are not unduly risked attempts should always be made to rescue animals. Under fire conditions, animals behave differently. Cattle when released usually find their own way out but will have to be driven well clear of the fireground or they will tend to wander back in. Horses will not pass through or near flame and should have their heads covered with, for example, a cloth or blanket before they are led out. There are a variety of ways of penning cattle and securing horses and firemen should visit farms and stables to note the methods used. Other animals overcome by smoke will often revive in the open air, especially if splashed with a little cold water. Firemen should not hesitate to ask for the R.S.P.C.A or P.D.S.A. or a veterinary surgeon to attend if an animal is injured.

As mentioned in Section 2 above, animals often stumble or fall into places from which they cannot escape. Boggy areas, shafts, ravines, ponds and culverts are examples. Here again, sheer-legs, slings, lines and tackle are useful, but in areas of soft ground firemen will have to improvise. Bales of straw, planks, tree branches and foliage have all been used to give an animal something more solid on which to push, to enable it, with assistance from firemen, to extricate itself. Hose passed under the animal's belly will help to keep its head above the mud until it can be hauled out. If an animal is unable to climb out of a steep-sided ditch it may be possible to lead it along to a less steep part or to a place where sheer-legs can be slung. Temporarily, the ditch could be filled with bales of straw so that it can scramble onto them and be led out.

Firemen should always if possible wear gloves when handling animals, especially cats. A trapped animal, being distressed and frightened, is very likely to claw at its rescuer. If firemen are clawed, bitten or scratched by animals, they should ensure that proper medical treatment is obtained as soon as possible. In most Brigades calls to animals trapped are usually only accepted from the R.S.P.C.A. or P.D.S.A. and the inspector in attendance will often bring a cat basket.

10 Tower cranes

One unusual and difficult rescue is recovery of a casualty from the cabin of a tower crane.

There are many different types of tower crane in use in this country and they can be found, free-standing, to a jib height of 140 metres. The towers themselves measure usually from 1.2 m. to 2.5 m. square and vary considerably in construction, in internal positions of cross-bracing, ladders, intermediate and external platforms, and slewing turrets. A variety of control cabins are found and their position and size are dictated by the type of crane [see Figs 5.3, 5.4]. The modern cabin is a very sophisticated piece of technology, probably at maximum one metre square by two metres high. Since it can be positioned in the tower, out under the jib or at one side of the jib, access varies greatly. Depending on design, normal entry can be from bottom, top, front or back.

The problems facing the officer in charge are:

(i) height;

(ii) difficulty in positioning rescue equipment;

(iii) limits on the length of rescue lines;

(iv) cramped conditions both for getting the casualty onto a stretcher or into a sling and for lowering;

(v) perhaps, in winter, lack of lighting;

(vi) limited access for T.Ls and H.Ps;

(vii) difficulty in communications.

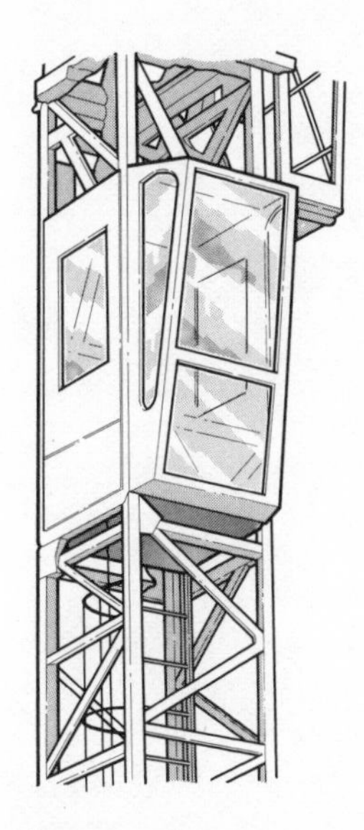

Fig. 5.3.

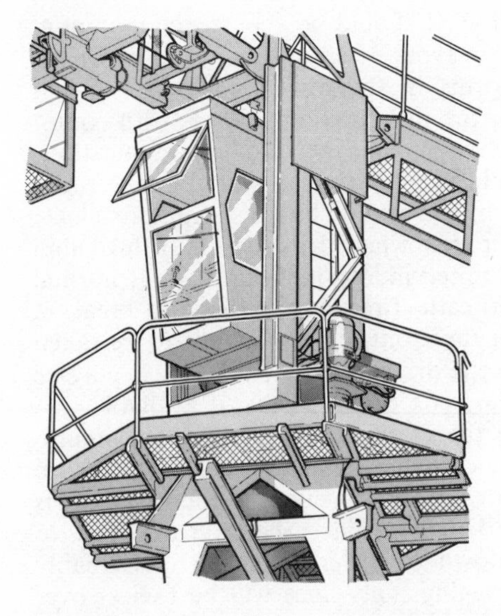

Fig. 5.4.

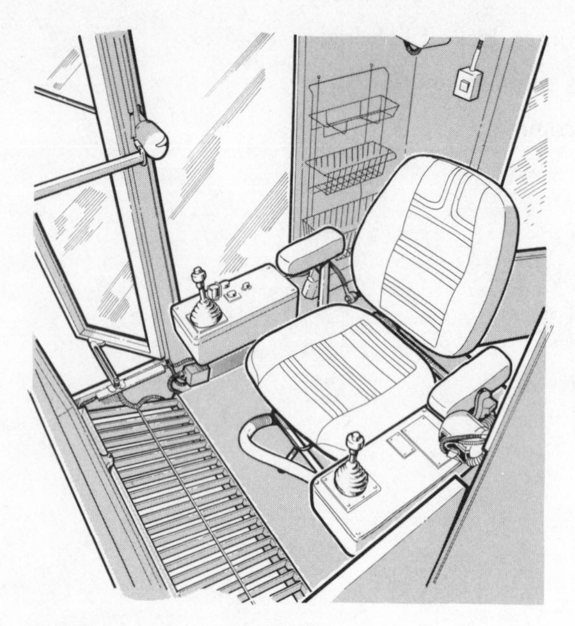

Fig. 5.5.

Figs. 5.3, 5.4 and 5.5 Examples of exterior and interior of tower crane cabins.

The number of personnel aloft should be kept to the minimum required, although, on certain types of crane, positioning men on intermediate internal platforms in the tower may have certain advantages. The physical effort just to climb 100 m. with equipment is considerable and obviously some means of communication, e.g. radio, would be helpful. Some sites may already have radio communication between cabin and ground but this is not prevalent.

Officers should remember that when the driver is in his cabin the available room is very limited indeed [see Fig. 5.5]. If normal access is by trapdoor underneath, firemen may have to break in elsewhere. If access is from the front, care will have to be taken in opening the door in case the driver's weight is on it. It may be prudent for the crew to wear hook or T.L. belts, if available.

The method of lowering the casualty will depend on circumstances, e.g. the state of the casualty, height, whether a platform surrounds the cabin, the internal construction of the tower. It is obvious that the inordinate length of line necessary may have to be paid out, e.g. internally down the tower, to ensure a reasonably steady lowering without snagging. Guy lines will be useless over about 35 m., even if they could be dropped accurately without drifting into the tower or other impediments. The assistance of the site engineer may enable the actual traveller and hook of the crane to be used for lowering.

On some cranes, mainly in Ministry of Defence dockyards, a Rescumatic or Davey type escape apparatus may be found slung under the counter-jib behind the cabin. This will, obviously, have sufficient line aboard to carry out the lowering under well-controlled conditions. This is another instance where an officer should note the presence of a transient risk, confer with the site management, and co-ordinate a plan, which may need modification as work on the site progresses. A list of emergency numbers for use on any out of working hours incident will also be useful.

Chapter 6
First aid and casualty handling

1 The importance of first aid

Incidents to which the Fire Brigade is called will have often caused injury to the people involved. This is particularly so with special service calls, especially road traffic accidents. Hospital services can do much for such patients but efficient and rapid on-site emergency care is vital if they are to have the best chance of recovery. At times firemen may be the only people in a position to offer this, or at least they may have to assist. Accordingly while they cannot undertake elaborate medical treatment and should leave the handling of casualties to ambulance crews and other qualified personnel as far as possible, there are certain first aid measures they should be ready and able to carry out. Even when only simple, these can, if correctly performed, preserve life, promote recovery, prevent the injury worsening and possibly remove the need for more complicated treatment later. Firemen should therefore familiarise themselves at least with the basic first aid techniques, such as those set out in *First Aid*, the authorised manual of the St John's and St Andrew's Ambulance Associations and the British Red Cross. To reduce the human and economic costs of accidents it is important that Fire, police, ambulance and, where appropriate, medical services, combine to offer the highest standards of care to the victims.

2 Safety considerations at incidents

Both in approaching the victim of an incident and in giving first aid and effecting release, fireman need to give due thought to the risks they might encounter. These include:

(i) structural collapse;

(ii) traffic;

(iii) electric shock from domestic, grid, motor vehicle or other equipment;

(iv) gas pipes and installations and liquid gases in transit: the release of gas may result in oxygen displacement;

(v) visible and invisible fumes and smoke;

(vi) water and effluent;

(vii) hazardous dusts, including asbestos;

(viii)petrol;

(ix) toxic chemicals;

(x) radio-active sources.

Firemen should handle the situation according to the principles set out elsewhere in the *Manual*. They should recall the need for care in using tools and cutting or lifting devices and should always use protective devices for head, eyes, hands, feet and ears where appropriate. Firemen also need to assess both the victim's condition and the situation generally in order to determine the type of supportive care and method of release necessary. They may need, for example, to offer immediate first aid or effect a snatch rescue in order to save life.

3 General principles

Throughout an operation the fireman should bear in mind the need to apply commonsense as well as actual knowledge. Once he has carried out any immediately necessary action, he should take time in handling casualties and avoid undue haste which could cause further injury. If a victim is conscious the fireman should identify himself and offer reassurance and comfort. A calm patient can materially assist rescue operations. Assessment of injuries is very important and above all a fireman should not assume that a victim is dead unless the visible injuries make this quite obvious.

4 Types of injury and their cause

a. General patterns

In the majority of cases it is most important to assess an accident victim's injuries before treating or moving him or her. A knowledge of what to look for and where enables the rescuer to approach the problem with a confident, controlled and informed manner. Understanding patterns of injury is a helpful part of this and is often a blend of commonsense and simple mechanics. For instance, in falling from a height a man may land on his feet and fracture his heel bones. In addition, the force may travel on up through his body and cause a collapse fracture of the lumbar spine in the small of the back. The first injury should be obvious, the second may not be unless the mechanism of injury is understood. Should the fall be a bad one, the transmission of the force along the length of the body could also cause a fracture at the hip and base of the skull. Armed with this understanding the rescuer can rapidly check the patient's conscious state, appreciate the significance of blood from the ear, note the shortening and external rotation of the leg, expect to find swelling and bruising of one or both feet, and remember to move the patient carefully with regard to the spine.

b. Road traffic accidents: general

These patterns of injury exist in various types of accident but nowhere are they more apparent than in road traffic accidents. This is useful in that road accidents represent the most frequent of special service calls, ranging in scale from the seriously injured individual trapped in a car to the problems of the large scale motorway incident with numerous casualties suffering widely differing degrees of injury.

The majority of special service calls to road accidents involve vehicle occupants. Amongst other factors the direction of impact will have a bearing on the assessment of their injuries. Within the vehicle the two main causes of injury to the occupants are deformity and deceleration. Deformity involves the intrusion of the vehicle shell or structures into the passenger carrying space. Deceleration involves the forced slowing of the vehicle at such a rate that the unrestrained occupant is thrown onto the interior structures. The laws of physics dictate that in a crash at speeds higher than 13 kilometres per hour unrestrained occupants cannot brace themselves to avoid being thrown onto adjacent interior structures. Seat belts do provide a valuable protection to their wearers but firemen must recognise that even if wearing belts, accident victims can still suffer injury.

c. Injuries caused by head-on collisions

The majority of collisions involve the front of the vehicle. They can be viewed in stages:

(i) In the first stage [see Fig. 6.1(1)] the victim's body slides forward and the knee strikes the lower edge of the dashboard or parcel shelf. It is possible to see an area of impact, typically the knee cap [patella] is fractured, and the leg may slide on under the dash area and become wedged in. A severe impact may cause distortion of the vehicle body shell, displacing the interior structures towards the occupant. The victim's legs may then be trapped and more seriously injured. The floor pan may, for instance, be distorted upwards; if the knee is then caught under the dashboard the lower leg and ankle may be compressed, fractured and trapped. If the direction of impact is at an angle towards the off-side front of the car, the force of the collision may push the front off-side wheel back into the wheel arch or even through it. When this occurs, it is common to find a fracture of the driver's right leg somewhere along its length;

(ii) In the second stage, heavy braking prior to impact causes the front of the vehicle to dip and this movement is continued by the collision. This has the effect of throwing the front seat occupant up from the seat, a movement added to by the hinge action at the knees. The occupant moves upwards and strikes the windscreen or windscreen header sustaining head injuries [see Fig. 6.1(2)]. Evidence of this contact between the head and the vehicle interior may be seen in the denting of the windscreen header, safety visors or rear view mirror, or by a greasemark of the face on the windscreen. When this happens the head is pushed back, arching the neck into extension, and the weight of the body coming up places great stress on the neck. The neck or cervical part of the spinal column may be damaged just by over-bending whereas the lower part of the spine is often damaged by a combination of bending and rotation. Also in this phase the thigh, which is under the dash or steering wheel, may be bent upwards and cause a fracture of the shaft of the femur;

(iii) In the third stage [see Fig. 6.1(3)] the chest comes into contact with the steering wheel. Ribs may be broken along the edge of the breastbone [sternum] at the point of impact. If severe enough the force on the ribs will compress them to the point where they snap again at the site of maximum bending along the outer margin of the rib cage. When this happens to four or more ribs, the segment between is loose or stove in. This grossly interferes with the mechanism of breathing and in combination with a serious head injury can carry a mortality rate of up to 40%. This violent force on the chest may also bruise the lungs, cause them to be punctured by broken rib ends, or allow escaping blood and air to fill the chest cavity. The effect of this is to make the lung collapse, thereby seriously affecting the patient's ability to maintain intake of oxygen and elimination of carbon dioxide. In extreme cases the blood vessels in the chest may be torn by the deceleration and compression. The abdomen may also be injured by the lower edges of the steering wheel causing internal injury [see Plate 7]. Recent improvements in the construction of the steering wheel do however offer some protection to the chest.

Occasionally the breastbone [sternum] is fractured against the steering column. The victim's spine should then be checked at the same level for a fracture. It is possible to find a similar combination of sternum and spine injury where the patient is doubled up with the spine bent forcibly forward from behind. This can happen, for instance, if a vehicle rolls over or if a load shifts forward onto the occupant of a van or lorry;

(iv) In the fourth stage, the head goes through the windscreen and moves down onto the edge of a column of broken glass [see Fig. 6.1(4)]. The weight of the head gives the kinetic energy necessary to produce facial lacerations with pieces of glass embedded in them. The eyes may also be damaged. In severe impacts the head may pass through the windscreen and hit the bonnet or other structures causing further injury. As the momentum of impact is spent the person sinks back into the car under the recoil effect and his or her own weight. The face is drawn back across the outward sloping broken glass edges to add to facial injuries. The modern laminated screen is, however, designed to resist penetration.

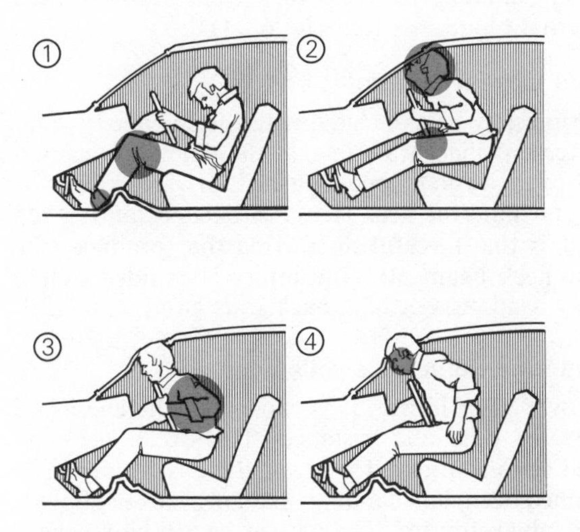

Fig. 6.1 Injuries caused by a head on collision.

A complicating factor in this stage of the crash may be the inward buckling and penetration of the bonnet through the windscreen towards the occupant's face. This may produce severe injury even though the person is wearing a seat belt;

When viewing the crash scene firemen must remember that the final position of the distorted structures may not represent their position at the point of maximum impact owing to the effect of recoil.

Should the impact to the vehicle be at an angle instead of from straight ahead, the occupant may be thrown onto the edge of the windscreen and sustain a severe head injury against the A post. The injury may even be of the open type with depression of the bony fragments and a linear wound caused by the edge of the A post.

d. Injuries caused by impact from the side

The side of a car is a vulnerable area. There is not much space between the exterior and the occupant and safety engineering has only focussed on this area in more recent years.

Research has shown that if the doors of a vehicle suffer an impact that results in more than six inches of intrusion then the incidence of serious injury rises steeply for occupants on that side. Limb and head injuries may be evident but firemen should make a conscious effort to look for the more serious internal injuries that may involve the pelvis, abdomen or chest. Patients with these injuries need careful handling to avoid increasing the likelihood of shock from internal blood loss [see Fig. 6.2 (1)].

e. Injuries caused by rear-end collisions

The rear-end collision may be associated with the so-called 'whiplash' injury. The term is inaccurate in that the damage is caused by the seated body of the casualty being pushed forward at impact, whilst the head lags behind the neck is arched baaaack and pulled along its length. It is this forceful distraction that produces the usual injury to the neck ligaments. The injury is avoided by the proper use of safety head rests or high back seats [see Fig. 6.2(2)].

f. Injuries caused when a vehicle rolls over

When a car rolls over after impact it is expending the energy of impact over a greater time and distance. The occupants may therefore be spared serious injury. However, there is an increased chance of unrestrained occupants landing on their heads or shoulders and sustaining spinal injuries. The patient has to be reached, examined, splinted, and removed from the vehicle in the face of such problems as difficulty of access, awkwardness of position, displaced seats or other contents and the hazards of spilled fuel. Obviously other injuries may be found in this type of accident but firemen must bear in mind above all else the possibility of spinal injury [see Fig. 6.2(3)].

g. Injuries caused by ejection from a vehicle

The casualty who is thrown from a vehicle is particularly at risk. He or she has the greater chance of serious or fatal injury because of the further impact suffered on landing. In rural areas the high impact speeds may throw the person even further from the crash,

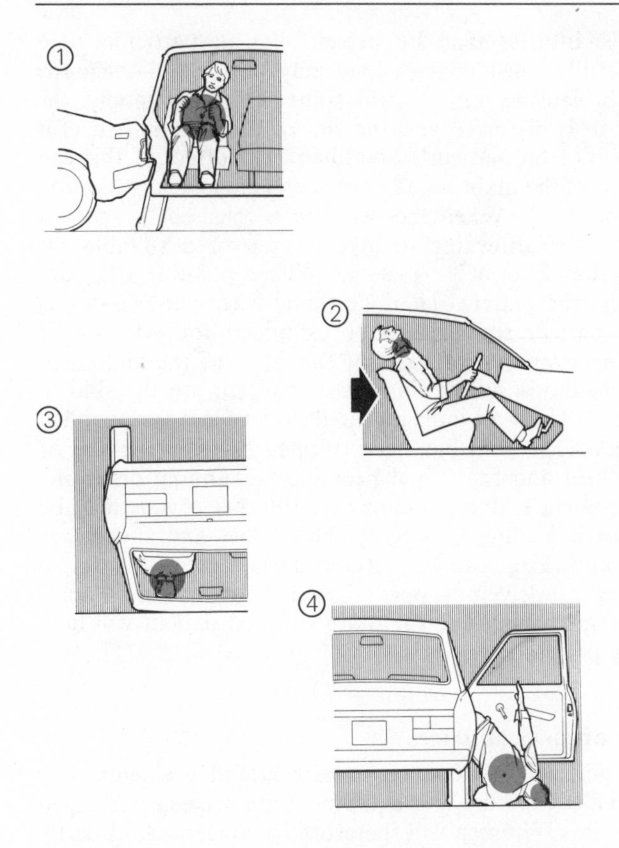

Fig. 6.2 (1) Injuries caused by a side impact. (2) Injuries caused by a rear end collision. (3) Injuries caused when a vehicle rolls over. (4) Injuries caused by ejection from a vehicle.

perhaps out of the area of immediate activity. Silent, seriously injured, possibly out of sight in a ditch at night, such a casualty runs an ever-increasing risk of deterioration. Firemen should search the surrounding area for such people. Whenever possible they should ask a conscious casualty how many were travelling in the vehicle. When they have found an ejected casualty they must remember to look for signs of a blow on the head, which will indicate the possibility of neck injuries, or for a shoulder injury that may be associated with a spinal injury lower down [see Fig. 6.2(4)].

h. Injuries to drivers of heavy goods vehicles

The driver of a heavy goods vehicle may be trapped by the legs and feet and his release may require considerable effort by the

Brigade. Other injuries may be present but in particular two should be carefully considered. A load may shift and damage the rear of the cab, causing injury to the spine. More commonly, the front of the cab is distorted and the rim of the steering wheel is pushed firmly into the patient's abdomen. The effect of this can be to clamp across the main blood vessels and alter the distribution of blood in the body. When the pressure is released the patient may collapse. It is allowable to give oxygen or a suitable gas mixture beforehand to help reserves. Where possible, the aim should be to lie the patient flat if he faints when the pressure is released. The patient should also be examined for evidence of pattern bruising over the soft part of the front of the abdomen. Classically, this shows as the imprint of clothing on the skin in bruise markings. This will indicate the degree of pressure applied to the abdomen. The skin has been trapped between the rim of the steering wheel and the spinal prominence running down the inside of the patient's abdominal cavity. Internal organs may be torn or ruptured, leading to internal blood loss and shock [see Plate 7]. This knowledge can be useful in the context of a multiple pile-up with several drivers trapped. Looking for maximum compression, pattern bruising and the more shocked patient will help in determining priorities.

i. Injuries to other road users

The Fire Brigade will, of course, usually attend accidents only where its specialist expertise and equipment are necessary to reach and release victims. Firemen will therefore be concerned primarily with the occupants of vehicles. It may happen occasionally, however, that a motor cyclist or pedestrian is trapped as the result of an accident.

(1) Motor cyclists

Motor cycle accidents produce some of the worst injuries: severe multiple injuries, head injuries, partial or complete amputation of limbs, and severe burns. Two other injuries motor cyclists may receive are local paralysis of an arm and dislocation of the hip. It is important that the first is not confused with the total paralysis that might result from a head injury. Dislocation of the hip is less common than a fracture of the femur, but is important to recognise as its treatment is different. A fracture needs traction and effective splinting, while a dislocation needs support behind the knee and gentle splinting of leg to leg. If both injuries occur in the same limb the fracture takes precedence. A dislocation can be recognised by shortening of the leg, turning in of the foot and inability of the knee to lie flat; a fracture of the femur results in shortening, the turning out of the foot, and the leg lying flat.

(2) Pedestrians

Adult pedestrians most commonly suffer injuries at the knees, hip, femur, pelvis, wrist and head. Violent movement of the head and arms after impact and their collision with hard surfaces can lead to further injury. Actual running over imposes a severe crushing and shearing force to the area affected, usually the leg. Children are particularly likely to be injured at the head, pelvis, legs, and then, less frequently, at the arms, abdomen and chest. They are also more likely to go under a vehicle and catch their clothing on projections there. The vehicle can then drag them along, causing friction burns and perhaps pulling clothing tight round their necks, resulting in partial strangulation. It is important to look for this and release such a constriction without delay [see Section 5a. below].

5 Assessment of injuries

Firemen automatically assess the general characteristics of an incident as they approach. To decide how to handle it and what first aid to apply, they must also assess the victim. Injuries are often difficult to detect, are complex and may interact with each other. If firemen know their cause and symptoms, they can make a quicker and more accurate appraisal of the victim's condition.

a. Lighting

In the assessment of a patient there is one vital factor that firemen must appreciate from the outset of an incident, especially one occurring at night. The recognition of a number of complications in emergency care depends on a clear sight of the colour of the patient's skin [or other areas]. Examples are:

(i) the blanched pallor of shock;

(ii) the blue or cyanosed appearance associated with lack of oxygen;

(iii) the cherry pink colour found with carbon monoxide poisoning;

(iv) the pinpoint skin haemorrhages found in strangulation or crush injuries of the chest.

All of these are valuable signs and are important in the assessment of the patient but they require good lighting to be seen clearly. The dim orange glow of a small torch with low batteries or the glare and shadow of over-bright spotlights can cause firemen to miss these subtle skin tones, perhaps with dire consequences. A victim's face may well be obscured by position or grime, but firemen should do what they can to ensure that the casualty can be seen properly from the earliest stage possible [see Plate 6].

b. Pairs of injuries

A common theme throughout the assessment of patterns of injury is the existence of pairs of injuries, with the obvious one often drawing attention to the less obvious and possibly more serious. Typical pairs are:

(i) head and neck injuries;

(ii) breastbone and mid-spine fractures;

(iii) lower ribs and internal injury;

(iv) pattern bruising and abdominal injury;

(v) shoulder injury and injury to the nerves, etc., of the arm;

(vi) fractured lower limb and dislocated hip;

(vii) fractures of the foot and of the ankle;

(viii) fractures of the heel and lower spine in falls from heights;

(ix) fractures of the pelvis and rupture of the bladder or urethra in crush injuries;

(x) burns to the face and breathing problems;

(xi) entry and exit point burns in electrocution.

c. Checking the casualty

Once the casualty has been categorised by the type of accident the fireman should make a general systematic check, looking for expected injuries. The most widely used system is probably the head to toe one. It has the great merit of having an automatic arrangement of priorities. Checking the patient over and considering the following key points should only take between one and two minutes and once learned is applied as an integral part of the over-all assessment.

(1) Head

(i)	airway	is it clear or blocked? What is the colour of skin and lips? What noise is there?
(ii)	level of consciousness	how conscious is the patient? Is the level of consciousness static or fluctuating?
(iii)	external injury	what was the direction of the blow? What is the degree of damage? Is there any effect of transmitted force?

(iv)	pupils of eyes	are they damaged? What is their size? Does it differ from one to the other? How do they react to light?
(v)	nose and ears	is there evidence of blood, suggesting a fractured base of skull?
(vi)	movement	can the patient move all four limbs?

(2) Neck and spine

(i)	external injury	can any injury be seen?
(ii)	local pain	does feeling down the spine gently whilst holding the casualty's chin cause pain at any point?
(iii)	paralysis	is there any loss of movement, numbness or tingling?

(3) Chest

(i)	breathing	is breathing normal, shallow, painful or rapid?
(ii)	local pain	is the casualty aware of any local pain? Is any felt when the casualty is touched gently? Can any broken ribs be felt grating with breathing?
(iv)	colour	are the skin or lips blue, indicating a shortage of oxygen?

(4) Abdomen

(i)	local pain	is any felt, with or without touch?
(ii)	bruising	is there any pattern bruising?
(iii)	pelvis	is there any pain when the hips are squeezed gently together? This indicates a fracture. If the casualty wants to urinate, this indicates internal damage.

(5) Arms and legs

(i)	external injury	are any wounds, deformity or swelling visible?
(ii)	local pain	does the casualty mention any? Does the casualty feel any when the arm is touched gently along its length from the collar-bone or the leg from thigh to foot?
(iii)	movement	is there any absence of movement, indicating injury or paralysis?
(iv)	pulse, colour and temperature	is the pulse absent, or the skin cool, dusky or pale? This indicates that the circulation is cut off.

(v) sensation — is there any numbness or tingling? This indicates spinal or local nerve damage.

When the casualty's injuries have been assessed, the information is used to determine the relative priorities and detailed treatment required.

d. Blood loss

For each injury there is an associated blood loss. The total blood loss determines the likelihood of the patient going into shock and the speed of its development. The basic factors in the calculation start with the determination of the normal blood volume of the casualty. A rough estimate is about one litre for each 13 kg. body weight. Loss of one third of that volume will result in the typical symptoms of shock developing: a pale, sweaty skin, faintness and a rapid, thready pulse. Thus a 64 kg. man starts to develop the signs of shock when he has lost one and half to two litres of blood.

Obviously the blood loss into fractures is not immediate and relates to time, effectiveness of first aid and other factors.

6 Principles of treatment

The preservation of the patient's vital functions heads the list of actions firemen should take at the accident, as far as first aid is concerned. Whilst the Brigade's responsibility for the actual process of extrication might seem to be the over-riding consideration, firemen must recognise that the process of extrication takes approximately 30 minutes on average. This contrasts markedly with the maximum of four minutes taken for a patient to choke to death or the death from severe blood loss that could take place in well under 30 minutes.

The principal points to which firemen should give attention are, in general order of priority:

(i) breathing;
(ii) bleeding;
(iii) unconsciousness;
(iv) pain relief;
(v) broken bones;
(vi) burns and scalds;
(vii) shock.

7 Breathing

a. The importance of respiration

Anything which interferes with the intake and absorption of oxygen causes asphyxia. If the lungs do not receive a sufficient supply of fresh air, important organs, especially the brain, are deprived of oxygen. This causes unconsciousness and subsequent heart failure. Victims who stop breathing will therefore die unless respiration is restored at once.

b. Signs and symptoms of asphyxia

Unless breathing has already stopped, the following are the principal signs of asphyxia:

(i) the rate and depth of breathing increase at first, but later breathing can become noisy and the victim may froth at the mouth;

(ii) there is congestion of the head and neck, causing swollen veins, lips and face, and dizziness;

(iii) face, lips, conjunctiva and finger and toe-nail beds turn blue;

(iv) there is progressive loss of consciousness;

(v) there may be fits.

c. Treatment of asphyxia

If there is an external cause, the first necessity will be to remove the cause from the casualty or the casualty from the cause. Next the fireman should tilt back the victim's head to secure an open airway [see Fig. 6.3] and ensure adequate air. He should start resuscitation without delay: he may use suitable equipment if it is to hand but must not wait for it. He should continue resuscitation until natural breathing is definitely restored or medical personnel and equipment are available.

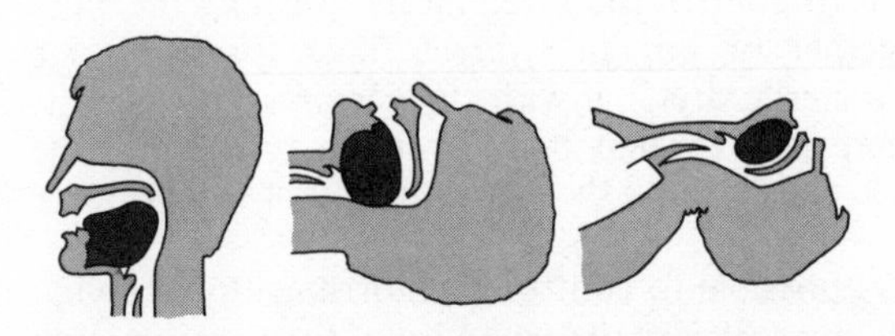

Fig. 6.3 Securing an open airway to assist breathing.

(1) Mouth to mouth resuscitation

Having secured an open airway, the firemen should clear the casualty's mouth and throat of mucus, saliva, blood or any foreign matter, and remove dentures. Pinching the casualty's nose shut, the fireman should then blow into the mouth until the chest rises. He should thereupon remove his mouth from the other person's, wait for the chest to deflate, then repeat the operation until breathing is spontaneous. The first four inflations should be as rapid as possible to flood the blood with oxygen.

8 Bleeding

a. Importance of blood circulation

An average adult's body has about six litres of blood. When a third or more is lost from the circulation, the vital organs are deprived of oxygen and nutrients and shock develops. Damage to arteries and, occasionally, veins, with severe bleeding, will lead to death if not checked. There is a particular danger where a casualty is suffering from a blood disease or under treatment to prevent blood clotting.

b. Slight bleeding

Slight bleeding comes from injured capillary vessels in or immediately under the skin surface. The blood is red in colour and may ooze from all parts of the wound. Such minor bleeding may appear alarming but usually stops of its own accord and is easily controlled by local pressure.

c. Severe bleeding [haemorrhage]

Severe bleeding results from damage to an artery or vein, or sometimes both together. Arterial blood is bright red and may come out in spurts which correspond to the heart beats; venous blood is darker and flows continuously or wells up in the wound. In treating severe bleeding the fireman should keep the casualty at rest, giving reassurance and explaining the need to relax completely. He should elevate the injured part and loosen tight clothing but remove as little as possible when exposing the wound. He should then attempt to control the bleeding by grasping the sides of the wound together or applying direct finger pressure. He should next apply a sterile dressing with further dressings over it, if necessary. If there is a foreign body or bone projecting, the fireman should place pads around the projection but avoid pressure on it.

It is nearly always possible to control haemorrhage by applying a large enough dressing to cover the wound and then maintaining firm pressure with hand, bandage or both. Rarely is anything else required. Just occasionally, however, the use of a blow-up plastic pneumatic or air splint, if available, may provide the over-all splinting and pressure for a difficult or extensive wound. Even more rarely a tourniquet may be called for. The extremes of injury that sometimes accompany entrapment may involve serious haemorrhage from an unreachable extremity. In such rare cases a tourniquet could prove life-saving, though they are usually regarded as being for use by professional medical personnel only. Ideally, a tourniquet should be made of soft rubber tubing and applied firmly enough to control arterial [spurting] blood loss. Thin string and bits of stick can inflict serious pressure damage to skin and nerves in particular and should be avoided.

d. Internal bleeding

Internal bleeding may occur in one of the bodily cavities such as chest, abdomen or skull, following a direct injury from a blow, crash or stab, or an indirect blow. It can also occur with crushed muscles or a fracture. In the case of a complicated femur fracture, for instance, the large thigh muscles can swell considerably because of the extra blood entering them which is lost to circulation. Internal bleeding can also result from certain medical or surgical conditions. It cannot be controlled in the same way as external bleeding, but firemen should be aware of the possibility of its occurrence and avoid actions that might worsen it; they must not delay the victim from full medical care.

9 Unconsciousness

Unconsciousness is the result of injury to, or disturbed function of, the brain.

a. Head injuries

In the context of an accident the cause of unconsciousness may well be an injury to the head. Such injuries may also be associated with breathing difficulties and each may worsen the other. Head injuries may be divided into open and closed types. The more rare open type, with a wound, fracture of the skull, and exposure of the brain is self-decompressing. Provided the injury is not fatal there is less likely to be the rapid deterioration that accompanies the more serious closed head injury.

When the head strikes a hard object, one of the three following results is likely:

(i) concussion: this is a temporary loss of consciousness due to the jarring effect of the blow. It lasts between a few seconds and a number of minutes;

(ii) contusion: this is a tearing of the brain substances due to the shock wave of the blow or movement of the brain inside the bony cavity of the skull;

(iii) compression: this is pressure on the brain due either to bleeding from a torn blood vessel which forms a clot or to a depressed fracture of the skull in which bone is pushed in to press on the brain.

The patient will recover from concussion spontaneously but may require surgery to relieve compression. Contusion cannot be repaired surgically. The history of a head injury is therefore very important in deciding on early surgery. Examples of two quite different types are (i) a person who loses consciousness immediately on impact, does not regain consciousness, has non-reacting pupils and no spontaneous movement of the limbs. In this case brain damage [contusion] occurred at impact and is unlikely to be helped by surgery; (ii) a person who loses consciousness briefly after a bang on the head [concussion], comes round, can talk lucidly and move, then becomes progressively more drowsy and develops a dilated pupil on the side of the injury, with weakness down the opposite side. The onset of drowsiness indicates that brain function is being impaired by something occurring after the impact. This is most likely the build-up of a blood clot, which will require urgent surgery.

b. Treatment of an unconscious person

A fireman should check whether the victim can speak or answer questions or respond in any other way. His first task will be to deal with any breathing problems, or bleeding, as outlined above. He should then place the victim in the recovery position [see Fig. 6.4]. This will allow any vomit to drain naturally without blocking the air passage. He should loosen tight clothing about the victim's neck, chest and waist. Heat should not be applied, but the fireman should, where necessary, wrap the victim in a blanket and put another underneath. He should not attempt to give food or fluid while the victim is unconscious. He should treat the cause of unconsciousness if known and attend to any other injuries.

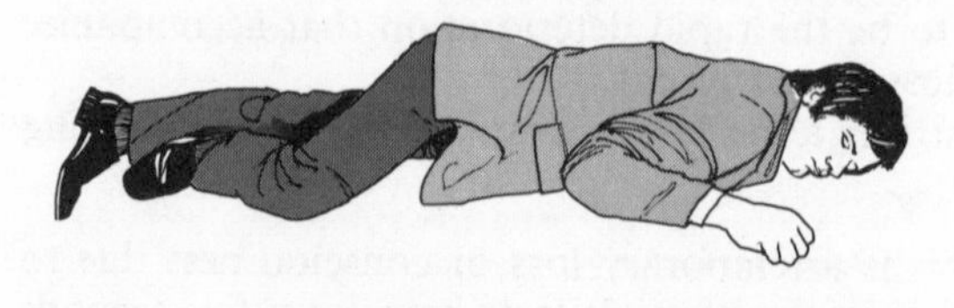

Fig. 6.4 Recovery position.

10 Relief of pain

Most pain felt by an accident victim results from bony damage. At its simplest, relief of pain comes from the immobilisation of fractured bones. In a rescue, however, it may not be possible to immobilise the fracture until the victim is released. The pain must therefore be relieved by other means. The ideal agent to use during rescue is one which starts working rapidly, lacks side effects and is easily discontinued. An agent that most nearly meets this criterion is a mixture of 50% Nitrous Oxide and 50% Oxygen, such as Entonox, which is administered through a demand valve and mask. It should usually be self-administered by the patient holding the mask, but exceptionally the fireman can hold the mask and the patient push his face against it to make the necessary seal which trips the demand valve [see Plates 6 and 7]. In both cases a patient who takes too much and becomes drowsy no longer maintains the seal and therefore breathes air, making the method fail-safe. Such an agent should *not* be used with victims who have an impaired level of consciousness, who cannot use the mask because of facial injuries, or who are drunk and liable to vomit. It should not be used at temperatures lower than −6°C. because the gases separate.

11 Broken bones

a. Types of fracture

A fracture is a broken or cracked bone. When force has been applied to a bone and the diagnosis is uncertain all injuries to that part of the body should be treated as fractures. There are three types of fracture:

(i) closed or simple: when there is no wound leading down to the broken bone;

(ii) open or compound: when there is a wound leading down to the broken bone or when the fractured ends protrude through the skin, thus allowing germs to gain access to the site of the fracture;

(iii) complicated: when a fracture involves another part of the body, such as a blood vessel or nerve.

b. Treatment of fractures

Attention to breathing, bleeding and unconsciousness must take priority over broken bones. Casualties should be dealt with where they are, unless life is immediately endangered. A fireman should at once steady and support the injured part and should maintain this control until the fracture is completely secured. He should immobilise the fracture either by securing the injured part to a sound part of the body with bandages, or by the use of splints and bandages.

(1) Splints

Splints must be well padded and sufficiently long to immobilise the joint above and below the fracture.

Suitable splints for different types of injury are as follows: [see Figs 6.5, 6.6, 6.7]

(i) spinal: it is possible to improvise with rolled-up newspaper, bandaged into place, but purpose-made plastic collars are more effective. Full spine splints include the workshop made shortboard, with its practical limitations. Commercially available alternatives include the Tynemouth Spinal Splint in fibreglass and the Sherman Splint, which is a combination of board and fabric corset. Both can be applied in situ and both could be used in conjunction with a folding lightweight frame stretcher, e.g. Paraguard or Chance type, for evacuation from awkward situations;

(ii) upper limb injuries: use of the conventional triangular bandage as a sling or board bandage is more than adequate for most injuries. An inflatable splint is rarely required. It is always necessary to take care with fractures of the elbow, which can interfere with circulation. The colour and temperature of the hand should always be checked, as should the pulse. A weak or absent pulse and a cold, pale, or dusky hand is indicative of trouble with the circulation, which requires urgent attention;

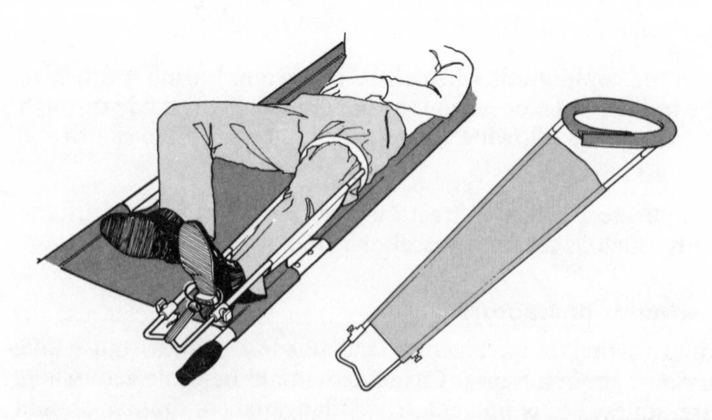

Fig. 6.5.

Fig. 6.6.

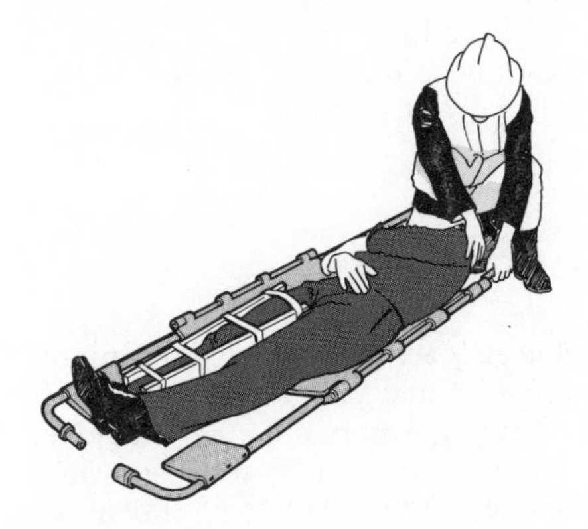

Fig. 6.7

Figs. 6.5-6.7 Various types of splint

(iii) lower limb injuries: fractures below the knee may be adequately splinted with broad bandages in many cases. Wooden 'L' splints are more rigid and blow-up plastic 'inflatable' splints are useful. Such fractures may often be displaced. An inflatable splint will force the leg straight. The fracture needs either traction and an alteration of the victim's position, with pain relief applied, or an alternative means of immobilisation.

It is best to immobilise fractures of the thigh in a traction splint such as the Tauranga Thomas, Trac 3, or Hare. These all use the principle of longitudinal traction to counter the muscle contraction of the thigh that causes shortening, pain, and space for bleeding into the fracture site [see Fig. 6.5]. They transform the transport of a patient, but have to be applied by trained ambulance or medical staff. However, conventional broad bandage splinting or the use of boards and foam pads from trunk to toes does immobilise a fracture somewhat, though both do little to reduce bleeding into the fracture site. Splints can be improvised from firmly folded newspaper or well-padded broom handles or pieces of wood.

Firemen must recall that a dislocation of the hip with shortening, internal rotation of the foot and slight bending of the knee should be splinted gently as found, with a support behind the knee. The casualty would not be able to tolerate traction.

(2) Bandages

When using bandages alone, the fireman should apply them sufficiently firmly to prevent movement but not so tightly as to prevent circulation of the blood. If the casualty is lying down, the fireman should use a splint or similar implement to pass the bandage under the trunk or lower limbs in the natural hollows of the neck, waist, knees, and just above the heels. He should then work the bandage gently into its correct position.

12 Burns and scalds

With both burns and scalds, skin cells are damaged and the injured area becomes red, swollen, blistered and painful. Since the skin damage has been caused by heat, the part affected should be cooled as soon as possible. The fireman should, where possible, immerse it in cold water or run cold water over it; he should not break any blisters that are formed. He should cover the area with a sterile dressing, clean lint or freshly laundered linen. This is particularly important with parts of the body liable to get dirty, such as hands. The fireman should remove from the casualty anything of a constricting nature, such as rings, bangles, belts and boots, before swelling starts. He need not, however, remove all burnt clothing as it will have been rendered sterile by the heat. He should beware of melted fabrics and plastics adhering to the skin.

13 Shock

Shock is a reaction of the body to an insufficient circulation of blood and consequent oxygen deficiency. It accompanies injuries, severe pain, or sudden illness and may vary in severity from a feeling of faintness to collapse and even death.

a. Causes of shock

Shock may arise either from an actual loss of blood through injury, thus decreasing the volume in circulation, or from the effect on the circulation of massive stimulation of nerves by pain, of heart attacks, or of toxic substances, including infections, bites, etc.

b. Signs of shock

Apart from actual collapse, typical symptoms and signs of shock are giddiness, nausea, pallor, a cold, clammy skin, and a pulse which becomes rapid and thready. The intensity of the symptoms and signs may be related to the degree of shock.

c. Treatment

The fireman can almost always reverse shock due to nerve reaction by simple measures, in particular by calming, reassuring and comforting the victim, laying the person down, and keeping him or her warm. Shock due to loss of blood or blood plasma is more serious. Transfusions and surgical operations will be urgent in severe cases of haemorrhaging. The priority will therefore be to remove the casualty to hospital without dèlay or obtain on-site medical aid. Until this can be done, first aid should concentrate on maintaining respiration and stopping bleeding.

14 Handling casualties

a. Preliminaries

In general, the casualty should receive any necessary first aid or extended care before or during extrication. This seldom interferes with the release of a trapped person. The principle of rendering the situation safe, treating the patient and then effecting removal is tried and established. In the last decade the techniques of emergency care that can be used by ambulance crews and medical personnel on site have developed considerably and can be most useful to the Brigade. They can extend the time available for extrication and increase safety for the casualty and emergency service personnel.

b. Protecting the casualty

Section 2 of this Chapter listed some of the risks which firemen have to bear in mind when tackling an incident. The following are further factors to which they should pay attention during their operations in order to make the rescue easier for a victim:

(i) heat: the casualty should be protected from the radiation, conduction or convection of heat. Fire blankets, water cooling or heat blocking agents are amongst the possible means;

(ii) vibration: movement and vibration can be very painful, for example, if transmitted to a fracture, and they could increase shock. Firemen should therefore take care to limit the degree of disturbance to which the patient is exposed;

(iii) sound: mechanical rescue tools are often noisy. So that the noise does not disturb the casualty too much, firemen should give warning and reassurance;

(iv) dust and fumes: the casualty should be given respiratory protection if the dust and fumes amount to anything more than a nuisance;

(v) electricity: firemen must obviously protect the casualty from electrocution. They should also remember that patients with certain heart conditions may be sensitive to lesser voltages than fit people.

c. Moving the casualty

The actual movement of the patient, once he or she is released, follows on from the previous considerations, and in many cases the assessment of the patient dictates the methods to be used.

Basically, the patient should not be moved unless it is of real benefit to do so; the aim should then be to make the move a continuous one from the position in which he or she was found to the stretcher. Exceptions to this obviously exist in such cases as the use of the recovery position, but general adherence to this guidance should ensure that the casualty is not dragged round unnecessarily. The stages in moving the patient may be categorised as below [there is further information on the handling of casualties in Chapter 1].

(1) Preparation for removal

Splints and dressings should be applied as necessary and firemen should follow the other first aid principles set out above. Before removal from a vehicle to a stretcher it may be necessary to reposition the patient, either by turning round [Fig. 6.6] or by leaning out [Figs. 6.8 & 6.9].

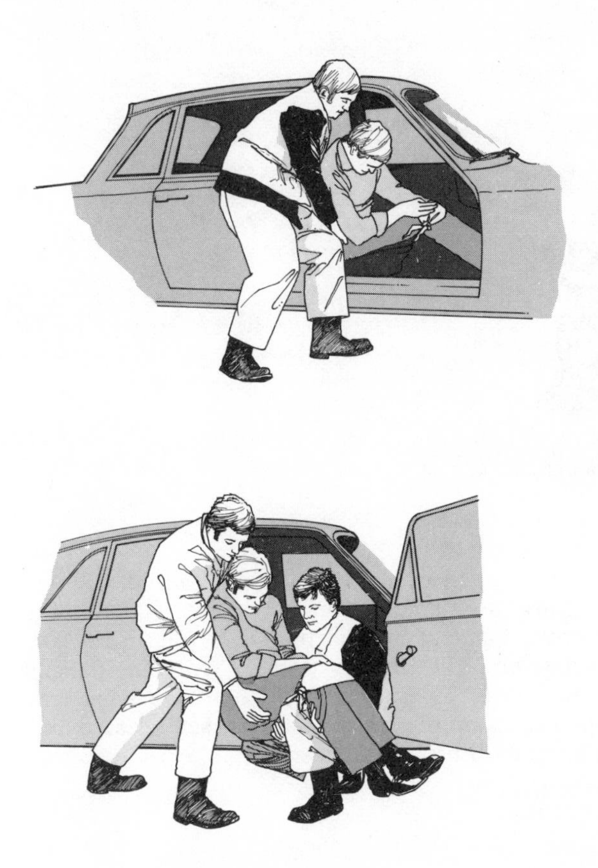

Figs 6.8 & 6.9 Leaning out a casualty before removal from a vehicle

As a general rule it is often possible to lift the patient by his or her clothing. This has the advantage of being possible in situ and does not involve the delay or disturbance that special equipment might.

Obviously, the presence of injuries may modify the way in which the patient is lifted at the point of injury. Special considerations include the avoidance of wrap-round compression on fractures at the shoulders, ribs, or hips and pelvis. Where a clothing lift is not feasible, then a fireman may slip a zig-zag folded blanket behind or under the patient, extend it to the shoulder and back of knee level, then roll it up to the edge of the patient in typical blanket fashion [see Fig. 6.10]. The patient may then be lifted in a sitting position.

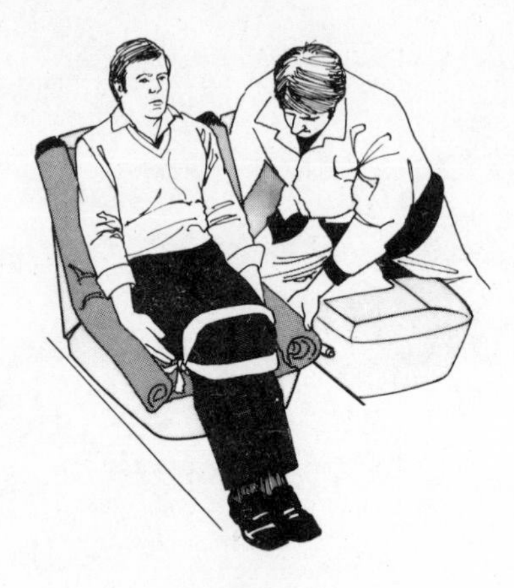

Fig. 6.10 Lifting a casualty in a sitting position.

The patient who is found in a sitting position with a fracture of the femur may also need preparation for the lift. The use of a figure of eight broad bandage around the knees (Fig. 6.10] is a great help in maintaining the fracture position while the patient is taken from the sitting/knees bent position to the lying/legs straight position. The figure of eight bandage is then released and repositioned as a standard broad bandage.

(2) Lifting

(i) To the standing position: firemen may roll the patient forward and help him to lift himself as shown in Fig. 6.11 left. This has much to recommend it in avoiding back strain in the rescuer;

(ii) to the sitting position: the Australian lift position of shoulders under the arms can be used to lift the patient into a chair and again avoids stress on the back of the rescuer, especially where the patient is overweight [see Fig. 6.11 right];

(iii) to the stretcher: lifting from a car to a stretcher is shown in Fig. 6.12. Where the patient is already on the ground it may be accomplished by a clothing lift. Firemen should either slip a pole and canvas or carrying sheet beneath or move the patient forward onto an improvised pole/blanket stretcher. This is useful where equipment is short. Using a folded blanket as a seat [Figs 6.13, 6.14] also creates a lifting aid out of minimal equipment.

1 A good example
›mplex and fragmented
lopments at the rear of
-city buildings, making
ss difficult.
o: London Fire
›de.

2a An example of
notor winding mechan-
of an escalator.

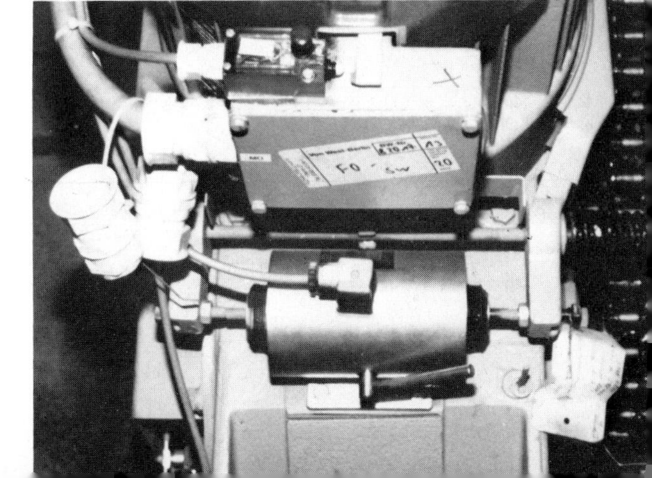

2b The lever at the
om of this photograph
example of the manual
e control of an escala-

o: Otis Elevator
pany.

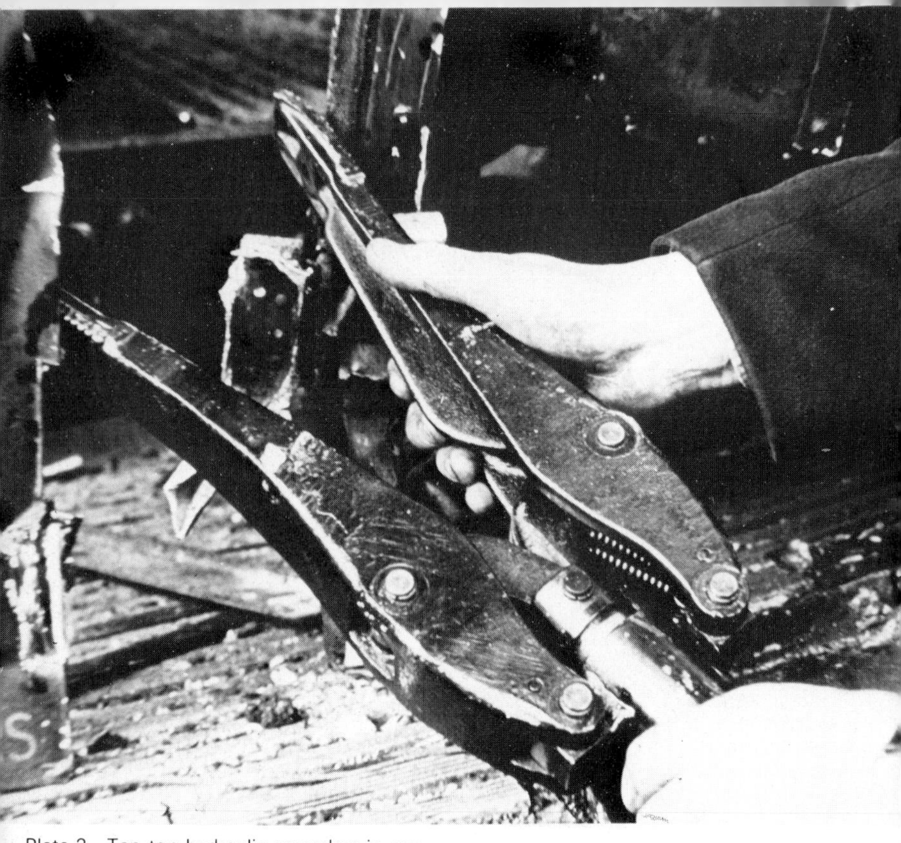

Plate 3 Ten ton hydraulic spreaders in use.

Plate 4 Hydraulic spreaders in use at an r.t.a. attended by all emergency services.
Photo: Avon Fire Brigade.

5 Method of using
pliance to assist in
ng a casualty from
p deck of a bus.
: *Fire Service College.*

6 A trapped diesel
otive driver. A medi-
am is in attendance
a drip feed and anaes-
ng gas, whilst the Bri-
provides lighting.
: *London Fire*
de.

Plate 7 A driver trap
his cab as the result
r.t.a. which has driv
steering wheel into h
abdomen. An anaest
ing gas is being adm
tered.
Photo: Avon Fire Br.

Plate 8 This car wa
erally wrapped round
a difficult and protra
operation was neces
release the casualty.
Photo: Surrey Fire B

9 A special service rescue being carried out following the collapse of trench shuttering.
o: Birmingham Post and Mail.

Plate 10 An unusu
special service invol
rescue of a trainee
from a glider which
become entangled i
tric power lines.
*Photo: West Susse.
Brigade.*

Plate 11 Cliff rescu
equipment, including
winch with 150 m. o
7 mm. diameter cab
stretcher cable guide
tector, strops and re
slings.
Photo: Kent Fire Bri

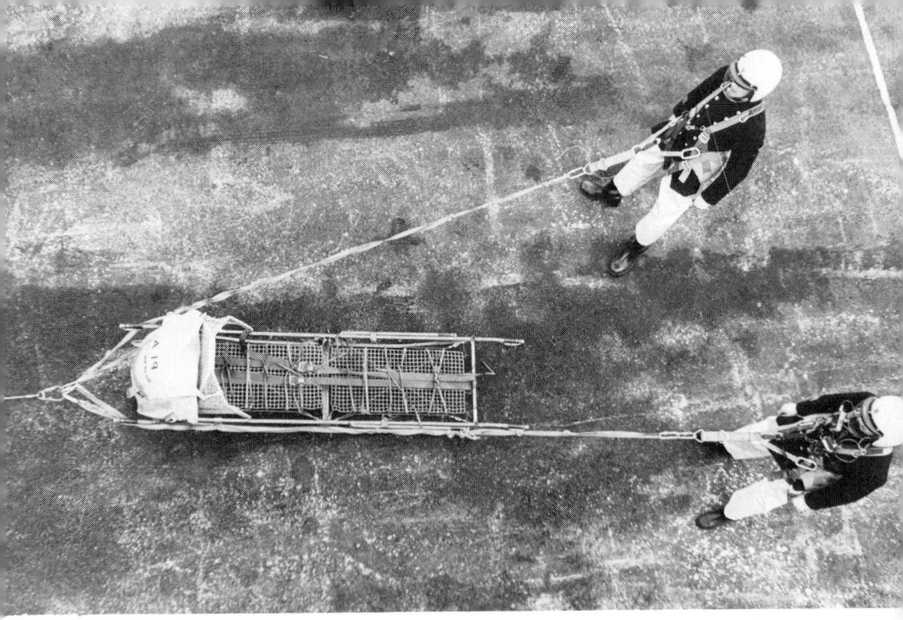

ı2 Cliff rescue equipment [see Plate 11], with two firemen ready to be lowered with a rescue ıer. The canvas bag at the head of the stretcher contains first aid kit, two padded rescue slings, arness for the cliff crew.
: Kent Fire Brigade.

13 Decontamination team at work with full equipment, including air-lines.
: Essex Fire Brigade.

Plate 14 Wet decontamination procedure being carried out.
Photo: Essex Fire Brigade.

Plate 15 Tarpaulins used to cover a roof should well overlap and be securely fastened. This roof covered by a Salvage Corps, but firemen should follow the same principles as far as possible.
Photo: London Salvage Corps.

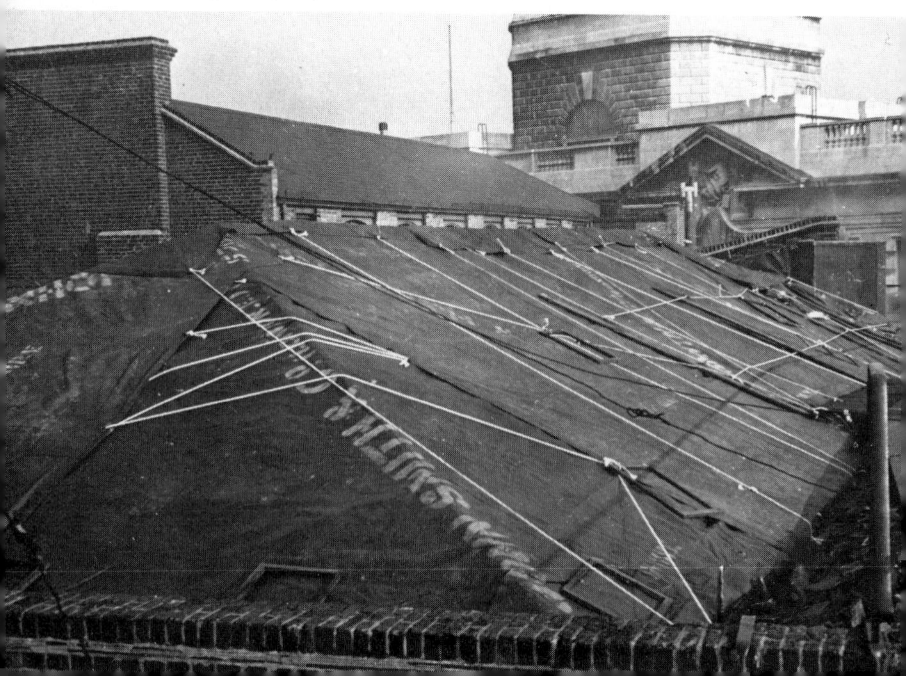

e 16 This wire mesh guard is protecting a drain from blockage by debris. Manholes should have
lar protection.
to: London Salvage Corps.

Plate 17 The Salvage Corps use hoppers like this to help remove water, usually in buildings with special drainage plugs.
Photo: Liverpool Salvage Corps.

Plate 18 The goods on these shelves are being protected by lightweight plastic sheeting. This is easier to support than salvage sheets and keeps the goods visible.
Photo: Liverpool Salvage Corps.

19 Goods in this warehouse are being protected by sheeting. The thorough covering and over-
g of sheets are particularly important.
: London Salvage Corps.

20 An example of the difficulty in identifying bodies after a fire. There are at least six bodies
ed here.
: Commissioner of Police, Metropolis.

Plate 21 The different degrees to which these chairs are burnt suggests that the one on the right was the seat of the fire.

Plate 22 The pattern of damage to this roof clearly suggests that the fire started at the left hand end. An eye-witness confirmed this.

e 23 The pattern of damage strongly suggested that an oil heater had flared up without warning. presence of glass fragments implied a shattering of the drip-feed heater's glass container.

e 24 The presence of an oil heater, paraffin cans and a funnel at the site of this fatal fire suggested the heater was being filled, but there was insufficient evidence for the coroner to record this.

Plate 25 Evidence of illegal entry before a fire. Note the two unbroken louvre panes carefully remov
and placed one under and one on the window-sill.
Photo: Commissioner of Police, Gibraltar.

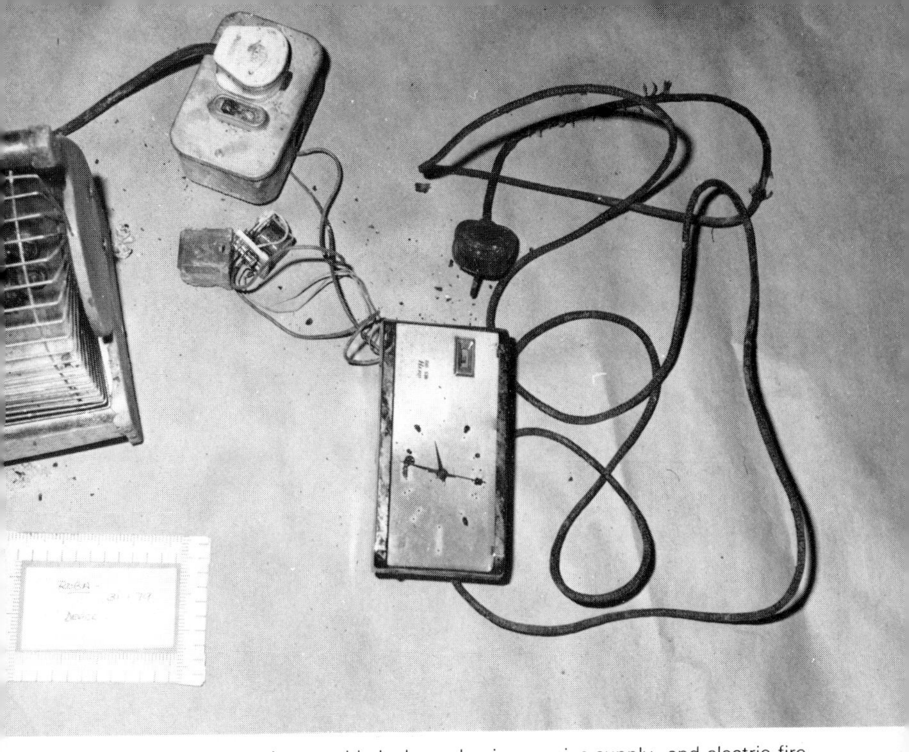

e 26 An incendiary device using an old clock mechanism, mains supply, and electric fire.
to: Chief Constable, Hertfordshire.

e 27 The device shown in Plate 26, as found at the scene.
to: Chief Constable, Hertfordshire.

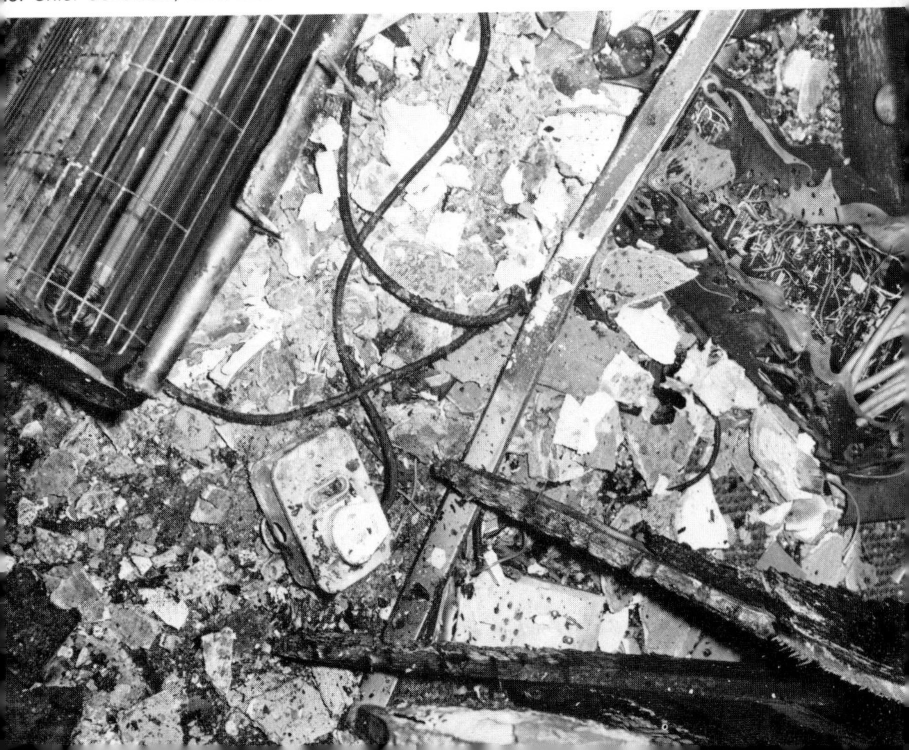

Plate 28 The removal debris and furniture ha revealed the distinctive pattern of an accelerar used in setting this fire
Photo: Commissioner c Police, Metropolis.

Plate 29 Clear evidenc arson in the attempt tc create a fire path from heads soaked in an acc ant.
Photo: Commissioner c Police, Metropolis.

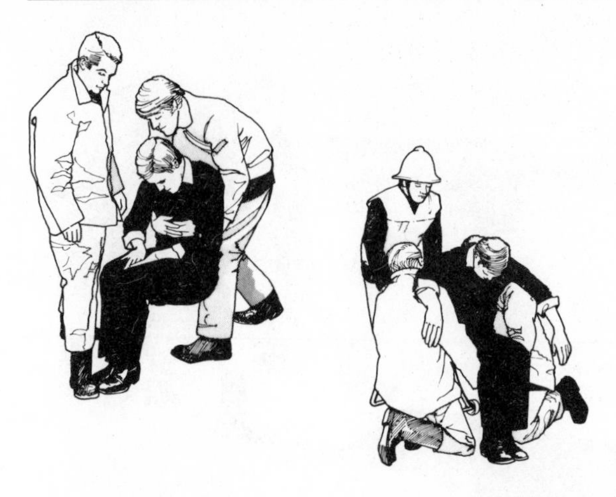

Fig. 6.11 Left: Lifting to the standing position. Right: to the sitting position.

Fig. 6.12 Lifting to the stretcher.

d. Special circumstances

(1) Snatch rescue

Encroaching fire, danger of drowning, dangerous fumes, etc. may require the immediate evacuation of injured patients to save their lives. To minimise injury, the fireman should grasp the patient from behind, as shown in Fig. 6.15, holding the head on either

Figs. 6.13 & 6.14 Lifting with a blanket.

side, take the weight under his arms, and pull the patient against his body and onto his forward leg. By this means, he disturbs spinal and other injuries as little as possible. In Fig. 6.16 one rescuer holds a zig-zag folded blanket by his heels whilst the other pulls the patient longitudinally onto the blanket, using blanket, clothing and positioning of hands to stabilise the neck.

Fig. 6.15 Snatch rescue.

Fig. 6.16 Snatch rescue using a blanket.

(2) Car seat

Occasionally, circumstances may justify cutting the seat mounts and removing the victim on the seat. He or she may then be tilted back to lie on a stretcher, the seat carefully slid out and the legs laid flat. A patient should not be left sitting upright if shocked, but otherwise could be taken to the hospital on the seat.

(3) Spinal injuries

Spinal injuries may be safeguarded with a Sherman Splint [Fig. 6.6]. This is applied before moving the patient and makes lifting much safer and easier. As a general rule, the patient should not be lifted by the splint itself.

(4) Continuous attendance

A seriously injured patient may need continuous surveillance, assistance with breathing, or other treatment during removal from awkward situations. The combination of frame stretcher and slings and lowering line [Fig. 1.16] allows this to be undertaken in situations such as quarry rescues and helicopter evacuation.

In some unusual situations the use of a frame stretcher with a spinal board is a practical combination. Firemen should fit the spinal board and move the patient on a carrying sheet to the nearest point where the stretcher may be used. In addition to the lifting straps illustrated, the stretcher may also be fitted with such additional aids as carrying handles, carrying yokes and a waterproof sheet.

(5) Inverted positions

People trapped upside down need very careful monitoring in case their condition deteriorates or complications set in.

(6) Rescues from under debris etc.

Firemen sometimes attend incidents where people are trapped under collapsed masonry or in a collapsed trench [see Chapter 5, Sections 3 and 6]. Their priority in these circumstances must be to get to the head and clear the airway. They must couple this with relieving any pressure on the chest which might interfere with breathing and brain function. Uncovering a trapped person's trunk and pulling him clear may seem an obvious course of action but is unlikely to succeed and carries the grave risk of aggravating the injury.

Part 2
Decontamination

Introduction

Firemen will often receive calls to fires and other incidents where it is known or suspected that dangerous substances are involved. These situations will arise not only on such obvious occasions as incidents at chemical factories but also in many other circumstances, such as road traffic accidents, material washed ashore from ships and calls to a wide variety of premises, e.g., farms, schools, laboratories or even private houses where dangerous substances are kept for study or use. The incidents may happen in industrial areas, residential areas or the countryside. Hazards will vary, the most likely being chemical, but there may also be a risk from radioactive or biological contaminants.

Clearly, firemen should avoid contamination from such substances as far as they can, but, equally clearly, this will not always be possible. The purpose of decontamination is to ensure that, on such occasions, the contamination is removed safely from their persons, clothing and equipment. The procedure aims at removing the contamination without the dangerous substance being inhaled or ingested, coming into contact or further contact with their skin, or spreading beyond the decontamination zone. There must also be decontamination of equipment but this is a secondary consideration and may be carried out elsewhere after the incident.

Firemen wearing protective clothing are those most likely to be contaminated, as they will have been committed to the affected area. The procedure must, however, also be able to cope with firemen in normal fire gear and members of the public who might have become involved. It should usually enable successful decontamination to be carried out at the incident but on occasion the nature or extent of the contamination will be beyond its scope to deal with thoroughly. Specialist treatment will then be necessary. This and the possible need for medical examination should always be borne in mind. The fireman must be ready to summon and take account of specialist advice.

The precise way in which decontamination is carried out will vary according to the nature of the dangerous substance involved. Its level will also vary: decontamination could be carried out initially using only equipment normally available on a pumping appliance, and at minor incidents this may suffice; at other incidents, however, a much more thorough procedure will be necessary. The initial action can only be a first aid measure. Full facilities for the more thorough procedure must be available for any incident where it is required and firemen must on these occasions follow the full procedure.

The success of decontamination will depend on the strict observance of a disciplined procedure within the defined zone where the whole process must be carried out. Firemen must familiarise themselves as far as possible with the hazards they are likely to face, particularly any which are fixed features of their own ground; they must familiarise themselves with the general principles of decontamination and with the detailed routines they must follow. These details will be laid down by each Brigade and will take account of local circumstances. This Part of the *Manual* attempts to set out some general principles.

Chapter 7
The identification of dangerous substances

1 The nature of the problem

The number of dangerous substances which might face firemen at an incident is immense. They can be in different forms and present a variety of hazards. While firemen should avoid contamination as far as possible, the presence of these substances may make decontamination necessary.

If firemen are to cope safely and efficiently with such an incident, they must be able quickly, and without difficulty, to discover the nature of the danger and how they should respond. Sometimes the substances will be at fixed sites, such as factories and laboratories. Then it is essential that firemen take active steps in advance to familiarise themselves with the dangers and how to cope with them. Section 1.1(d) inspections provide a good opportunity for this. Sometimes a building might carry some indication as to its contents, but firemen must not rely on this.

However, while many incidents do involve goods being kept in one place, a greater problem could arise with goods in transit, particularly those in bulk tankers. Clearly it would be difficult for firemen to know in advance the details of all the dangerous substances being transported within their areas. They must therefore be able to obtain the information they require at the time and to rely on it.

This Chapter briefly describes the indicators that should be present at the scene of an incident, the information they convey, and how firemen should ensure they have adequate data to deal with the situation. A later Book of the *Manual* will deal with the actual handling of incidents.

2 Types of dangerous substances

The United Nations Committee of Experts on the Transport of Dangerous Goods has classified nine types of hazard, some of which are themselves sub-divided. These are as follows:

(i) Class 1: explosives;

(ii) Class 2: gases;

(iii) Class 3: flammable liquids;

(iv) Class 4: flammable solids;

(v) Class 5: oxidising substances and organic peroxides;
(vi) Class 6: poisonous and infectious substances;
(vii) Class 7: radioactive substances;
(viii) Class 8: corrosives;
(ix) Class 9: miscellaneous dangerous substances [presenting during transport a hazard not covered by the preceding eight classes].

Full definitions of these classes appear in *Transport of Dangerous Goods: Recommendations prepared by the Committee of Experts on the Transport of Dangerous Goods*, published by the United Nations.

3 The labelling of dangerous substance containers

The number of dangerous substances covered by the nine classes is very great and their physical characteristics—colour, smell, etc.—even if apparent, are not necessarily such as to distinguish clearly one from another. This is particularly so for non-experts. When goods are in transit, the driver of the vehicle and the consignor's documents on it may be of help, or the vehicle may carry special instructions on the action necessary in the event of an incident [see, for example, 6a below]. In some accidents, however, firemen would not be able to consult these. In such circumstances, unless they have obtained information in advance, they must rely on the labelling of the container.

In the past such labelling has varied with regard both to its presence or absence and to the information it has conveyed. Increasingly, however, various voluntary schemes have come into operation and legal obligations have been imposed. There have been similar developments in some foreign countries and considerable international action through professional associations and such organisations as the United Nations, Council of Europe and European Economic Community. The arrangements are subject to continuing development but firemen should expect usually to find at least certain information given by means of labelling.

4 Hazard warning panels [The United Kingdom Transport Hazard Information System]

The U.K. Transport Hazard Information System was introduced on a voluntary basis on 1 July 1975. It has subsequently been the principal system for marking road tankers carrying dangerous substances in the U.K. British Rail also adopted the system for rail bulk tank wagons during 1976. The system was the basis for legislation in 1978. The subsequent *Dangerous Substances [Conveyance by Road in Road Tankers and Tank Containers] Regulations 1981* now make the labelling of tankers compulsory where they contain any of almost 1000 prescribed dangerous substances or any other substance offering a comparable risk. The prescribed substances are those named in the 'approved list' published by the Health and Safety Commission [*Approved Substance Identification Numbers, Emergency Action Codes, and Classifications for Dangerous Substances conveyed in Road Tankers and Tank Containers*]. The list is subject to revision.

The *Regulations* require that each vehicle should display at its rear and on both sides a composite hazard warning panel divided into five sections [see Fig. 7.1]. The panel is black and orange, except for section 1, which shows a variously coloured diamond symbol on a white background.

Fig. 7.1 Example of a hazard warning panel.

a. Section 1: hazard warning diamond

The first part of the hazard warning panel contains a symbol in the shape of a diamond [see Fig. 7.2]. This indicates that the contents of the vehicle are dangerous and shows the broad nature of the principal hazard they present. The symbols are internationally agreed under the auspices of the United Nations and relate to the classes listed in Section 2 above. In the U.K. the Health and Safety Commission assigns dangerous substances on the approved list to these classes and thus determines which diamonds shall apply to them.

Class 2(a)-Flammable gas

Class 2(b)-Non flammable compressed gas

Class 2(c)-Toxic gas

Class 3-Flammable liquid

Class 4(a)-Flammable solid

Class 4(b)-Spontaneously combustible substance

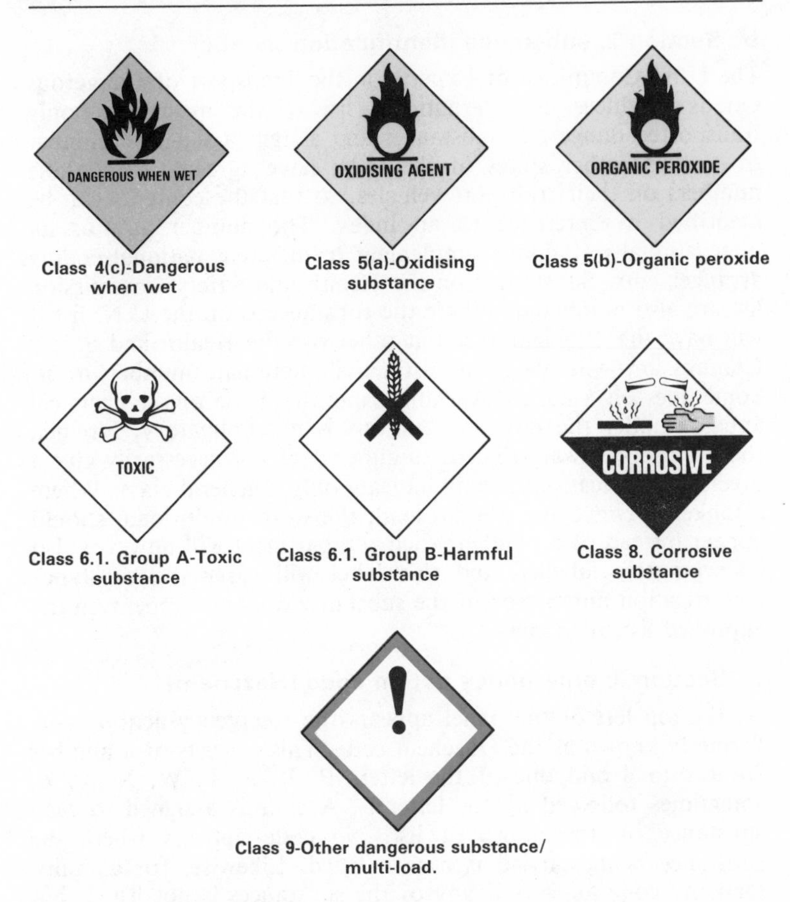

Class 4(c)-Dangerous when wet

Class 5(a)-Oxidising substance

Class 5(b)-Organic peroxide

Class 6.1. Group A-Toxic substance

Class 6.1. Group B-Harmful substance

Class 8. Corrosive substance

Class 9-Other dangerous substance/ multi-load.

Fig. 7.2 Hazard warning diamonds.

b. Section 2: substance identification number

The U.N. Committee of Experts on the Transport of Dangerous Goods produces an international list of the most commonly transported dangerous substances and assigns a separate number to each. Member states of the U.N. have agreed to use these numbers on their transport vehicles, so that the contents can be identified by reference to an index. The number acts as an internationally standard supplement to different national coding arrangements. Substances on the Health and Safety Commission list are also numbered. Where the substance is on the U.N. list it will have the U.N. number but otherwise the Health and Safety Commission will assign a distinctive, national, number to it. Sometimes on a hazard warning panel the name of the chemical appears under the number, but this is not obligatory. Firemen should also be aware that the number does not necessarily give a precise identification: it may indicate only a general class. Where a tanker is conveying a multi-load, the word 'multi-load' should appear instead of a number; each compartment will however also be separately labelled and this label will carry the substance identification number or, if the substance does not appear on the approved list, its name.

c. Section 3: emergency action code [Hazchem]

At the top left of the panel appears the emergency action code, formerly known as the Hazchem code. This consists of a number from 1 to 4 and one of the letters P, R, S, T, W, X, Y, Z, sometimes followed by the letter E. A code is assigned to each substance on the approved list. No code appears where the substance being carried is not so listed. Likewise, for a multi-load, no code appears if any of the substances is not listed, but if all are a composite code is given. The code does not identify the contents of a vehicle. Its purpose is to indicate the basic method of dealing with an incident. Fig. 7.3 shows a card setting out the meaning of the different numbers and letters. Each operational fireman should carry one of these cards. They should note the following points:

(i) if necessary, they can use a firefighting medium represented by a higher number than that shown, but not one represented by a lower;

(ii) where the letter appears as orange on black, police and other non-Fire Service personnel need to wear breathing apparatus only for a fire not for a spillage, but firemen will wear it in both cases;

(iii) the letter E indicates that the officer in charge should consider civilian evacuation of the area: it does not make evacuation obligatory or inevitable;

(iv) the letter V is a reminder that the coding letter concerned indicates a violently reactive substance; it does not appear on the hazard warning panel itself.

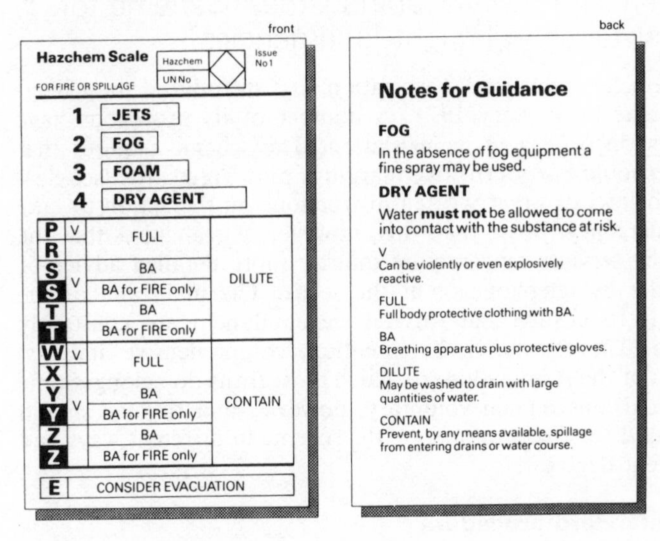

Fig. 7.3 Fireman's card summarising the emergency action code.

d. Sections 4 and 5: specialist advice

In the last sections of the panel, there appear a telephone number [section 4] and possibly [in section 5, which otherwise remains blank] a manufacturer's name or symbol. Contact with the number brings into operation the Chemsafe scheme organised by the Chemical Industries' Association [see Section 5 below]. If the manufacturer has lodged relevant information with the Chief Fire Officer and the latter has agreed that the arrangements are satisfactory, this section may read instead 'Contact local depot'. The manufacturer's identity must however be clear from the vehicle's markings.

e. Special arrangements for crop-spraying aircraft and inland waterway vessels

Crop-spraying aircraft also use the hazard warning panels on a voluntary basis. In their case, the panel will be smaller, the hazard warning diamond will always show a black skull and crossbones and the word 'toxic' underneath and the emergency action code will always be 3WE; there will be no substance identification number. Inland waterway vessels likewise make voluntary use of the panel but at present [1982] this does not include an emergency action code.

5 Chemsafe [Chemical Industries' Scheme for Assistance in Freight Emergencies]

The Chemical Industries' Association first introduced the Chemsafe scheme in January 1974. A number of its provisions have now been incorporated in legislation. The scheme requires that vehicles should carry effective markings plus Tremcards [see Section 6a below] or other written instructions on the action to take in an emergency. More than this, however, it recognises that the emergency services may require quickly more detailed advice or help either by telephone or at the scene. The main aim of the scheme is to ensure that this advice aand help are constantly available. The scheme is, by intention, comprehensive amongst members of the Association, to which most firms do belong. Some of its provisions remain voluntary, however, and firemen should be prepared for firms to operate the scheme in different ways and to different degrees.

a. The standard procedure

Under the standard procedure, each firm ensures that its vehicles are clearly labelled with an emergency telephone number. By calling this number the Fire Service should be able to obtain advice and help at any time. Each firm, with assistance from the Association, makes its own arrangements for guaranteeing 24 hour coverage and these may include co-operation with other firms.

b. Long-stop procedure

Contact with the emergency number should be the first course of action. In some circumstances, however, the number may be missing or obscured or the arrangements may break down. In this case, there is a long-stop procedure for obtaining assistance, even though the manufacturer or trader is unknown or unobtainable or the product is unidentified.

(1) National Chemical Emergencies Centre [N.C.E.C.]

The principal element of this long-stop procedure is the National Chemical Emergencies Centre at Harwell. This has a continuously manned telephone through which the public emergency authorities can ask for advice on the chemical hazards of a product involved in an incident. In order readily to identify hazards and the emergency action that should be taken for the numerous different products being marketed, the Centre has established a computerised chemical data bank to which members of the Chemical Industries' Association are invited to contribute information on their products. N.C.E.C. duty officers, who are scientifically qualified and experienced in handling hazardous materials, have access to this.

If assistance is needed at the scene the Centre will turn out its own qualified staff or, if it is more convenient, request a particular company to send help. The manufacturer or trading company actually involved should take over as soon as its identity is known. The other assistance provided will, however, remain until no longer required.

The data bank at the Centre is very extensive but firemen should appreciate that the standard of information it can give will vary. The Centre depends on manufacturers to supply information, which it cannot then alter. Accordingly the data bank does not cover some chemicals at all whilst on others it has different information from different sources.

Where the standard procedure does not apply, a telephone call to N.C.E.C. is the normal course of action. A Brigade may contact a local firm directly if this seems likely to provide the required help more quickly. Such a firm may not, however, have detailed knowledge of a chemical it does not handle itself.

6 Foreign and international arrangements

Some foreign countries have developed their own methods of giving information on dangerous goods. Firemen may have encountered some of these in incidents involving foreign vehicles. Sections 3 and 4 above have pointed out that there have also been considerable international activity and attempts at standardisation. Firemen should ensure they are familiar with the arrangements which have resulted. Apart from those already mentioned, two will affect them in particular.

a. Tremcards [Transport Emergency Cards]

C.E.F.I.C. [the European Council of Chemical Industries' Federations], of which the British Chemical Industries' Association forms part, has reached agreement that each vehicle conveying a dangerous chemical should carry a Tremcard. This is a standard A4 size card in red and black issued for each of a number of common hazardous chemicals. Fig. 7.4 shows a typical example. The card gives:

(i) the chemical name of the substance;

(ii) its appearance and chemical properties;

(iii) its hazards and the precautions against them;

(iv) the action necessary in the event of fire or spillage;

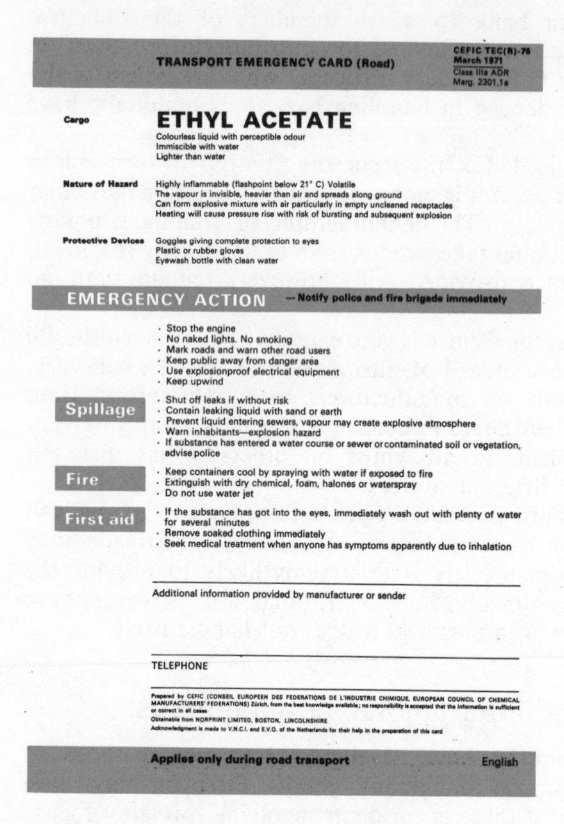

TRANSPORT EMERGENCY CARD (Road)

CEFIC TEC(R)-76
March 1971
Class IIIa ADR
Marg. 2301,1a

Cargo **ETHYL ACETATE**
Colourless liquid with perceptible odour
Immiscible with water
Lighter than water

Nature of Hazard
Highly inflammable (flashpoint below 21° C) Volatile
The vapour is invisible, heavier than air and spreads along ground
Can form explosive mixture with air particularly in empty uncleaned receptacles
Heating will cause pressure rise with risk of bursting and subsequent explosion

Protective Devices
Goggles giving complete protection to eyes
Plastic or rubber gloves
Eyewash bottle with clean water

EMERGENCY ACTION — Notify police and fire brigade immediately

- Stop the engine
- No naked lights. No smoking
- Mark roads and warn other road users
- Keep public away from danger area
- Use explosionproof electrical equipment
- Keep upwind

Spillage
- Shut off leaks if without risk
- Contain leaking liquid with sand or earth
- Prevent liquid entering sewers, vapour may create explosive atmosphere
- Warn inhabitants—explosion hazard
- If substance has entered a water course or sewer or contaminated soil or vegetation, advise police

Fire
- Keep containers cool by spraying with water if exposed to fire
- Extinguish with dry chemical, foam, halones or waterspray
- Do not use water jet

First aid
- If the substance has got into the eyes, immediately wash out with plenty of water for several minutes
- Remove soaked clothing immediately
- Seek medical treatment when anyone has symptoms apparently due to inhalation

Additional information provided by manufacturer or sender

TELEPHONE

Prepared by CEFIC (CONSEIL EUROPEEN DES FEDERATIONS DE L'INDUSTRIE CHIMIQUE, EUROPEAN COUNCIL OF CHEMICAL MANUFACTURERS' FEDERATIONS) Zürich, from the best knowledge available; no responsibility is accepted that the information is sufficient or correct in all cases
Obtainable from NORPRINT LIMITED, BOSTON, LINCOLNSHIRE
Acknowledgment is made to V.N.C.I. and E.V.O. of the Netherlands for their help in the preparation of this card

Applies only during road transport English

Fig. 7.4 Example of a Tremcard.

(v) the appropriate first aid treatment;

(vi) possibly, an emergency telephone number.

The carriage of Tremcards is not mandatory, but the *Dangerous Substances [Conveyance etc.] Regulations 1981* do require some of this information to be carried in writing on vehicles. The cards are issued also in sets which can be used as manuals for reference purposes. 'Group text' cards are now available for substances which do not have a card of their own. If, at an incident, the card is not present or not accessible but Brigade Control has the sets other indicators at the scene may make it possible to ascertain which card is applicable.

b. International conventions etc.

The principal international agreements on the transport of dangerous goods are A.D.R. [European agreement concerning the carriage of dangerous goods by road] and C.I.M. [International convention for the conveyance of goods by rail], particularly in the latter case the R.I.D. annex [Regulation on the carriage of dangerous goods]. Signatories have agreed that their bulk tankers will carry two warning symbols. The first is a hazard warning diamond of the type described in Section 4 above. The second is a rectangular plate, coloured orange, containing two numbers in black. Fig. 7.5 shows an example: at the bottom is the U.N. number, at the top, the Kemler code. The first digit of the code indicates to which of the classes listed in Section 2 above the substance being carried belongs. The second and third digits indicate associated hazards: 0, no meaning; 1, risk of explosion; 2, gas may be given off; 3, flammable risk; 5, oxidising risk; 6, toxic risk; 8, corrosive risk; 9, risk of violent reaction from spontaneous decomposition or self-polymerisation. Firemen should note the following special points:

(i) where the first two digits are the same, they indicate that the primary hazard is intensified;

(ii) if the letter X precedes the code, the use of water is absolutely prohibited;

(iii) 22 indicates a refrigerated gas; 42 a solid which may give off a gas on contact with water.

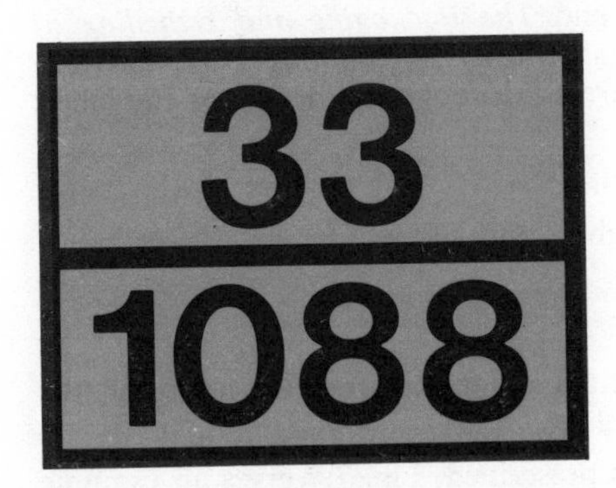

Fig. 7.5 Example of an A.D.R./C.I.M. Label

Vehicles engaged in international transport operations which comply with A.D.R. or C.I.M. need not also comply with the *Dangerous Substances* [*Conveyance etc.*] *Regulations 1981.*

7 Other labels and means of identification

a. Labels on wagons

Conveyors of dangerous goods sometimes use their own labelling systems in addition to any laid down by law. An example is the British Rail wagon label [Fig. 7.6]. This shows a hazard warning diamond (1), the class of dangerous goods which this indicates (2), the U.N. number (3), and British Rail's own Alpha code (4) which indicates to their staff a source of specialist advice. British Rail can also advise on the contents of any goods train by reference to their records. Firemen should note that in some cases, e.g. petroleum fuel, the number at (3) may identify the contents more precisely than the substance identification number in the hazard warning panel. Where the contents are mixed the number 8969 will appear here and the hazard warning diamond will show an exclamation mark.

Apart from these labels the tank wagon colour may also help identify the contents. Those carrying liquefied gases have a white barrel with a horizontal orange stripe and those carrying highly flammable liquids are dove grey with signal red sole bars.

b. Packages

In addition to the regulations concerning the labelling of road tankers, there are also labelling requirements for certain goods carried or stored in packages. These are currently [January 1982] prescribed by the *Packaging and Labelling of Dangerous Substances Regulations 1978*, and *The Packaging and Labelling of Dangerous Substances (Amendment) Regulations 1981*, but new regulations are being prepared. Although the design of the labels can vary, all must include:

(i) the name of the substance;

(ii) one or two danger symbols and key words;

(iii) risk phrases;

(iv) safety phrases;

(v) the name and address of the manufacturer, the importer, the wholesaler, or the supplier.

The wording of (i)–(iv) is prescribed. Fig. 7.7 gives an example of a typical label and Fig. 7.8 shows the danger symbols. These are used throughout the E.E.C.

c. Supplementary information: protective clothing code

Chemicals covered by Tremcards and emergency action codes have been allocated letters as follows, to indicate what sort of protective clothing is required:

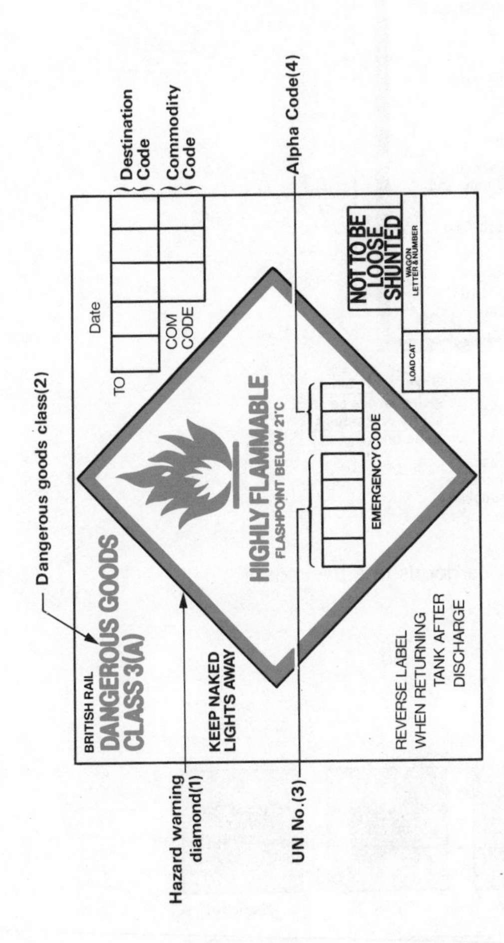

Fig. 7.6 British Rail wagon label.

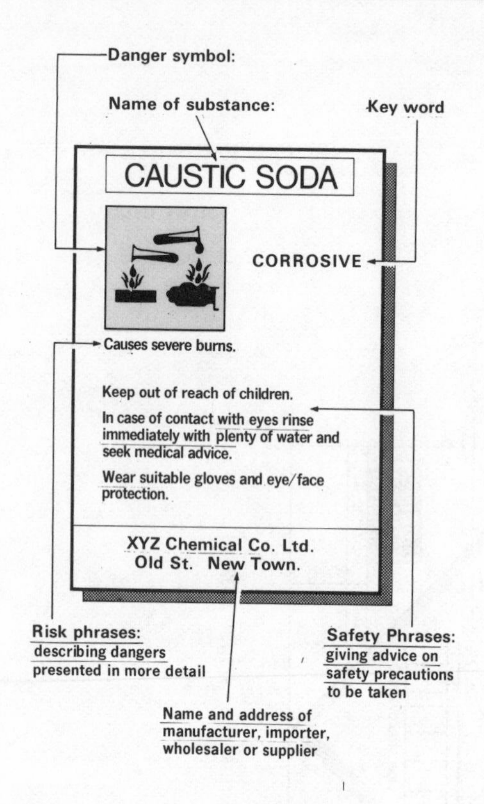

Fig. 7.7 Label for dangerous goods in a package.

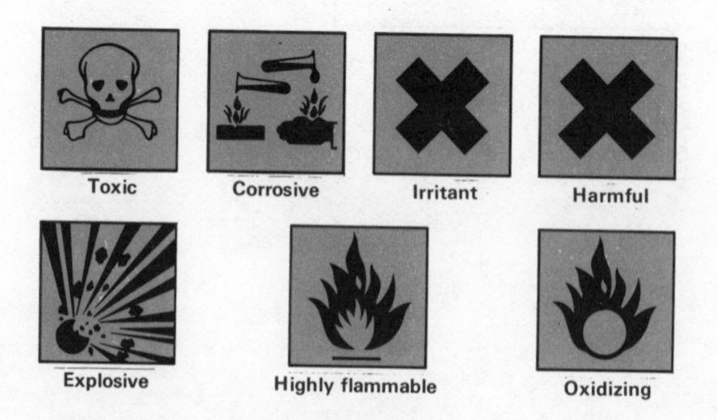

Fig. 7.8 Danger symbols for packaging labels.

(i)	no letter	self-contained breathing apparatus and a chemical protection suit will be adequate;
(ii)	A	the chemical severely attacks protective clothing, especially that containing rubber or p.v.c., and exposure should be limited;
(iii)	B	a gas-tight chemical protection suit is necessary;
(iv)	C	the chemical is highly toxic and positive pressure breathing apparatus is necessary;
(v)	AB	exposure even in a gas-tight chemical protection suit should be limited;
(vi)	AC	a chemical protection suit with positive pressure breathing apparatus is required;
(vii)	F	no form of protective clothing is adequate and firemen should take special care to avoid contamination.

The protective clothing code is not included in labelling. When a chemical has been identified and the emergency action code indicates that full protection is necessary, firemen should seek this information from their Control.

d. Non-chemical dangerous substances

Firemen will occasionally encounter dangerous substances other than chemicals. The most serious danger of contamination will come from radioactive and biological hazards. Where the labelling arrangements referred to above do not apply, the symbols shown in Figs 7.9 and 7.10 are often used for identification purposes.

Fig. 7.9 Symbol used to indicate a biological hazard. The word BIO-HAZARD, also in red, may appear underneath.

Fig. 7.10 Symbol used to indicate a radioactive hazard.

Dangerous substances which are not contaminants, such as explosives and gases in cylinders, also have means of identification. These will be dealt with elsewhere in the *Manual*.

e. Substances of low hazard

The Chemical Industries' Association has introduced a voluntary scheme, known as the black and white marking scheme, for the marking of domestic tanker vehicles carrying substances of low hazard. The substances concerned are those not covered by the *Dangerous Substances [Conveyance by Road in Road Tankers and Tank Containers] Regulations 1981*. The scheme provides that such tankers should be labelled with panels similar in general appearance to the hazard warning panels described in Section 4 above but using only the colours black and white. The panels convey the same general information as the hazard warning panels. The two principal differences are:

(i) there is no hazard warning diamond but words of warning may appear in the same place;

(ii) there is no substance identification number but in the same place there appears some descriptive term: the chemical name, a common name, a trade name, or, if appropriate, the expression 'multi-load'.

An emergency action code does appear: this is allotted by each firm separately on the basis of advice given by the C.I.A.

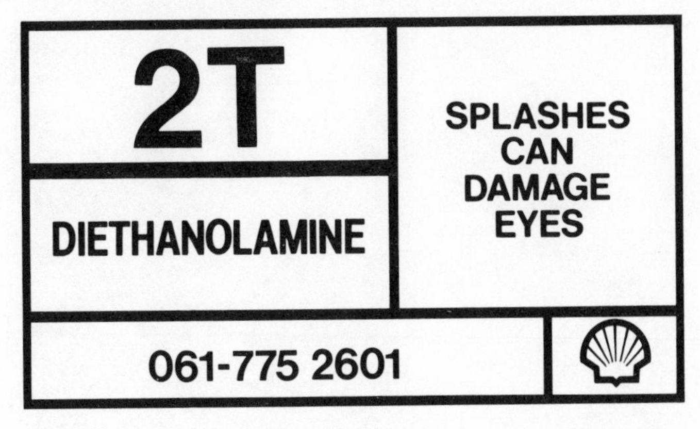

Fig. 7.11 Example of a panel giving warning of a substance of low hazard.

8 Obtaining further information

Some of the information available at an incident, for example Tremcards or the emergency action code, will enable firemen to know at once the basic action they should take. If, however, this information is missing or firemen require more details, they must make further enquiries. In some Brigades appliances carry a certain amount of information and firemen can refer to this on the spot. Otherwise the officer in charge must contact his Brigade Control. Control may refer first to the various resources some Brigades maintain themselves or it may, for example, telephone to the chemical manufacturer or National Chemical Emergency Centre.

Attempts at improving the availability and usefulness of the information available to Brigades are constant. Experiments are now concentrating on computer based systems. Firemen should ensure they remain familiar with new developments.

Chapter 8
Chemical decontamination

1 General

Chemicals are the contaminant a fireman is most likely to face. There are very many different sorts, both powder and liquid, but generally they fall into one of three broad categories:

(i) those which are soluble in water;

(ii) those which are insoluble in water; and

(iii) those which react violently with water or are flammable.

The degree of danger they present will vary. They may be, for example, toxic or corrosive; sometimes they may be harmless. If the latter is definitely known to be the case, a simple brush- or wash-down, as appropriate, will be adequate. Where decontamination is necessary the level and method employed will depend on the amount and nature of the chemical involved. These factors will also determine such points as what protective clothing is required, what cleansing agent is to be used, and what is to be done with the contaminant once removed.

2 Chemical incidents

a. Dealing with chemical incidents

The first attendance at an incident may not be aware initially that a dangerous chemical is involved. Even when the firemen concerned do know or learn this they may not know the nature of the chemical and how they should deal with it. The officer in charge can take certain precautions from the start. He can, for example, as far as possible keep appliances and men up-wind, clear of any vapour cloud and out of contact with the chemical; he can order B.A. to be worn; he can arrange for an ambulance to be standing by. He must in any case get what information he can and summon further assistance if necessary. He must also take any other action that is immediately necessary—evacuation, perhaps. In the meantime, however, firemen will have to be rescuing people trapped or at risk, dealing with the material affected, and stopping the incident from spreading. They are likely, therefore, to become contaminated and the initial decontamination procedure is designed as an immediate first aid measure to cope with this. It uses only equipment normally found on a pumping appliance.

b. The initial decontamination procedure

When contaminated firemen emerge from an incident the officer in charge should first establish a zone where decontamination can be carried out. He should appoint a suitably trained person as decontamination officer or, if necessary, assume this role himself. He should see that whatever other help is available and necessary is provided [he will already, of course, have summoned further help via Brigade Control if that is required and not already on its way].

The decontamination officer should instruct personnel in the procedure to be followed, making use of any protective clothing or breathing apparatus available. He should direct a contaminated person to the decontamination zone and tell him to stand in a plastic bag or on a salvage sheet so arranged as to hold water if that is used. The detailed decontamination procedure laid down in advance by the Brigade, and including if necessary the removal of contaminated clothing, after it has been wet or dry cleaned, should then be implemented. Any parts of a person's body which have been contaminated should be cleansed thoroughly with soap and water and at the end of the procedure the person should step out of his boots and onto a designated clean path. A fireman wearing breathing apparatus should remove this when appropriate but keep on the face mask till the last moment. The breathing apparatus tally of each man leaving the incident should be collected from the control board and checked to ensure it corresponds with the man concerned.

3 The decontamination team

a. Mobilisation

Where the contamination is such that the initial procedure will not be adequate to deal with it, a special decontamination team should attend. It may be obvious from the first call that the team will be necessary, in which case the Brigade Control will dispatch it automatically. Otherwise, the officer in charge at the incident should request the team as soon as the need for it becomes apparent. He should pass on any information he already has about the chemical concerned.

b. Composition of the team

The team should comprise a decontamination officer, an assistant decontamination officer, and a number of suitably trained Fire

Service personnel as operatives. One officer who has received appropriate training and has a knowledge of and interest in chemistry and chemicals should be available to act as supervisor if this is necessary in the absence of a specialist adviser to fulfil the role.

c. Assistance to the team

The decontamination officer must find out what he can about the chemical involved as soon as possible. Some of the schemes for providing him with basic information have been described in the preceding chapter. If these give him a contact point for advice on the particular chemical concerned the officer should get in touch as soon as possible; otherwise, there may be a source of general advice locally on which he can call. If at all possible there should be a specialist scientific adviser to act as supervisor of the team's operations.

d. The team's equipment

Each Brigade will decide separately what equipment a decontamination team will have and how this should be carried and brought to an incident, for example, in a specially maintained Chemical Incident Unit. A typical set of equipment, however, might include the following:

(i) protective clothing [see Fig. 8.1];

(ii) breathing apparatus;

(iii) compressed air cylinders with air-lines;

(iv) vacuum cleaners [complying with British Standard 5415, Parts 1 & 2];

(v) plastic bags with ties and labels, for storing clothing that has been removed, etc.

(vi) traffitape, cones and warning signs to mark the decontamination zone;

(vii) polythene sheeting or other material to provide a clean path;

(viii) detergent, sawdust, sand, earth, soda ash;

(ix) chemical absorbent pads [for chemicals that do not mix with water and detergent solutions] or dry agents;

(x) cleaning cloths;

(xi) empty containers with lids, labelled as to their contents;

(xii) portable dams;

(xiii) shovels and brooms;

(xiv) brushes, soap, disinfectant, towels;

(xv) clean overalls and footwear; blankets.

Special consideration should be given to using air-line equipment rather than breathing apparatus sets for the team operatives. They would then have less weight to carry and be less encumbered. Accordingly they could work in the decontamination zone for longer periods and it would be possible to augment their air supply with less hazard, since the change of cylinders would take place outside the zone.

Fig. 8.1 Examples of chemical protective clothing.

4 The decontamination zone

a. Siting the zone

When the team arrives the decontamination officer will determine the current situation with the officer in charge and estimate the size and nature of the incident. He will then decide on a suitable location for a decontamination zone, taking into account:

(i) the type of decontamination to be conducted;

(ii) the general weather conditions and wind direction;

(iii) the safety and comfort of personnel;

(iv) the slope of the ground;

(v) the location of drains;

(vi) the operational circumstances;

(vii) the location of the breathing apparatus entry control point;

(viii)the location of a pump to supply hose reels for wet decontamination if needed.

He will see that all decontamination is carried out in this zone in accordance with a strictly disciplined procedure.

b. Establishing the zone

The size of the zone will depend on operational circumstances, including the equipment available. It should, however, be as small as possible. The officer should see that it is clearly defined, for example by traffitape, or, if a building is used, that the entrances are clearly marked. A sign should indicate the entry to the zone and warn other personnel and the public to keep away. The zone can be laid out on the lines shown in Fig. 8.2. The officer should consider providing some screening or shelter for the disrobing and dressing area, if possible.

5 The full decontamination procedure [basic]

a. Control

The decontamination officer will issue all instructions on the procedure to be followed and must ensure that the instructions have been properly carried out before moving on to the next stage. He should pass all relevant information about the chemical involved back to his Control and obtain back-up information from or via there, as necessary. He should work throughout under the guidance of the supervisor. He will operate at all times in fire gear and will stay outside the zone. His assistant will wear fire gear, gloves and breathing apparatus, enter the zone on the clean path and remain on it throughout. Other members of the team will wear chemical protective clothing and breathing apparatus or air-line equipment and should stay within the decontamination zone. To avoid spreading contamination personnel awaiting decontamination should remain in or next to the zone, as directed. The Operational Procedure for the Use of Breathing Apparatus [see *Manual*, Book 6, Chapters 10–12] should apply in respect of the operatives when this is warranted by the numbers to be decontaminated.

b. Carrying out the decontamination procedure

The decontamination officer or supervisor will decide the method of decontamination according to the nature of the contaminant. The basic methods involve the use of the following means to clean clothing, before its careful removal:

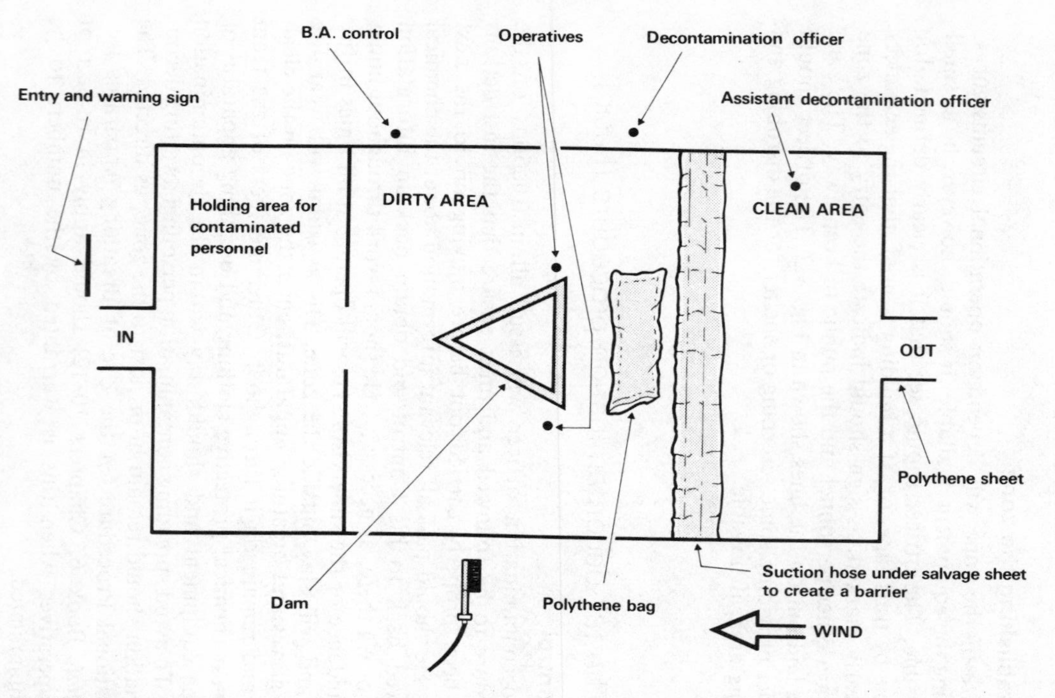

Fig. 8.2 Typical lay-out of a decontamination zone using two overlapping salvage sheets and traffitape to mark the boundaries.

(i) water;
(ii) neutralising solution;
(iii) detergent;
(iv) dry agents;
(v) brushes;
(vi) vacuum cleaners.

The contaminant removed will be contained or allowed to drain away according to its nature. The details of the procedure will vary according to such factors as:

(i) the method used;
(ii) the type of protective clothing and breathing apparatus employed;
(iii) the amount of contaminant;
(iv) the equipment available.

The decontamination officer should have the procedures clearly set out on easily available boards; he should read out each stage and ensure it is satisfactorily completed before moving on to the next. Whatever method is used, the decontamination officer should take care to prevent people spreading the contaminant, particularly when decontamination takes place inside a building. The procedure will end with the cleansing and disrobing of each other by the decontamination team members. [See Plates 13 and 14].

c. Personnel wearing breathing apparatus

When a fireman wearing breathing apparatus is contaminated he should, if possible, leave the incident in time for decontamination to be completed before his cylinder runs out. A minimum reading on the gauge of 80 atm/bars is desirable. All cylinders should be checked before decontamination starts and if any is dangerously low [say, below 50 atm/bars] the decontamination officer should use any means available to ease the situation. He could supply the wearer by air-line or, if that is not possible, change the cylinder. When breathing apparatus is removed during decontamination the wearer should, if necessary, be protected by air-line mask, dust mask, or respirator.

6 Decontamination in special circumstances

a. Decontamination of clothing and equipment away from the incident

The supervisor will give instructions as to the disposal, cleaning and thorough decontamination of affected gear. It is important that contaminated clothing and equipment is not moved unnecessarily from the incident to an area where it might present a greater problem. When it must be moved, this should only be done under the close scrutiny of the supervisor. The supervisor may well direct in some circumstances that certain items be decontaminated at some other suitable location where there are appropriate facilities and adequate supervision.

b. Persons not wearing protective clothing

Members of the public or firemen in ordinary fire gear may sometimes become contaminated. When this occurs the decontamination team should normally give them priority over protected firemen. They should follow the normal procedure as far as possible. It is essential, however, that since ordinary clothing will not provide adequate protection, any which might be contaminated is removed without delay and the person's body is cleaned with particular care. The person should then be dried and reclothed or given a covering at once and sent for medical check-up. The team should take care throughout to reassure members of the public and to explain the procedure. There should be provision for taking care of, and returning, their property as appropriate.

Although those not wearing protective clothing are particularly at risk the team must recall that the effectiveness of protective clothing can be lessened by damage and that it can only provide protection for a limited time against some substances. Against some particularly dangerous substances, such as liquid oxygen or sodium, there is no adequate protection. When dealing with these at an incident, it is particularly important to avoid contamination.

c. Injured persons

The severity of a person's injuries may make the normal procedure impossible or the need for rapid medical treatment more important than the need for decontamination. An ambulance should already be standing by and in these circumstances the decontamination officer should act in consultation with medical personnel. Arrangements for the safe transport of the person to hospital without spreading the contamination, for assisting medical staff to carry out their duties without themselves becoming contaminated, and for any decontamination required at a later stage will be determined locally.

7 Liaison with other bodies

In addition to contact with sources of special advice, there will be a need for liaison with other organisations. This is especially so where, for example, people need medical treatment, an area needs sealing off or evacuating, or contaminant requires disposal. The decontamination officer should liaise with hospitals and the ambulance service, police, relevant departments of the Local Authority, the Water Authority, and any other bodies necessary, as locally determined.

8 Record keeping

The decontamination officer should ensure that a record is maintained showing:

(i) the names and stations of firemen who have been decontaminated;

(ii) the chemical concerned;

(iii) any other relevant information such as

  (a) their role in the incident;

  (b) how contamination occurred;

  (c) the period of contamination;

  (d) the areas of their bodies contaminated;

  (e) the decontamination procedure used.

These details should ultimately be recorded at Brigade Headquarters. Such information can also helpfully be recorded in respect of members of the public who have to undergo decontamination in case it is needed for medical purposes.

Chapter 9
Other decontamination

1 General

Although chemicals are the contaminant a fireman is most likely to encounter he will, on occasions, also have to deal with others. The need for decontamination may then arise, and he must be familiar with the procedure to be followed, particularly where this differs from the standard procedure outlined in Chapter 8. Precise details of the action to take will again be laid down locally and will take account of local circumstances. Apart from accidents with goods in transit incidents involving these hazards are more likely to take place at certain fixed locations and firemen should familiarise themselves with those on their ground and establish close liaison with the people in charge.

2 Radiation

Radioactive materials have come into increasing use in industry, hospitals and scientific establishments as well as for military and energy generation purposes. The possibility of incidents involving them has therefore grown. Though they do not, by virtue of their radioactivity, form any greater fire risk they can cause contamination and this can be a danger to health. Radiation cannot be perceived by the senses and its effects can be delayed. It can, however, cause biological, chemical and physical changes which may be harmful. It can also have a genetic effect which will be apparent in any future offspring of the person affected.

Where premises house radioactive materials in hazardous quantities special precautions are taken; the same is true when radioactive materials are being transported in bulk. In both cases there are special procedures arranged between the authorities concerned, the police, and other interested bodies, to deal with incidents when they do occur. Ordinarily, however, the radioactive sources involved in incidents will probably be small and there is little risk of firemen being seriously affected. To ensure their safety, however, there must be provision for effective decontamination on such occasions and they must be able to carry it out efficiently.

Where radioactive materials are involved in an incident, the police should be notified immediately, as should any available source of technical advice. It may also be necessary to alert local hospitals, with which arrangements should have been made in advance. Where a military aircraft is involved it should be assumed that it is carrying a nuclear device and the Royal Air Force should be informed via the police. When a nuclear device is involved the R.A.F. will advise the police and Fire Brigade of its presence and dispatch a team from their Special Safety Organisation which will take over operations on arrival. The officer in charge will tackle the incident in accordance with procedures laid down locally by the Brigade [see also *Manual*, Part 6c, Chapter 45], using any means of protection available and exposing as few men for as short a time as possible. He should take particular care to protect firemen from the effects of smoke from a fire involving a radioactive source. Irrespective of what decontamination measures are implemented, when he suspects or has evidence, such as a dosimeter reading, that a fireman has been exposed to excessive radiation, the officer in charge should see that the man attends hospital for examination. Anyone who receives an open wound or feels unwell should also attend hospital [anyone receiving an open wound should withdraw from the incident immediately]. Details of exposure to radiation should be entered on a fireman's personal record and the information kept available for reference. Particular care should be taken that a fireman is not, by the cumulative effect of radiation on different occasions, subjected to more than the maximum permissible dose as promulgated to Brigades and laid down in Brigade orders or operational notes.

When an incident involving a radioactive source occurs, a decontamination zone should be established as usual and the normal procedures followed as far as possible, particularly those relating to specialist supervision. Where circumstances demand, control of the area should be handed over to police, specialists, or the local Medical Officer of Health. The decontamination officer should not remove restrictions without consulting specialists. He should allow no-one to enter the zone without breathing apparatus, plastic gauntlets and personal dosimeter. He should allow no-one to eat, drink or smoke in the presence of radiation.

Decontamination will as usual consist principally of cleansing and removing contaminated clothing and washing possibly affected parts of the body. The decontamination officer should see that particular attention is paid to clothing joints and fastenings, to the areas between fingers and toes, and to nails, hair, eyes, mouth, and any cuts that have been received. The person being decontaminated, assisted by the decontamination team, should take care that skin is not broken by scrubbing, that plenty of water is used to wash off the contaminant, that as far as possible water is not allowed to run onto an unaffected area, and that uncontaminated wounds are covered before washing. Nose, mouth, eyes, breathing apparatus mouthpiece and interior of face mask must not be touched with a hand or glove that might be contaminated, to prevent ingestion. Before decontamination starts the decontamination officer should take a reading of the background radiation: he will not regard decontamination of a fireman as complete until a reading of no more than five counts per second above the background reading is obtained. It is important that all of a person's body, clothing and equipment are checked. Men and equipment will only leave the zone at an approved point and will be checked for contamination before being allowed to proceed. Contaminated clothing etc. should be placed in sealed and specially labelled plastic bags for removal.

The disposal of contaminant [e.g. water used for cleaning] should be checked with specialists in the usual way. The decontamination team will be concerned only with the decontamination of persons and Fire Brigade equipment. It will not be a Fire Brigade responsibility to decontaminate premises, vehicles other than their own, etc. involved in an incident.

3 Biological hazards

A rarer danger firemen might have to face is that of biological contamination. Nevertheless the possibility may arise during incidents at such places as hospitals, medical schools, or pathology, veterinary, pharmaceutical or research laboratories. As with chemicals, the degree of danger will vary widely according to what is involved and specialist advice will be vital both in dealing with the incident and carrying out any necessary decontamination.

Again, apart from goods in transit, the location of possible biological hazards will generally be known in advance. Firemen should familiarise themselves with these premises and establish an efficient liaison with those in charge. They should encourage the taking of proper precautions and ensure they are aware of the action to take in the event of an incident. The normal decontamination procedure should be followed as far as possible, under specialist guidance.

Medical advice is particularly important where the most dangerous contaminants [Class A pathogens] are involved and should usually be available. In these circumstances the decontamination team should wash and thoroughly disinfect a man's protective clothing, then remove it, making sure that parts which may have been contaminated do not touch the wearer. The wearer should then wash thoroughly, preferably under a shower; he should pay particular attention to hair, nails, etc. It is essential that water is not splashed around or clothing shaken as this might spread microorganisms [disposal of water used in decontamination should be discussed with the specialist adviser and the water undertaker]. Further treatment of those contaminated, including any referral to hospital either immediately or later, will be as advised by the specialist. Records should be kept and medical advice sought on any personnel experiencing ill effects within 21 days of attending an incident involving biological contaminants. Personnel and equipment must not enter or leave the decontamination zone except as authorised, at fixed points, and all items of clothing and equipment that could possibly be contaminated must be disinfected, placed in plastic bags, sealed and labelled with all relevant details, before removal from the scene. They should be isolated until they can be thoroughly cleaned and a specialist can verify that they are free from contamination. If this should not be possible, they should be disposed of safely.

4 Other hazardous substances

Firemen will often encounter hazardous materials of different sorts in the incidents they attend. With the exception of chemicals, biological hazards and radiation sources, however, the danger will not usually be such as to require decontamination. Where such incidents do occur the procedure already outlined should be followed, adjusted if necessary according to the special circumstances.

a. Asbestos

A substance from which decontamination may more commonly be required is asbestos. If firemen use the dry method for cleaning protective clothing they should use a vacuum cleaner complying with the requirements of the Asbestos Research Council. They should also use such a cleaner in decontaminating uniform. They should then pack the uniform in a suitable container to prevent the escape of residual dust and send it for cleaning. The cleaners should be aware of the health risks from asbestos and take precautions against them, and they should be told of the reason why cleaning is necessary and of the decontamination already carried out. Asbestos dust on a person's body should be washed off.

Part 3
Ventilation at fires

Introduction

Ventilation, to the fireman, is the art of inducing heat and smoke to leave a building as quickly as possible, causing the minimum damage. Its purposes are primarily three-fold:

(i) to prevent or reduce damage to the building and its contents from smoke and heat;

(ii) to prevent the spread of fire by a build-up of heat;

(iii) to enable firemen to enter, find and extinguish the fire quickly without suffering excessive punishment from heat and smoke.

Problems have increased over recent years with the introduction of modern materials which produce, more rapidly and in greater quantities, smoke which can have a far more damaging effect than hitherto, even to the extent of attacking steelwork.

If correctly carried out ventilation can assist in reducing damage; however, if incorrectly carried out, it can cause the fire to spread and lead to unnecessary and excessive damage. To have the desired effect, the fireman must therefore know how, where and when to ventilate. This will vary according to circumstances and an ability to decide on the correct course will come only from training and experience.

Ventilation can be assisted by certain features of construction, such as stage lantern lights in theatres and glazing over staircases. These are covered in the *Manual*, Book 8, *Building construction and structural fire protection*, which also deals, in Chapter 11, with the natural and mechanical ventilation of buildings for the normal and everyday purpose of renewing and circulating the air inside them. Systems introduced into a building to assist with ventilation for firefighting purposes are dealt with in the *Manual*, Book 9, *Fire protection of buildings*, Chapter 19.

Chapter 10
Ventilation

1 Nature and behaviour of smoke

Smoke is generally a mixture of fine solid particles, droplets of water and other liquids, and products given off by the materials involved in the fire. The fire will heat the air surrounding it and since hot air is lighter than cold, it will tend to rise very rapidly and with great force. The smoke will be carried with it.

a. Smoke explosions

Firemen should already be familiar with the explosion hazards due to vapour and air mixtures from flammable liquids and with the phenomenon of 'flash-over'. They should be aware too of the serious risk which may exist in other circumstances when flammable smoke and vapours collect in an enclosed space. When mixed with air these can ignite suddenly, causing a dramatic rise in pressure like a blast wave. This risk of explosion is liable to arise when certain substances, such as foamed rubber, are smouldering in an enclosed space. Open flaming is unlikely but there are likely to be considerable amounts of relatively cool smoke, perhaps only just above the surrounding temperature. Experiments have suggested that smoke from smouldering foamed rubber will be white at first but, after a few minutes, off-white with yellow streaks and brown streaks; it may also produce brown condensation on walls etc. If the seat of smouldering is uncovered or has extra air introduced it may become a source of ignition and cause the type of smoke explosion described. The sort of ventilation discussed below is particularly important in lessening the risk but should be conducted with great care. Firemen should take particular care to protect themselves from any possible blast wave, e.g. by avoiding the front of openings and keeping close to the floor.

2 The value of ventilation

a. Preventing and reducing damage

The constituents of smoke can be corrosive, oily or otherwise injurious. If it is not controlled, smoke can therefore cause damage even to parts of the structure or the contents of a building which the fire itself does not reach. Furthermore, if a building is not ventilated and a fire is large or burns so long it becomes partially starved of oxygen, the production of incompletely burned hydrocarbons will increase. Unburnt flammable gases may collect beneath ceilings and roofs. These may subsequently ignite and lead to further, unnecessary, fire damage.

b. Preventing fire spread

Hot gases will rise via lift shafts, staircases, and any other pathway available carrying with them smoke, flame and burning materials. If they cannot escape by way of a vent, they will mushroom out under the ceilings and roofs that confine them [see Fig. 10.1]. In this way the fire may spread to other, hitherto unaffected areas; mushrooming is in fact one of the most common causes of fire spread through roof spaces or from floor to floor. Although other precautions are necessary to prevent fire spread by radiation, ventilation can prevent or hinder fire spread by convection.

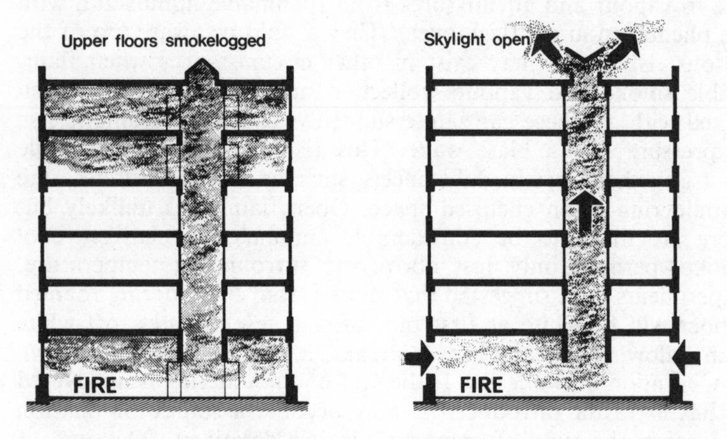

Fig. 10.1 Left: mushrooming caused by failure to ventilate. Right: effect of ventilation.

c. Assisting firemen

Heavy smoke with its irritating properties and reduced oxygen content always makes working conditions more severe. By reducing visibility it can also hinder the speedy location of the seat of a fire and assessment of how best it should be tackled. If the smoke is cleared by ventilation firemen will face less difficulty and danger and will be able to fight the fire more effectively and more efficiently. When a compartment or building is completely on fire, ventilation will not enable firemen to enter but it can help by ensuring that flames and hot gases flow out only through vents while air flows in through all other openings. This will help to counter the further spread of flame and assist firemen in their approach.

3 When to ventilate

Ventilation generally has little effect on the rate of burning of a fire in a large building in its initial stages, though it would eventually cause an unattended fire to burn more rapidly than it would otherwise do. If unwisely or incorrectly performed, however, ventilation can lead to the rapid spread of the fire within the building and endanger people present. Releasing the fire can also put neighbouring structures and combustible roof coverings at risk.

Accordingly, firemen should not start ventilation until they are sure it is safe and have branches in position to guard against the risk of fire spread. Subject to the necessary precautions, however, it is important that they should start ventilation as soon as possible.

4 Types of ventilation

a The principle of ventilation

Ventilation depends for its effectiveness on the behaviour of smoke. This is governed basically by the principle that hot gases rise. Ventilation employs this principle to achieve the results described in Section 2 above, by removing heat and smoke through openings in the structure of the building and replacing them with cold air [see Fig. 10.2]. Firemen may create such openings themselves; they may be able to use doors, windows and other openings already provided for other purposes; there may be a mechanical fire venting system [these are described in the *Manual*, Book 9, Part 3]. The openings may be at the top or side.

b. Ventilation from the top

Generally, firemen should start their ventilation of a multi-storey building at the highest points they can reach, such as staircases or lift shafts. The officer in charge should automatically be on the look-out for vertical shafts and other means of assisting top ventilation on his arrival. If firemen cannot reach the necessary points from the inside they may be able to from the outside. Once the heat and smoke are released from the top, the atmosphere will clear rapidly.

When ventilation from the top is carried out, there must be adequate inlets for cold air lower down the building, otherwise the vents at the top will behave as though their capacity was

Fig. 10.2 Venting a building. Left: initial stage of establishing a flue by opening roof and ground floor. Right: later stage of ventilating intervening floors by opening doors and windows.

reduced. The inlets should ideally be as close to the ground as possible, below the level of hot gases and smoke. There is otherwise a danger that the incoming cold air might entrain the hot gases and smoke, causing them to spread back to the lower part of the building. Normally the openings through which the fire is being fought will be adequate but, if not, their number should be increased at ground level.

c. Ventilation from the side

Top ventilation will not always be practical for various reasons: location, the physical properties of the building and its contents, the extent of the fire, the accessibility of points for ventilation, etc. Even where possible, top ventilation may not be helpful. In an ordinary dwelling house, for instance, opening the roof will not benefit firemen through ventilation unless the roof, or attic, is itself involved in the fire.

In such a case, firemen should ventilate from the side [see Fig. 10.3]. This shows how a sash window can be used in ventilation. Windows are the natural form of ventilation for a private house.

The weather is particularly important when ventilation is carried out from the side. There is a greater danger of spreading fire than when vertical shafts are used. The inadvertent opening of another window or a shift in the wind can prevent heated gases and smoke escaping and perhaps drive them back on firemen and occupiers. High humidity and rain will lower the buoyancy of smoke and gases and slow up air currents, perhaps making more openings

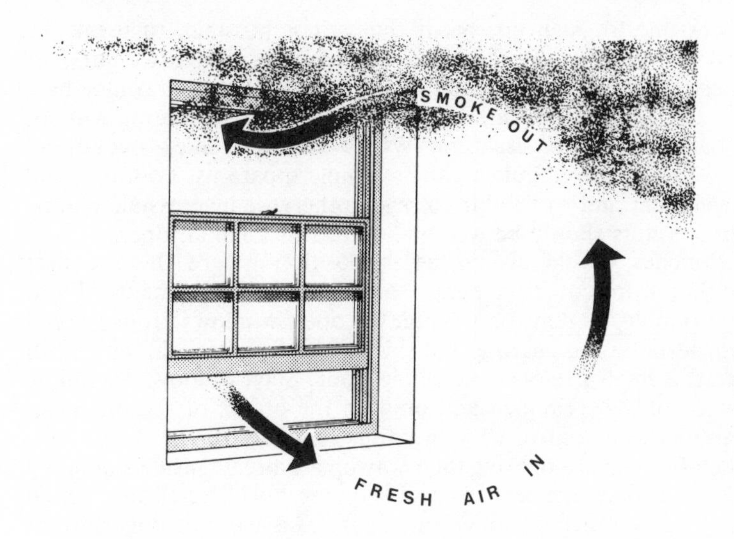

Fig. 10.3 Clearing a room of smoke by opening a window one-third at bottom to admit air and two thirds at top to release smoke.

necessary to achieve effective ventilation. Firemen should therefore not undertake ventilation from the side without considering:

(i) the direction and force of the wind;

(ii) which is the windward side of the building;

(iii) the humidity and temperature.

Wind blowing into low-level openings will tend to create an internal pressure which will act like the pressure due to a hot gas layer and increase the flow through the vents. It is an advantage to have firemen in control of the low-level openings to ensure that in general only those on the windward side are open.

5 How to ventilate

Correct ventilation technique is very important and when necessary one or more crews should be specifically assigned to this work. The men should carry out their task as speedily and as thoroughly as possible if the ventilation is to achieve its aim of assisting the extinguishment of the fire and reducing damage.

a. Ventilation from inside

The importance of early ventilation, subject to certain precautions, has already been noted. Firemen should therefore enter as soon as possible to open up, or, if that is not possible, to break the glass of windows at the head of staircases and lift shafts, or otherwise create some openings. They should still of course bear the same precautions in mind and be sure that ventilation will not in fact worsen the situation. Where there are thick smoke and toxic fumes they should wear breathing apparatus, both to avoid punishment and to be able to reach otherwise inaccessible points. Egress points should be well maintained throughout operations.

Branches should always be in position before firemen start ventilation, to cover the danger of fire spread. In some buildings, for example, it may be possible to open windows from ground floor level by rod gearing, but this can cause a draught which will spread a small fire over the whole floor. Such windows should be opened only by firemen and only on the orders of the officer in charge. Close control of ventilation generally is very important. When firemen are fighting their way up a staircase inside a building it is important that jets from outside are not directed in through windows or other openings carelessly. This can not only prevent ventilation but also drive the heat and smoke back inside, involving the men there. It is, of course, particularly important not to direct jets into openings specifically made for ventilation; those outside who are controlling branches must know why the openings have been made.

b. Ventilation from outside

If it is essential to ventilate from outside, men should get to the roof via adjacent buildings or ladders. If they cannot do this, they may be able to break or open windows from a ladder or smash a skylight by the use of a T.L. monitor. On the roof they may find that skylights can be removed or lifted off with relatively little damage. Actual cutting into the roof should only be undertaken as the last resort. When it is necessary, a fireman should position himself on the windward side so that any sudden emission of smoke and hot gases is carried from him. To make a roof opening, the fireman should first remove the slates or other covering as necessary where he wishes to work, then cut out a section initially about 600 mm. x 600 mm. It may also be necessary to cut through a lath and plaster ceiling below. Depending on the amount of smoke bottled up, a larger opening or more small openings may be necessary. It may be better to have several small openings rather than one large one, as this reduces the distance travelled by flying brands and the height of the flames. Neighbouring structures are at less risk from radiated heat if the flames issuing from a vent are small.

6 Practical applications of ventilation

a. Single storey buildings

The mechanical ventilation of single storey buildings is described in the *Manual*, Book 9, Chapter 19. Automatic venting is not, however, always installed. In such cases the officer in charge must consider whether it would be worthwhile to attempt ventilation from the outside. Often a rapid and intense fire will have developed over the whole floor area at an early stage. In such circumstances, ventilation at a later stage would release vast and dangerous amounts of heat, smoke and fire. Where ventilation is desirable, as in the early stages of small fires, firemen may be able to work on the roof, positioning branches to better effect and helping ventilation by breaking roof glazing or stripping roofing. Valleys between the roofs and bays will help provide access in one direction and on large roofs there may also be transverse access areas [see *Manual*, Book 2, Chapter 7].

b. Mechanical ventilation systems

Mechanical ventilation systems of the sort described in the *Manual*, Book 9, Part 3, usually work automatically but there may be a manual over-ride. Where firemen require the special operation of these systems, they should if possible consult the engineer responsible, as incorrect use could result in spreading the fire. This also applies when firemen have to face the fire hazards presented by the sort of ventilation system described in the *Manual*, Book 9, Chapter 20, 'Ventilation and air conditioning systems', and on underground railways, where ventilation is effected by fans.

c Basements, projecting shops, theatres and cinemas, etc.

Different sorts of buildings and the different areas within them are described in the *Manual*, Book 8, while the *Manual*, Book 11, describes how to tackle fires involving them. Ventilation should be carried out in line with the principles already described, but bearing in mind any special factors which may be present.

Part 4
Salvage

Introduction

Section 1.1(e) of the *Fire Services Act, 1947* requires Fire Authorities to: 'secure efficient arrangements for ensuring that reasonable steps are taken to prevent or mitigate damage to property resulting from measures taken in dealing with fires in the area of the fire authority'.

In Glasgow, Liverpool and London, the Salvage Corps provide extensive and specialised facilities to minimise losses and damage caused by firefighting in their areas. All firemen too, however, must bear in mind this additional duty and take whatever steps are practical and necessary, from the start of firefighting operations.

The effectiveness of salvage operations depends on the speed and skill with which Brigades can put such operations into effect. Front-line appliances should carry the basic items of salvage equipment and when calling for reinforcements an officer should make adequate allowance for the needs of effective salvage.

At a large fire, a good 'stop' plus effective salvage can mean the difference between a total loss and, possibly, closure of a firm, and comparatively minor disruption. At a small fire, lack of proper salvage work can result in greater damage from smoke, water and other causes than from the fire itself. The fireman should always bear these points in mind.

Chapter 11
Salvage operations

1 The value of salvage

a. Damage attendant on a fire.

The damage attendant on a fire is not restricted to the burning of property. Damage may also be caused by:

(i) heat, smoke, steam, fumes, condensation;

(ii) water or other extinguishing agents;

(iii) debris, dirt and breakages;

(iv) the effect of adverse weather conditions on exposed interiors and their contents;

(v) deterioration of stock, plant, machinery, furniture etc. which is not properly attended to immediately after the incident;

(vi) vandalism and pilfering at insecure premises.

The losses attributable to these factors often considerably exceed those due to the actual fire damage and the differential appears to be increasing.

b. The aim and potential of salvage

The aim of salvage is to minimise the losses due to a fire and the operations undertaken to extinguish it, however these losses are caused. It thus has a considerable economic potential. The financial benefit derived will depend on the circumstances of each incident — the salvage work carried out, the nature of the premises and contents involved, the state of the fire when salvage began, and so on. Studies have shown, however, that even limited salvage can save a considerable sum of money. Firemen should always bear in mind that not only a quick extinguishment of the fire, but also an effective salvage operation, both during and after firefighting, is very important in reducing damage and consequent cost.

2 The extent of salvage

The level of specific salvage work undertaken can vary considerably, from that which only uses salvage sheets which may be on a front-line appliance, through work made possible by the attendance of a special salvage tender, to the specialist work in Glasgow, London, and Liverpool, of the Salvage Corps. Much effective salvage is in fact achieved solely by good firefighting practice and many activities contribute to both salvage and the efficient tackling of a fire; ventilation [see Chapter 10] is a good example. The extent of the salvage operations necessary will in any case vary according to the circumstances of each fire. It does not automatically increase with the scale of firefighting required. At a large fire there may be little potential for salvage, while at a small one the risk of avoidable damage from other causes may be much greater than the actual fire damage. The salvage possible will, of course, depend on the equipment and manpower available, the primary obligations of the Fire Brigade — to extinguish fire and save life — and the speed with which salvage work can be conducted. The success of salvage decreases as the delay between the start of firefighting and the start of salvage work increases.

3 Salvage procedure

Effective salvage is a continuous process and involves a wide range of activities and considerations. Tasks may arise in varying orders, or simultaneously, and there is no clear demarcation between different phases of the work. Figure 11.1 shows various aspects of salvage work. The various aspects can, however, be arranged in the following groups, which follow a rough sequence:

(i) preliminary work;

(ii) considerations to be borne in mind whilst fighting the fire;

(iii) active measures to prevent avoidable damage;

(iv) mitigating the effects of the fire and firefighting operations;

(v) subsequent rehabilitation and protection of a property and its contents.

4 Preliminaries

a. Before a fire

As with other aspects of the fireman's job, training is very important. The value of salvage should be stressed and the fireman should ensure that he naturally has salvage considerations in mind when fighting a fire and that he is familiar with the salvage operations he should undertake. As far as possible he should be familiar with the salvage potential of the different premises on his station's ground. Inspections carried out under section 1.1(d) of the *Fire Services Act 1947* provide a good opportunity to find out about this [and also to advise occupiers on the measures they themselves can take to assist salvage. It is generally beneficial to include salvage advice with advice on fire prevention].

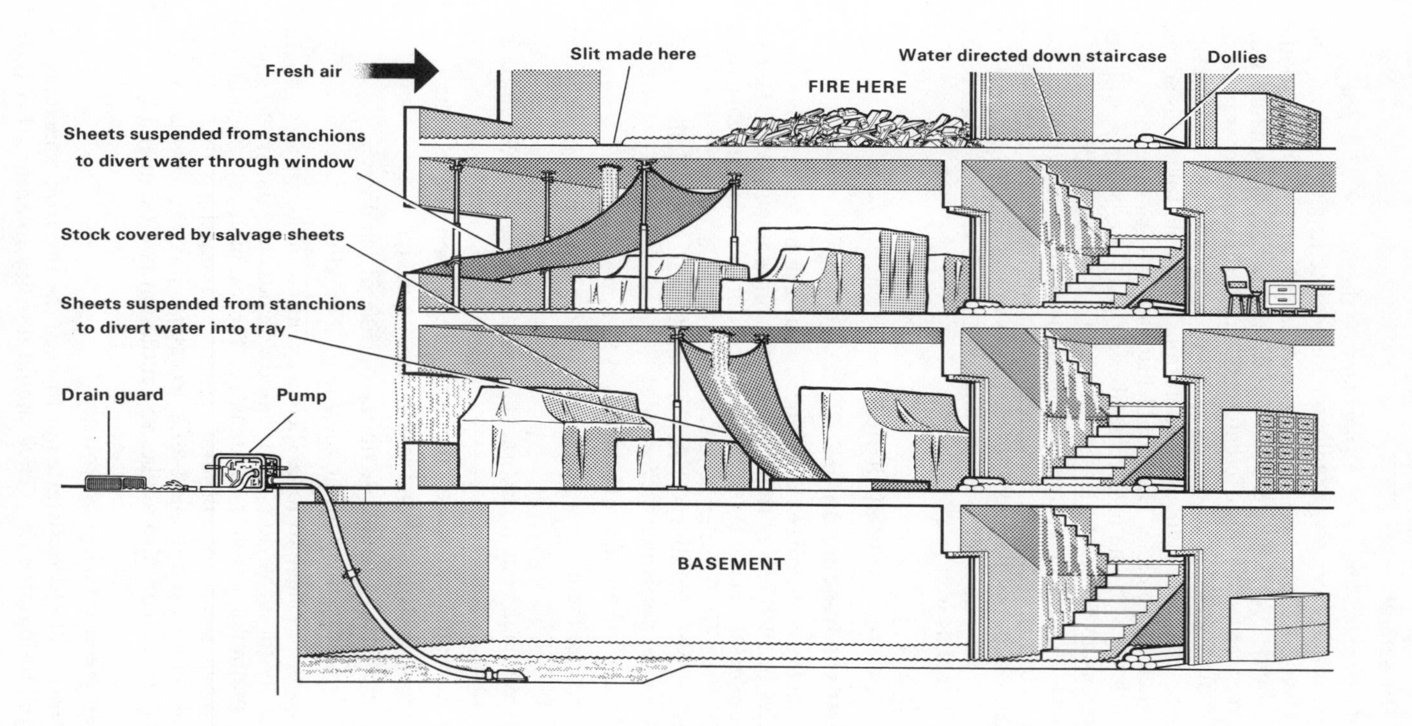

Fig. 11.1 Various aspects of salvage work.

b. On arrival

The officer in charge of an incident or the officer with delegated responsibility for salvage will note immediately the type of building involved, its use, the position and extent of the fire, and the possibilities for salvage. He should be familiar, in general, with the recovery value of different items but, if the occupier is present, he should seek his advice on areas or items of value. Subject to any general, over-riding, considerations he should follow his advice as much as possible. He should instigate salvage operations with as little delay as he can, remembering that later salvage will not compensate for early losses. In some cases the employees at a particular work place may be able to help; the owner may in fact have already established a damage control team. Such assistance must, of course, be under the direction of the Fire Brigade officer in charge who will pay particular attention to the safety of personnel as well as salvage.

5 Salvage considerations

a. At the building on fire

Firemen can give basic assistance to salvage by undertaking their duties in such a way that they do not cause unnecessary damage or undo salvage work already carried out. This is particularly so where the firefighting is less urgent, as at a chimney fire, but firemen should always bear in mind their obligations in this respect. In particular they should:

(i) keep the amount of water used to a minimum;

(ii) reduce the number and size of nozzles as soon as the situation permits;

(iii) use hand-controlled branches and hose-reel jets where possible;

(iv) move to smaller jets, fog, or spray as soon as they can;

(v) replace damaged and leaking hose quickly;

(vi) use lines to haul hose up the outside of buildings;

(vii) drain dry risers to the outside of a building.

When they have to force their way into a building, they should enter by the back door or a window if possible and try to cause the minimum amount of damage, for example by opening or removing means of entrance rather than smashing them or by breaking only the smallest area necessary. [See the *Manual*, Book 11, Part 2]. This also applies to ventilation [see Chapter 10].

b. At neighbouring premises

Firemen will obviously attempt to keep the fire from spreading to neighbouring premises. They should also try to ensure that their firefighting operations do not cause damage there. Water is the most likely cause. It can enter under doors or through defective brickwork in separating walls, via dislodged or broken slates or tiles, through broken or partially open windows, and through flooding due to the blocking of drains. When firemen have to take hose through neighbouring buildings to direct their jets effectively, water can spread from burst hose, couplings blowing out, the turning on of supplies before the branch is connected, and improperly drained hose being carried out of the building. Firemen should guard against these possibilities. They should also take care if they have to climb or drag hose over the contents of the building.

6 Active prevention of avoidable damage

a. Covering goods

Whatever care firemen take in their use of water there will remain some risk of damage from that which has to be used. It will therefore be of prime importance to provide some protection against this. Covering items susceptible to damage with waterproof sheets is a good way of giving protection. The items most at risk are those on the floors below the fire. In private dwellings, offices and medium sized shops, firemen should move furniture and fittings to the safest place in a room, lift stock from the floor onto tables, counters, benches, shelves or other support, improvising if necessary, and sheet them over. They should repeat this procedure from room to room and floor to floor. They should put dry rugs and carpets onto furniture before covering them and collect together fragile items such as glass, china and pictures, putting them somewhere where they will be safe from breakage, before covering them: the seats of armchairs and settees are a good place. It is often better to use transparent polythene sheeting rather than salvage sheeting when covering fragile items, so that it is possible to see what is underneath [see Plate 18].

It will be faster and more efficient if men work in pairs when covering goods, and they must be well trained. They must ensure that items are thoroughly covered at top and sides with the bottom of the sheet reaching but not dragging on the floor [see Plate 19]. Where one sheet is not sufficient, they should cover the top first, then place successive sheets round the side so that they are overlapped by the upper sheets and water can drain off [see Fig. 11.2]. When covering shelves, firemen may find it necessary first to empty the upper shelves. If the greater part of the sheet has to hang, it may become dislodged by its own weight. To overcome this, firemen should tie the top in position or weight it down.

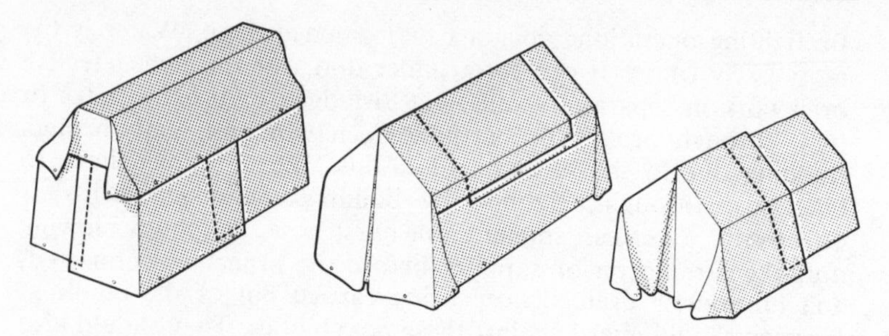

Fig. 11.2 Various methods of arranging salvage sheets to provide an over-lap.

b. Moving goods

While it is desirable to move the contents to a safer part of a room when possible, they should not be taken from the premises other than in exceptional circumstances. If they are, they may be in the way, they may suffer from exposure and they may be subject to theft and vandalism. If items have to be moved outside, any doors, drawers, controls etc. should be turned to the inside and the whole sheeted over.

c. Damming and removal of water

(1) Holding water back

Firemen should prevent water flowing into unaffected areas by damming the openings into them. They can use dollies for this, but, to avoid problems over finding the right size, it may be better to use salvage sheets or other material to hand, such as sacking, which can be folded to size. Firemen can also use salvage sheets as dams to collect water dripping from a floor above. They should place the sheets on the floor, then fold the four edges several turns inwards, as shown in Fig. 11.3.

(2) Diverting water

It is also desirable to divert water out of a building or into suitable drains. Firemen can improvise a trough by opening a salvage sheet to its full length but only half its width, then folding in the edges lengthways to give the depth required. Several sheets so arranged can be placed end to end with an overlap in the direction of flow [see Fig. 11.4]. Another method when more time can be spared, is to sling one end of a salvage sheet from the ceiling — as close to it as possible — and pass the other end out of a window or other opening at a lower level [see Fig. 11.5]. It is also possible to divert water by means of a hopper [see Plate 17]. The amount of water this can handle is, however, limited by the size of the

Fig. 11.3 Using a salvage sheet to create a dam.

hose. Hoppers are used mostly by Salvage Corps, especially in warehouses, where special provisions have been made for them. If firemen do use them, they should put them into place, connect the hose, and direct it outside, before opening a hole in the floor above. The hole must not be larger than the hose coupling orifice, otherwise the hopper will overflow.

d. Use of drains and manholes

During large fires at industrial or commercial premises it is of prime importance to locate the drains and keep them clear of debris. A wire mesh guard is the most suitable means for achieving this [see Fig. 11.6, Plate 16] but it is often possible to find suitable material on the premises and improvise a barrier. Where there is a lot of debris it may be desirable to assign a man specially to keep the guards clear, but otherwise occasional visits should suffice. The covers of manholes should be lifted and placed across openings so that people do not fall in.

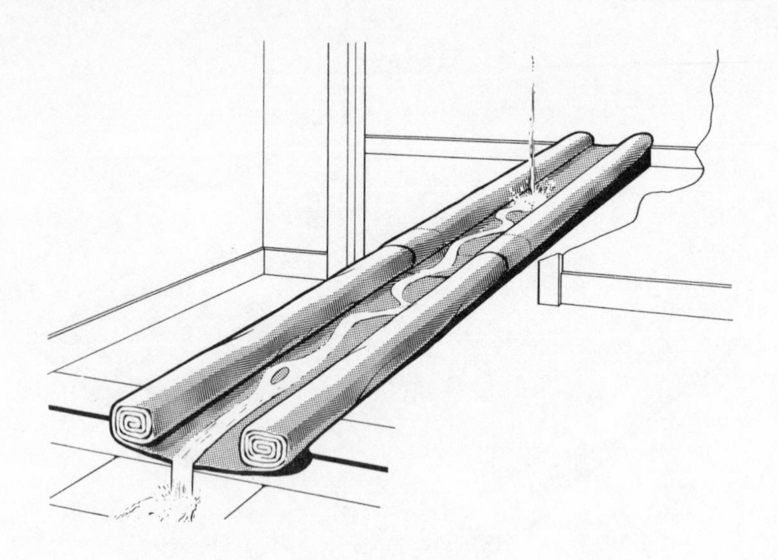

Fig. 11.4 Using salvage sheets to create a trough.

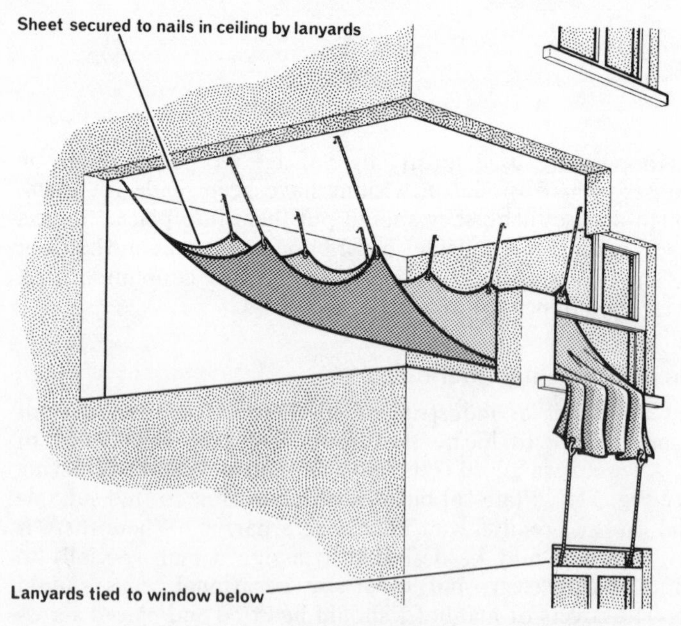

Fig. 11.5 Using a salvage sheet to direct water from a building.

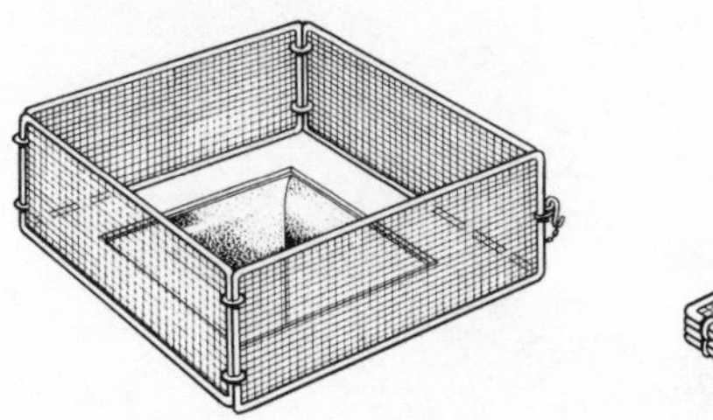
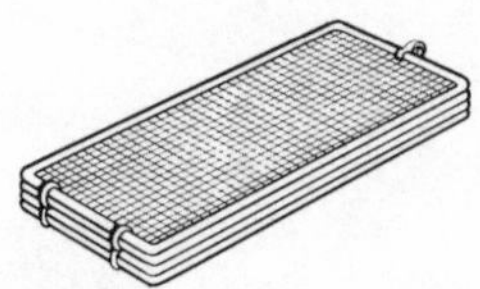

Fig. 11.6 Wire mesh drain guard. Left: open for use. Right: folded for storage.

e. Preventing other damage

Firemen should consider moving items aside or covering them up as a protection not only from water damage but also from the general mess caused by their activities. They should give special attention to carpets and rugs. In some shops, in hotels and in offices, losses from damage to carpeting alone can be very extensive, while elsewhere individual carpets and rugs may be very valuable. Firemen should therefore prevent dirt and debris being trodden into carpets as far as then can. They should take them up and put them in a safe place, where possible, and if that is not possible, cover them with salvage sheets or other materials.

7 Mitigating the effects of the fire and firefighting operations

a. Reducing water damage

Although firemen can provide a first line protection against water damage in the ways described, further action will subsequently be necessary. They should keep water on the move with brooms and squeegees so that it does not collect and increase in depth, possibly overflowing dams. They can help removal of the water by boring small holes in the floor with an auger or by using a crowbar to prise up a floor board where it joins with another and using a wedge to keep the joint open [see Fig. 11.7]. They should, of course, check that any openings they make are not over valuable or important items below and take care that no-one trips over the raised floor board. Large strips of floor board should not be torn up, as this causes unnecessary damage.

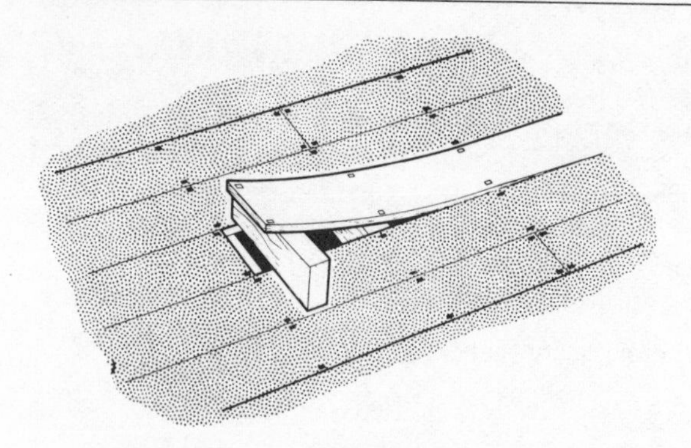

Fig. 11.7 Wedging up a floor board to let water escape.

Water can also be directed down lift shafts and, if there is no other outlet, can be removed from a basement by means of a pump. When no more water can be lifted by the pump, firemen should consider making a sump in the floor to remove it or else bale and remove it in buckets. There are of course low level pumps, some of the floating type.

As far as practicable, however, firemen should not use petrol driven lightweight pumps in basements or poorly ventilated areas, because of the dangers from carbon monoxide and other fumes produced. These can rapidly cause collapse and may be fatal. If firemen must use them, they should ensure that the flexible exhaust extension tubing provided for the purpose is correctly connected and led outside to direct fumes safely from the building. At the end of operations they should ventilate the building thoroughly to clear any exhaust gases remaining. The occupier must be warned of the possible danger. Firemen should consider the use of breathing apparatus in such operations.

b. Reducing damage from water installations.

(1) Burst pipes etc.

Water escaping from burst or fractured pipes or from overflowing tanks can cause additional damage. When this is happening, firemen should close the stop-cock or, if that is inaccessible, flatten lead pipes on either side of the burst. Water from a fractured pipe can be diverted to a suitable place for disposal. If defective tank ball valves are letting a tank overflow, firemen should secure them closed.

(2) Sprinklers

Firemen should check that any activated sprinkler head is operating over the fire and not merely adding to water damage. Any which are can be put out of action with a sprinkler stop, which can be inserted into a head. Firemen should only shut down a sprinkler system altogether on the orders of the officer in charge. When so doing they should operate the main drainage valve immediately the main stop valve is closed, so that water does not drain from the head apertures [see *Manual*, Book 9, Part 1].

c. Reducing smoke damage

The damage which can be caused by smoke is described in Chapter 10 and the importance of early ventilation both to reduce this and to assist firefighting is stressed. It will play an important part in salvage but firemen must bear in mind that careless ventilation can have a serious effect on the fire and cause it to spread. They must therefore carry it out only on the orders of the officer in charge and in the manner he prescribes. When appropriate they should use any forms of artificial ventilation available to assist them, such as fans or smoke extractors. They should also see that smoke doors remain closed and that other communicating doors are not opened unnecessarily if this would cause the smoke to spread.

d. Reducing damage to stock

Where stock has collapsed or been dislodged into a gangway firemen should not leave it there to be trodden on and further damaged. As soon as practical they should replace it or remove it to a safer position. They should not however place wet goods on top of dry.

8 Subsequent restoration and protection

Towards the end of firefighting firemen should be able to move on to work of recovery and protection of the property and its contents against deterioration or further damage and loss.

a. Drying premises.

The actions firemen will have already undertaken should have protected goods against water damage and removed the bulk of waste water. Any remaining should now be drained away e.g. by making channels through debris or piercing a ceiling with a ceiling hook to release water trapped there, having first placed a suitable container below. Drying of the premises will be assisted by ventilation, and heating plant, if available, can also by used. With heating plant, however, care is necessary. The equipment can in itself be a fire hazard and in some places, such seed warehouses, can cause changes in heat and humidity leading to serious harm. Firemen must also bear in mind the effect of any possible condensation on metal parts. Another drying agent is sawdust, which can be used to help absorb water. It is particularly valuable on wood block floors, which can be easily damaged by swelling.

Firemen should exercise caution in handling debris, both because it may contain items of value and because its examination whilst undisturbed can help investigation into the cause of the fire [see Chapters 14 and 15]. It may help, however, to remove water soaked debris from areas where it is slowing the natural drying process, provided it is done with care.

b. Removing covers

Firemen should begin uncovering items they have sheeted over as soon as conditions allow. First, they should dispose of any water that may have accumulated in the hollows of the sheets, then lift the sheets off carefully to avoid damage to any fragile items underneath and damage to the sheets from any sharp edges. The best way to remove heavy sheets from fragile goods is for four men to roll the sheet inwards from its corners until it is square again, then repeat the process until there is a compact bundle they can lift off without risk of damage [see Fig. 11.8].

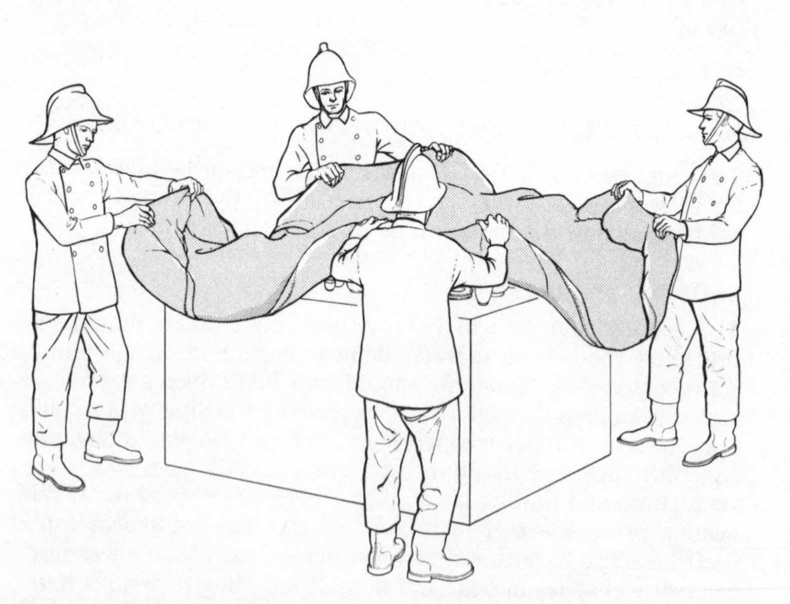

Fig. 11.8 Removing a salvage sheet from fragile goods.

c. Protecting items from deterioration

(1) Recovery

Firemen should replace in their original locations any items they may have moved, especially any taken outside, provided that the original location is dry and secure. Otherwise they should arrange alternative cover, perhaps with a waterproof sheet or tarpaulin. They should check in particular that small, valuable items are not mislaid.

(2) Furniture, fittings, etc.

Wooden furniture should be dried with cloths and drawers and doors opened to assist drying by air circulation. Water-soaked carpets should be taken up and left to drain. Light shades should be emptied of any water they may have collected.

(3) Stock

Where possible, firemen should remove the wet wrappings from stock so that the water does not soak through and damage the contents.

(4) Machinery

Machinery is quickly affected by water and atmospheric changes due to steam, condensation or damp. Surface water should be removed as soon as possible and parts likely to rust oiled. This has to be done with care, since different machinery requires different oils applied in different ways and some machinery parts, such as printing press rollers, can be damaged by oil. The occupier can best advise on the right course of action. On no account should firemen simply wipe over machinery with paraffin and leave it, since without the application of lubricating oil rusting will be inevitable. In any handling of machinery firemen should beware of cutting themselves on sharp edges.

d. Protection from the weather

(1) Roofs

In addition to covering any item which might have had to be taken outside, firemen may also have to protect a building and the goods still within when the roof has been damaged. It may be necessary to move items directly below a hole in the roof, but in any case firemen should try to cover the hole if possible. If the hole is of a suitable size [see Fig. 11.9 and Plate 15] they can use a tarpaulin for this purpose, but where a tarpaulin is not available they can give some protection with roofing felt or salvage sheets, if the damage is of limited extent.

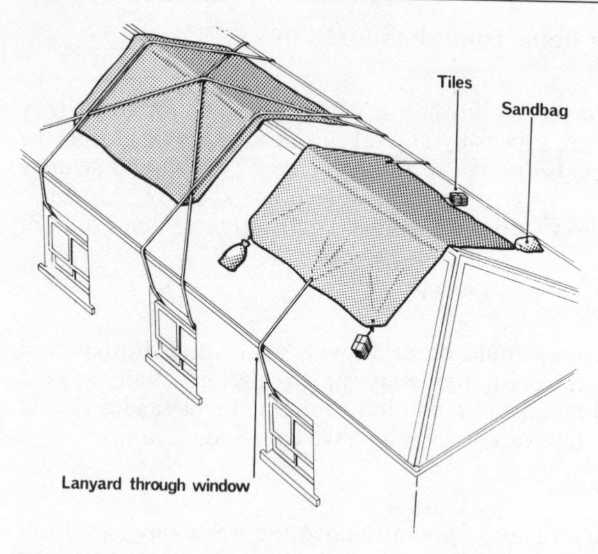

Fig. 11.9 Using a tarpaulin to improvise a roof repair, with various ways of securing it.

Before spreading a tarpaulin, firemen should remove loose tiles, slates, timber, etc. and hammer projecting nails flat. They should ensure that gutters and other channels for water drainage are free from obstructions. The tarpaulin should be secured by nails through the eyelets into available timbers or by the use of lines tied to firm fixing points. All available securing points should be used to resist the strain that will be applied to the tarpaulin from different directions. Heavy objects can be used to help hold the tarpaulin down but will not usually be sufficient by themselves to hold it in place. Firemen should check that where a number of tarpaulins are used they overlap sufficiently to form cover and that lines are not in danger of being frayed.

Instead of tarpaulins it is possible to use disposable polythene sheeting. This is much more difficult to secure, especially in adverse weather conditions. Because of its light weight it will require more extensive and careful securing than heavier tarpaulins, salvage sheets, or roofing felt. In some cases the roof timbers may be too badly damaged or the size of the hole too big for the use of tarpaulins in this way. Suspending the tarpaulins below the roof or below the ceiling of a lower room or, in extreme cases, spreading it on the floor, may provide some protection.

(2) Windows etc.

Adverse weather can cause damage and inconvenience through broken windows, skylights, etc. These should also be covered over. It is necessary first to remove cracked or broken glass, then cover the hole with a tarpaulin, roofing felt, or other material, if the window is at a high level, or with corrugated iron or boarding, if it is lower [for security reasons].

e. Security

If present, the key-holder will be responsible for the security of the premises once the fire has been extinguished. If the key-holder is not by then present, the Fire Brigade officer in charge will hand the premises over to the Salvage Corps if they are in attendance or otherwise ensure before leaving that doors and windows are as well secured as possible. Where there are any problems with security, the police should be informed and asked to take responsibility.

Chapter 12
Salvage equipment

1 Provision of equipment

The most extensive and specialised range of equipment for salvage operations is that maintained by the Salvage Corps of Glasgow, Liverpool and London. Fire Brigades, which are not devoted exclusively or mainly to such work, cannot provide as much but will need a certain amount of simple equipment at least, if they are to fulfil efficiently their duties under S.1.1(e) of the *Fire Services Act 1947*.

Some Brigades maintain special salvage tenders for this purpose, but there is a tendency away from such a course. One other option is to load the equipment in a demountable pod, which does away with the need for a separate, specialist, vehicle. Whatever course is followed, it is helpful, in any case, if all front line appliances carry at least some of the basic items.

2 Items of equipment

The following are among the principal items of equipment used by Salvage Corps and Brigades in carrying out salvage: air heaters; augers*; axes; bale hooks; bins; bolt croppers; brooms, hard and soft*; brushes [hand]; buckets*; ceiling hooks*; chamois leather* ; chisels; cleaning rags*; corrugated iron sheets; crowbars; cutting tools for steel and brickwork; dams; de-ionised water sprays; deodorant sprays and other deodorising equipment; dollies*; drain cover keys; drain guards*; drain rods; drills; electric lights [hand lamps, floodlights]; foam extractors; forks; gimlets; gloves, rubber and plastic; hammers; hoppers; jacks; knives; lanyards*; lines*; maps*; nails*; nail firing guns; oil*; oil sprays; padlocks; pickaxes; plungers; polythene rolls and sheets, heavy duty and lightweight* ; pumps, light, ejector and submersible*; roofing felt or sisalcraft; salvage sheets*; saws, hand, chain; sawdust*; scoops*; shovels*; slate rips; smoke extractor fans; spades; sponges; sprinkler heads and spanners; sprinkler stops; squeegees*; suction devices; tarpaulins; telescopic stanchions; trays; two-wheeled trolleys; wedges; vacuum cleaners. Not all these items are used exclusively for salvage; conversely, firemen should bear in mind the possibility of using other Fire Brigade equipment, not supplied specially for salvage, in salvage operations. The list is not comprehensive but probably covers a wider range of items than is usually available to most firemen. Brigades will decide individually the items to supply, their numbers, availability, etc. The more basic and probably most commonly used items are those marked with an asterisk.

3 Salvage sheets

The salvage sheet is one of the simplest and most useful items employed in salvage work. Examples of its use in covering property and diverting water are given in the preceding Chapter.

a. Types

Brigades still use a variety of salvage sheets. The older ones are of heavy canvas or are rubberised, but those now in general use are of nylon or terylene coated with P.V.C. Sheets are oblong in shape and usually provided in standard sizes. There are eyelets at each corner and along each edge.

Canvas, tarpaulins, and polythene sheeting are sometimes used in place of salvage sheets in particular circumstances and again examples are given in the preceding Chapter.

b. Folding and carrying salvage sheets

Sheets must lie flat, so they can be stowed easily, one man must be able to carry a number, usually on his shoulder, two men must be able to open out a sheet quickly without dragging it on the ground, and it must be possible to spread or throw a sheet over items to be covered. Firemen should fold sheets so as to meet these requirements, bearing in mind also the amount of space available on the appliance. Fig. 12.1 shows one good method. The sheet is spread out flat with the P.V.C. coated side to the bottom if only one side is coated. Two men fold the sheet in half lengthways, then repeat the process, bringing the open side to the closed. Standing at the closed, long side they next make a fold in the middle, bringing the right hand end over to the left. Finally, they make three more similar folds, left to right, right to left and left to right, always bringing the end with the corners over to the other end. A fireman can carry a number of sheets so folded over his shoulder. The open edge should be towards his neck and the corners of the sheet to his back [see Fig. 12.2].

c. Spreading salvage sheets

A fireman would find it difficult to unfold and spread a salvage sheet by himself. To ensure it does not drag on the floor and become dirty and wet, two men should work together. The one holding the sheet should grasp the third fold from the top with

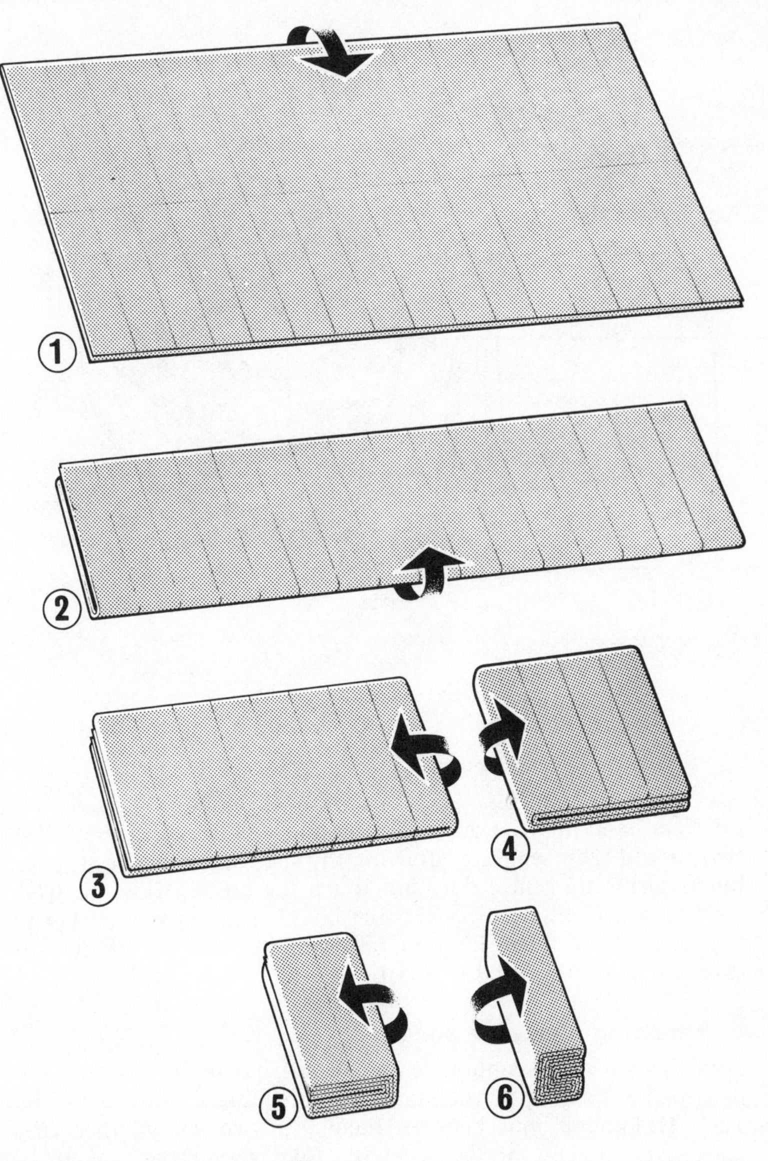

Fig. 12.1 Folding a salvage sheet.

Fig. 12.2 Carrying a salvage sheet.

his right hand and the other the second [see Fig. 12.2, inset]. The two should then separate, drawing the sheet apart between them, but ensuring its centre does not touch the ground [Fig. 12.3(1)]. Changing grip as necessary, each should then grasp a corner of the sheet nearest the item to be covered, raise the sheet, and spread it over [Fig. 12.3 (2 & 3)].

d. Throwing a salvage sheet

Sometimes a sheet cannot be spread but has to be thrown. The two men should open the sheet for spreading as shown in Fig. 12.3. Holding it taut between them, the two should then turn back over the rest of the sheet the fold nearest the item to be covered. They should then separate the sheet in the centre so it can be thrown in either direction [Fig. 12.4]. In throwing the sheet, each should keep a hold on it with the hand nearest the object to be covered until it has settled [Fig. 12.5].

e. Care of sheets

When using salvage sheets, firemen should take care not to tear them on sharp edges and projections. They should never nail them

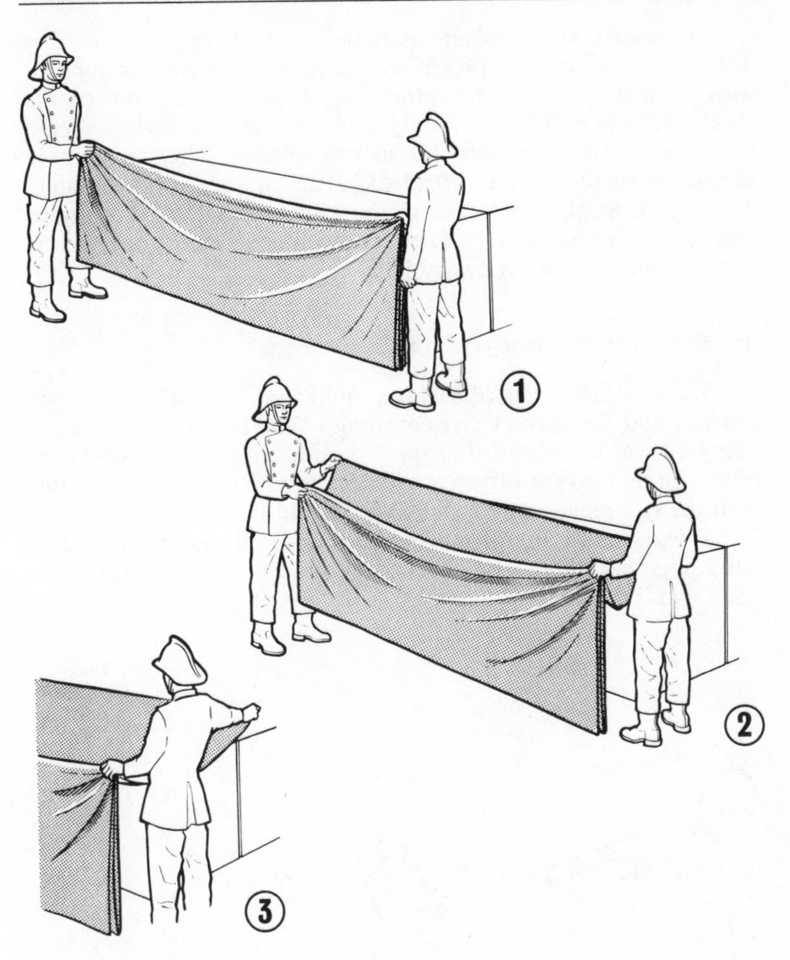

Fig. 12.3 Spreading a salvage sheet.

down except through the eyelets. When removing sheets, firemen should lift, not drag them off, and fold them. At the station, they should clean, dry and examine the sheets for damage before restowing them. Firemen should also check the sheets regularly whether they have been used or not. They should look after their sheets as they would their hose and many of the comments on hose in the *Manual*, Book 2, Part 1, apply also to salvage sheets.

f. Repair of sheets

Station personnel can usually repair salvage sheets that have been damaged. One way is to sew on a patch. The area around the tear is cleaned with a solvent suitable for the material; when it is dry any special solution prescribed by the manufacturer is applied, then a patch is placed over the tear at top and bottom of the sheet. This is sewn on usually with terylene or nylon thread [sailmaker's twine is used for canvas sheets]. The needle used should be small and the thread of sufficient size to fill the holes it makes. It a solution was used, the stitches should also be sealed with this. It is also possible to effect repairs by welding on patches, if a suitable machine is available.

4 Other equipment

The use of other items of salvage equipment is for the most part obvious and Chapter 11 gives examples. The following comments may however be helpful. For the rest, firemen should always bear in mind the need for effective salvage and the operations possible with the equipment they have. They should familiarise themselves in particular with any of the special items that may be available. All equipment should be checked periodically to ensure it is in good condition.

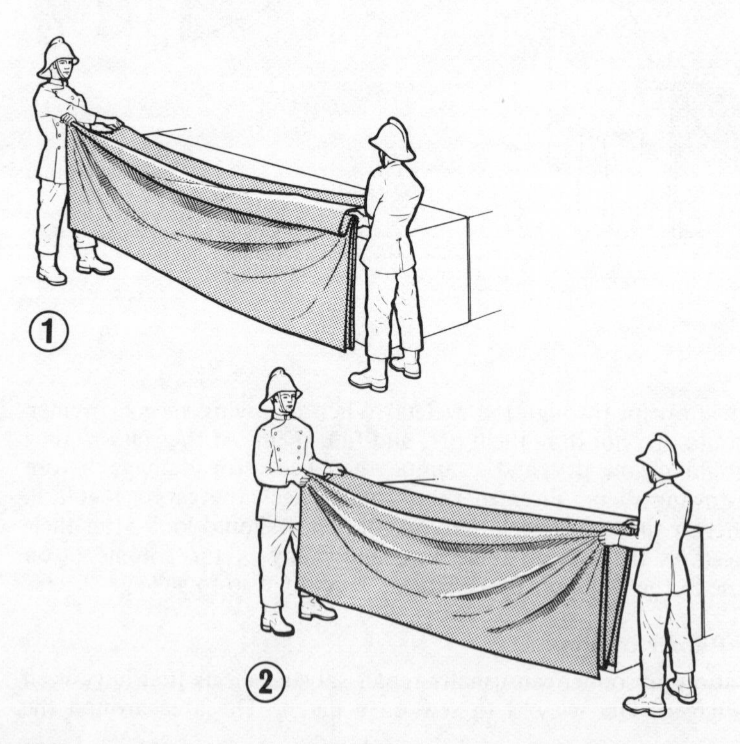

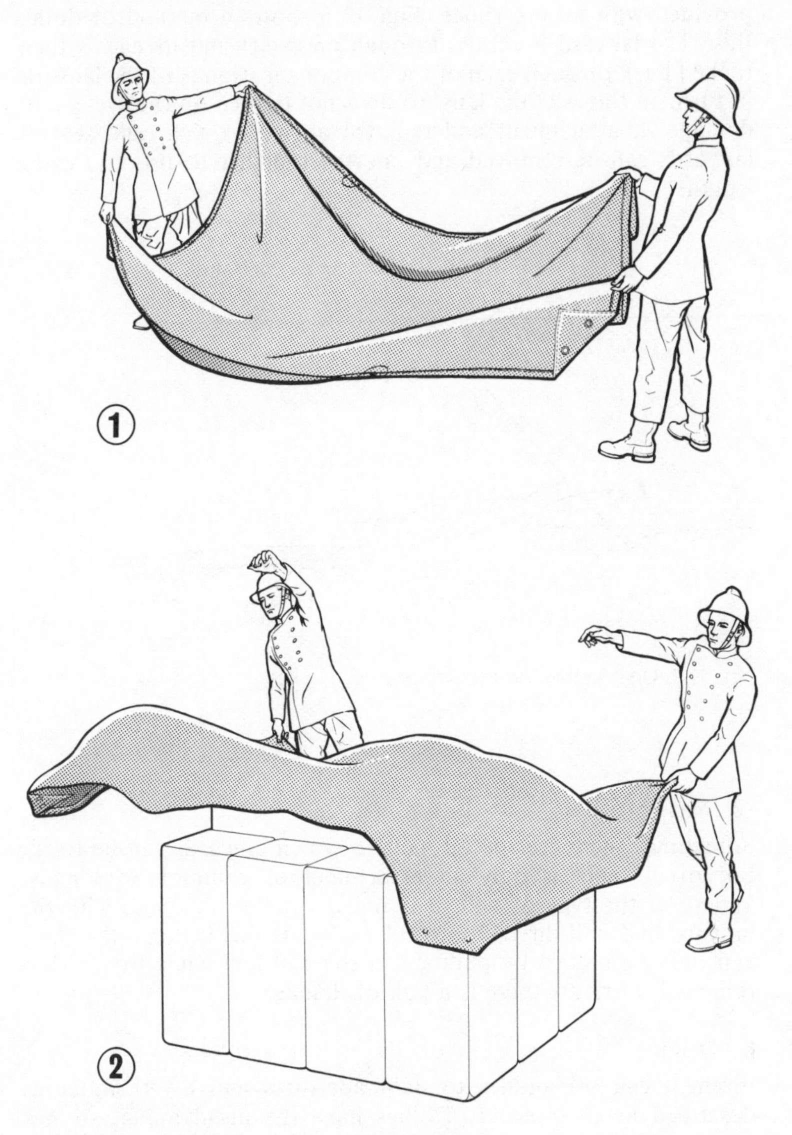

Figs 12.4 and 12.5 Throwing a salvage sheet.

a. Items for use with salvage sheets

(1) Lanyards

Each eyelet hole on a sheet should have a lanyard by which it can be secured. The length of lanyards varies but is usually about 1 m. The ends of lanyards should be whipped and one should be provided with an eye splice. Fig. 12.6 shows a method of doing this. The lanyard is reeved through an eyelet and its end is then tucked back through each of the component strands of the lanyard in turn. In this way the lanyard does not tighten on the eyelet and damage it, attachment and removal are very quick, and several lanyards can be removed and knotted together to produce extra length.

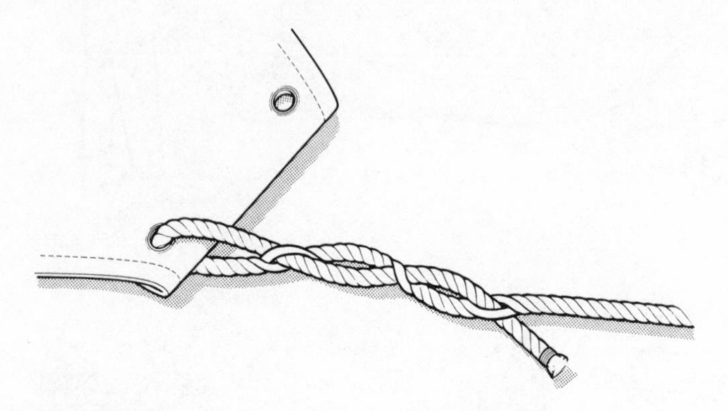

Fig. 12.6 One method of providing an eye splice.

(2) Nails

Sometimes there are special nails to which lanyards can be fixed, but often there is only an assortment of common wire nails. Whatever the type of nail, it is not desirable to dispose with the lanyard and nail directly into the eyelet. If this is done, the sheet can only be moved by pulling out the nail and when the sheet is removed hurriedly there is a risk of damage.

b. Dollies

Firemen can use dollies to dam apertures and divert water as described in Chapter 11. Dollies have the disadvantage of not necessarily being the right length and alternatives, such as folded salvage sheets or sacking, can be used instead. Dollies can be in the form of a hessian bag, about 1 or 2 m. in length and 125 – 150 mm. in diameter. These are about seven-eighths full of sawdust, which swells to fill the bag when saturated. The bag remains flexible and can be moulded to shape. After use, the dolly has to be emptied, cleaned, and refilled with clean, dry sawdust. Another form of dolly is a length of condemned non-percolating hose filled with sand and sewn at the ends [if filled with sawdust rather than sand the dolly would tend to float]. This dolly only needs to be washed down and dried after use. Fig. 12.7 shows both types of dolly and their use in forming a dam.

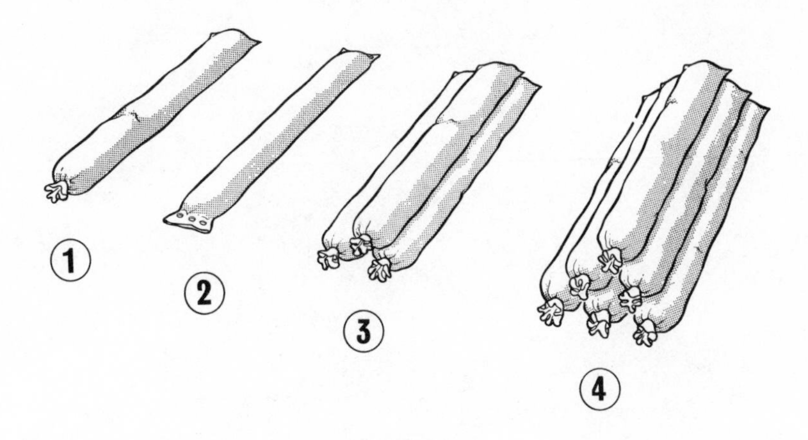

Fig. 12.7 Dollies and their use in forming a dam. (1) Hessian bag type. (2) Hose type. (3) and (4) Piling of dollies where one is not sufficient to hold back the water.

Part 5
After the incident

Introduction

The fireman's responsibilities do not end when a fire is, to all appearances, out. He will have first to ensure that it is properly extinguished and that there is no possibility of recurrence. There will be other jobs at the scene and he will have to attend to hydrants, sprinklers and dry risers. Appliances will have to be made up and, on return to the station, made fully operational again. Various pieces of equipment will have to be checked, tested, and if necessary, replaced.

One of the fireman's major duties will be determining the cause of fire, a controversial topic on which much has been written. There are methods of investigation which can be recommended and factors of which he should be aware but largely it is patience and attention to detail which are paramount. The fireman should not ignore the possibility of arson, a crime with which there has been increasing concern over recent years, and he should make a particular effort to acquire a feel for this. He must resist the temptation of recording a cause as, for example, 'unknown' or 'children' when with a little effort he might produce a number of possible causes from which he can then select a probable.

Finally, there will be action to be taken away from the scene of the fire. A report will always have to be made, information and advice may have to be given, and a fireman may have to give evidence at an inquest or elsewhere.

Chapter 13
The end of an incident

1 Victims of fire

At any stage of a fire a fireman may discover bodies of victims. Bodies, burnt and often semi-buried in debris, are often difficult to recognise [see Plate 20]. They are frequently in the most unlikely places because people tend to try and hide from the effects of the fire and are overcome. Children, especially, have been found in very small places e.g. under settees and in cupboards. Often the only indication, unless a fireman has been told of their likely location, is the distinctive smell of burnt flesh.

Obviously, if there is any reason to believe that a victim is still alive it will be essential to move him to hospital as quickly as possible. If an ambulance is not already in attendance one should be summoned immediately and first aid given until it arrives [see Chapter 6]. If the victim is obviously dead the fireman must inform the police and take such other steps as his Fire Authority requires, e.g. ask for the attendance of a senior officer and a photographer.

a. Handling bodies

The police will need full information about the circumstances in which a body was found, for presentation at the subsequent inquest. Pending their arrival firemen should therefore leave a body, and the debris surrounding it, undisturbed as far as possible. It may nevertheless be necessary to move it on rare occasions, as when it is at risk from spreading fire. The fireman must then record details of where and how it is lying, etc., as carefully as time allows. Any articles which may have fallen from the body should be recovered and handed to the police at the first opportunity.

If a fireman must move a body he should wear protective gloves, to avoid the risk of blood poisoning, and wrap it in a blanket, salvage sheet or other covering. He can use a short extension ladder as an improvised stretcher. Police will arrange for the body to be taken to a mortuary. If a fireman's bare skin does touch a dead body he should apply a suitable disinfectant as soon as possible and visit a hospital.

The officer in charge will need to enter 'Unrecorded pending inquest' in Part 6 of the report of fire FDR 1 and, usually, prepare a statement for the coroner [see Section 6b, below].

The fireman may also discover animals burnt by the fire. He should remove the bodies and place them in a garden, yard or other convenient place in the care of occupants or neighbours. He should remember that owners may have been very fond of pets and that any callousness on his part could increase their distress. Accordingly he should be considerate and offer any assistance practicable. In difficult cases, local officials of the Royal Society for the Prevention of Cruelty to Animals might be able to help [see also Chapter 1, Section 5].

2 Final extinguishment of the fire

Once the main body of fire has been extinguished a fireman must ensure that no 'pockets' or 'bull's eyes' remain and that there is no possibility of re-ignition [a 'bull's eye' is a very small core of burning material often found in beams, panelling, etc. after the main fire has been extinguished]. To receive a second call to a fire left as extinguished would not help the image of the Brigade. If there is any doubt in the mind of the last officer leaving, he should arrange for a visit, or visits, by crews until it is definite that there will be no further developments.

a. Scaling down operations

As the fire comes under control, branches should be worked in closer and then closed down. Unless collapsed floors or other results of the fire make the approach especially difficult the fireman should be able to get close to any burning material that is left. He will only need relatively little water to extinguish the fire completely. Accordingly, the size of nozzle and pump pressure should be reduced as soon as practicable. If water is only required from time to time, hose lines should be connected direct to hydrants and hand-controlled branches used. The fireman can greatly increase his manoeuvrability by using hose-reel hose connected to full-size lines by adaptors or hose-reel branches giving valuable extra control. The use of 45 mm. hose with a hand controlled branch and dividing breechings will also make it easier to move about whilst damping down.

Manpower requirements rather than pumping capacity will determine the number of appliances that stay on the fireground. As few pumps as possible should remain to supply hose-lines and surplus appliances should be made up and returned to their stations.

b. Damping down and turning over

All large fires are likely to produce debris under which small pockets of fire can continue to smoulder for some time. This debris can contain useful information on the possible cause of the fire, particularly in the area where it is thought to have started. The fireman should therefore try not to disturb debris in that area more than necessary before investigations into the fire's cause are complete. This consideration should not however hinder the proper extinguishment of the fire.

The fireman should recall that toxic vapours or liquids may be a greater source of danger at this stage than during the actual firefighting. In certain circumstances breathing apparatus and protective clothing may be necessary.

If possible, firemen should remove the debris to an open space. Otherwise they should make a small clearing and methodically turn over the debris onto it, working from one end of the affected area to the other. Firemen should be careful not to bury their own equipment whilst doing this. In industrial premises, where a lot of turning over has to be done it may be possible to get assistance from drivers of forklift trucks and dumpers. The permission of the management must first be obtained and the safety of non-Brigade personnel kept in mind. Assistance in turning over will be at the discretion, and on the responsibility, of the officer in charge. He should bear in mind particularly the provision of adequate protective clothing. During turning over, a hand-controlled branch of hose-reel jet should be available to damp down where necessary. It is useless to pour water onto debris in the hope of drowning any fire there without turning over.

The fireman should not break open and spread out baled goods such as cotton or rolls of paper. If he suspects one to be on fire internally he should remove it to the open air, preferably a yard or field where it can be opened safely. Water should again be available.

c. Checking for fire pockets

Even after a fire has apparently been extinguished, pockets of fire, bull's eyes, or other possible causes of re-ignition may remain. The fireman should thoroughly search and examine all parts of a building where there has been a fire, along with any adjacent properties which might have been affected, especially those with broken windows. He should thoroughly damp down large areas with small jets or hand-controlled branches but may need a small high pressure jet for some jobs, such as a bull's eye in a difficult high position.

Burning materials can linger in various places, many not immediately obvious. Dust for example may become ignited and burn slowly in a trail from one compartment to another, setting it alight some time after the main fire has been extinguished. Bull's eyes may smoulder for long periods, often in unlikely positions, and cause a later recurrence. The fireman's examination must therefore be meticulous. Bull's eyes will show up in darkness or a small jet played on suspected sites will reveal them by producing steam. A small jet will usually be sufficient to extinguish a bull's eye but sometimes cutting out may be necessary. The fireman must also check panelling, skirting boards, lintels and other woodwork by hand and cut away any traces of fire. He must look carefully at sash window cords. If these have burned through, the cords will have run over the pulleys into the weight recesses at the sides of the window: neglected, they will smoulder and finally set alight the dust there. The fireman must take particular care with hearth fires. If he does not remove every possible trace of burnt or charred timber, it may re-ignite as soon as a fire is lit again there.

Fire is often undetected in upholstered furniture such as settees, chairs and beds. At small incidents it is often preferable to take such items outside to finish extinguishing the fire, since they are then more accessible. Firemen should check whether owners themselves have taken furniture outside.

3 Protective measures

The fireman should avoid unnecessary damage, make as little mess as possible, and try to be considerate. Occupiers greatly appreciate this and it reflects credit on the Fire Service.

a. Avoiding unnecessary damage

Much unnecessary damage can be caused by careless cutting away, removing undamaged goods and excessive use of water.

Where goods have to be removed they should be returned after the fire is extinguished or, if that is impossible, protected from the weather with salvage sheets. The fireman should also take any practical measures to avoid or lessen water damage. Scaling down operations in the manner described above will help this. Additionally, where possible, when branches inside a building are being shut down to be made up the fireman should first break a coupling outside to allow the water to drain to a place where it will do no damage. He should then under-run the hose from inside the building before uncoupling individual lengths.

b. Closing up premises

Police will normally inform the occupier or keyholder of the premises involved of the circumstances. The Fire Brigade officer in charge should however confirm that this has been done. The Fire Brigade is not entitled to keep an occupier off premises once the fire is extinguished and it is the occupier who will then be responsible for security. However, if the occupier is not present by the end of operations, windows and doors should be shut and made secure before firemen leave. If it is impossible to secure them effectively the officer in charge should ask police to assume responsibility and should hand to them any valuables which have been found. It is advisable to make a note of these and agree it with the police. Police should also be informed of damaged gas or electricity meters or telephone boxes containing money. If a Salvage Corps crew is in attendance however the premises should be turned over to their officer in charge.

c. Utility services and structural safety

Representatives from the public utility services [gas, water, electricity] may already be in attendance at some fires. If not, and supplies have been affected, the officer in charge should arrange for the appropriate service to be notified. He should in their absence check that the gas has been turned off at the meter, the main electricity switch opened and the fuse withdrawn, and the water cut off at the main. Leaks in damaged lead water pipes can often be stopped or diminished by flattening the pipes.

Where there is a danger that the external walls of a building might collapse, the Local Authority surveyor should be asked to attend. If he certifies the building as unsafe it will be the responsibility of the police to prevent the occupier from re-entering and to divert traffic as necessary. It is however quite normal to find that external walls are stable but there is extensive damage to roof and floor timbers. In such circumstances, it will be the responsibility of the officer in charge to warn police, the occupier and any other interested party of the danger from collapsing timbers.

d. Fixed firefighting installations

(1) Sprinklers

It is essential at the end of an incident to see that any sprinkler heads which have operated are replaced and the system recharged if possible so that sprinkler protection is maintained. This will be the responsibility of the occupier, who should be so informed. If a system must remain shut down when firemen finally leave, the officer in charge should ensure that a prominent notice to that effect is displayed on the main stop valve. If the local station crew is not present that station should also be notified.

A sprinkler system may consist of several self-contained sections. The fireman ordered to shut down will normally only close the one that has operated. This will be indicated by the gauge [see *Manual*, Book 9, Chapter 4]. However, firemen should check the gauges of other sections to ensure they have not operated and search the building carefully to confirm that no head is discharging.

The system plan, usually found near the valves, will make this easier. The number of heads which have operated should be noted for the fire report, FDR 1.

(2) Dry risers, etc.

Firemen should drain any dry risers which have been charged, by opening the valve near the inlet. If there is no automatic air valve at the top of the riser, they should open the highest hydrant to allow air to enter and release the water. They should check internal hydrants to ensure that all valves are closed and remind occupiers of the need to dry and restow any of their own hose which has been used.

(3) Hydrants

Before leaving the fireground the officer in charge should ensure that the valves of hydrants which have been used are properly closed and that frost valves are working. Pits should be cleared of any debris and baled out if necessary.

e. Advice to occupiers

The officer in charge should advise occupiers of the need to refill and replace extinguishers they may have used on the fire before the arrival of the Brigade. They should also be advised to contact their maintenance service engineers to reinstate fusible links, automatic fire alarms, etc. where necessary.

4 Restoring operational availability

a. Leaving the fireground

The officer in charge will order what appliances he can to make up and return to their stations as soon as the situation permits. He should give priority to first-line or special appliances and then to crews which have been on the fireground longest.

As far as possible, appliances should always leave for their stations ready to respond immediately to another call. The tank should be replenished if necessary and any gear which has been removed but not used should be restowed. Other equipment should, as far as possible, be replaced in its correct position on the appliance. It should not, however, be allowed to contaminate other gear if it has been in contact with acid, oil, etc., and wet hose, after being under-run and rolled, should be carried somewhere other than a dry hose locker. Firemen should remove the overhand knots tied in damaged hose and roll it up on the male coupling. They should treat frozen hose very carefully. If speedy under-running and rolling-up immediately after knocking off are possible before freezing takes place it will be easier to transport the hose back to the station for thawing, cleaning and drying. In some exceptional cases, however, it may be necessary to leave hose where it is until it thaws. Firemen should always thaw hose completely before trying to manipulate it: otherwise it is liable to crack if bent. The same considerations apply to frozen lines.

The officer in charge of an appliance will be responsible for seeing that his gear is complete. If operations make it necessary to leave any on the fireground he should list the items missing and ensure the deficiencies are noted on return to the station. A large fire uses a lot of equipment and it may be desirable to collect it at one convenient centre for sorting and returning to the correct stations.

b. On return to the station

Getting the appliance back on the run will be the first priority. The officer in charge should turn out all station personnel as necessary for this but, if spare personnel are not available for the purpose, he should not allow the crew to leave the appliance until the work is done.

He should, if possible, fill the places of crew members injured and have the appliance/equipment made up, if necessary, from reserve stock, pending the return of items left behind or repair of items damaged. The fireman should follow any particular routine laid down by his own Brigade, noting damaged items and shortages, and ensuring that the repair procedure is put into effect as soon as possible. All equipment should be examined, cleaned, put into full working order and, where appropriate, tested. The results of these tests should be recorded.

5 Giving information

The fireman is likely to receive enquiries about the fire from a number of sources: police, the occupier, the media, and the general public. Such questions should be directed to the officer in charge. While enquiries should be dealt with politely they should not be allowed to impede operations. Firemen should not comment independently on the incident and must avoid addressing to each other remarks which could reflect badly on the Fire Service when they are within the hearing of strangers.

(1) Police and occupiers

As far as operations permit, the officer in charge should give police any information they want. He should also answer any reasonable questions put to him by the occupier. In so doing, however, he should realise that his statements might be quoted later, when possibly further information will have come to light.

He should therefore avoid commenting on matters where a difference of opinion might arise, perhaps in connection with an insurance claim or legal dispute. He can give a possible cause of the fire but should impress on the occupier that it could, in the light of later evidence, be changed. On insurance matters, he should direct the occupier to the relevant insurance company. He should not, however, allow insurance company representatives on the premises (a) whilst firefighting is continuing or (b) without the consent and presence of the occupier.

(2) The media

Representatives of the media should not be allowed to obstruct operations but otherwise the officer in charge should co-operate with them and give relatively full information. The same need for care and discretion applies, however, especially when there is a possibility of subsequent legal proceedings. The officer in charge should obviously not reveal any information of a confidential nature gained during operations. He should restrict his comments to the factual. Subject to the foregoing considerations, such information might include: the names of the officer in charge and other senior officers; the numbers and types of appliances attending; their functions; the stations from which they came; the time of the call; whether any rescues were effected; and, firefighting measures taken. The extent of the building and/or stock saved from fire should be emphasised. Media representatives should not be allowed access to the premises whilst operations are in progress; subsequently this will be a matter for the occupier.

(3) The general public

The officer in charge should not normally give information to members of the general public unless they have some special interest. There may, however, be no harm in giving general information on such matters as the reasons for the use of various pieces of equipment, provided this causes no inconvenience.

6 Legal proceedings

Fire Brigade officers and men will, on occasion, have to give evidence in court about incidents they have attended. This could be for legal disputes of various kinds, insurance claims or coroner's inquests. Often the hearing will be long after the incident, perhaps as much as six or seven years. Unfortunately, too, disputes can arise from quite minor occurrences to which Brigade personnel gave little attention.

a. Giving evidence

Firemen must remember that there are two types of evidence, *expert* and *direct* and the rules for each are different. When giving *expert* evidence, e.g. on the cause of a fire, a fireman may theorise. He must say 'in my opinion' not 'I think', but may pass comments based on his experience. He will not be at fault if contradicted. When giving *direct* evidence, however, he must state only what he observed and not guess or theorise. He must beware of giving expert evidence where he is not appropriately qualified. Counsel may, for example, encourage him to comment on electrical equipment but could then try to discredit his expertise generally by calling an electrical engineer to contradict him. Officers and men must beware such tactics.

Firemen will be able to answer better if photographs or notes were taken at the time. The court will, however, appreciate that the incident might not then have appeared noteworthy and that considerable time may have elapsed. If a fireman does not remember detail he must say so and not guess.

b. Inquests

(1) England, Wales and Northern Ireland

An inquest follows any sudden, unexpected or unusual death, including those in fires and other incidents attended by the Fire Service. Its purpose is to investigate publicly the circumstances of the death, to establish the identity of the deceased, to determine the cause, time and place of death, and to inquire into anything unusual or suspicious. It is primarily an investigation, not a trial, and though witnesses are under oath, proceedings are less formal than in most other courts. A coroner usually sits alone but is obliged to call a jury in some cases and may do so in others if he thinks it necessary.

Normally Brigade personnel will have submitted statements about the finding of the body to the Coroner's Officer, who will then inform about the inquest those required as witnesses. Quite often only the fireman who found the body and the officer who determined the probable cause of fire will be required. The coroner may take the fireman through his statement to confirm the circumstances of finding the body and ask a few questions to clarify minor points. The coroner will also consider photographs or sketches of where the body was found, ask the officer for evidence of the probable fire cause, and again put clarifying questions. The officer must be factual but must also give his expert opinion. Brigade personnel should listen carefully to all the evidence. Witnesses may be called more than once if it is conflicting or confusing. Once satisfied with the evidence, the coroner will sum up and either give a verdict at once or ask the jury to deliberate and give one. The verdict and cause accepted by the coroner should be entered on the FDR2.

(2) Scotland, Channel Islands, Isle of Man

In Scotland the Procurator Fiscal usually puts an inquest in train but procedures are different although the purpose is the same. *The Fatal Accidents and Sudden Deaths Inquiry [Scotland] Act 1976* abolished the need for a jury. Elsewhere in the British Isles procedures will follow local law.

Chapter 14
Fire investigation

1 Preliminaries: the importance of proper investigation

Every year Her Majesty's Stationery Office publishes, under the title *Fire Statistics, United Kingdom*, a statistical analysis of fires in the U.K. attended by Fire Authority Fire Brigades. This analysis is prepared by the Home Office from fire officers' reports and includes details of the supposed causes of fires which they have reported. The information is valuable in many ways. As well as being used by insurance companies in particular, it is most important in indicating areas for research which can lead to a reduction in the number of fires and amount of fire damage. Firemen should therefore make every effort to determine and report the probable cause of a fire as well as to describe its material circumstances.

Investigation of the cause of the fire will be one of the most important tasks of the officer in charge before he leaves the fireground. Such investigation is a highly skilled and often difficult task calling for great experience. The officer in charge should not hesitate to obtain any helpful advice which might be available. In many Brigades there are specialist officers, usually in the Fire Prevention Branch, who are particularly versed in this work and can assist him in making a correct assessment of the cause. Some Brigades have specialist Fire Investigation Teams which work closely with local police. Forensic scientists and others may also be able to help.

An officer should not jump to conclusions, even at the smallest fires, nor should he at once accept what appears the obvious cause. Evidence can be misleading and he should collect, sift and assess most carefully all that can be obtained, even if this means using valuable time after the incident. He must not guess at a cause or put forward one which is superficially possible, or likely, merely to complete the fire report or to release appliances and men. Specialist advisers, who may be able to devote more time to the work, can help achieve this end. The officer must consider all possibilities that could fit the evidence and only by the exercise of his skill, experience and impartial judgement select the one he favours. This he will then give as his expert opinion of the probable cause.

2 Frequent causes of fire

a. Sources of ignition

Excluding the categories 'other' and 'malicious/doubtful' *Fire Statistics, United Kingdom 1979*, [the latest available at the time of writing] records the most common sources of ignition in occupied buildings as: cooking appliances, 23% of the total; electrical equipment excluding heating devices, cookers and welding or cutting equipment, 16%; smokers' materials and matches $10\frac{1}{2}$%; space heaters, $8\frac{1}{2}$%; and children with fire, $8\frac{1}{2}$%. These have remained the five principal categories since 1969. Nevertheless the statistics do show many other sources, e.g.: central heating installations, welding and cutting appliances, blowlamps, ashes and soot, explosives and fireworks, naked lights, spontaneous combustion, and natural occurrences.

b. Establishing the cause

Clearly therefore the officer in charge must keep an open mind about possible sources of ignition. He must consider further however that a decision about this does not, of itself, necessarily amount to a full statement of the cause. In addition to determining the source of ignition and material first ignited he must be able to suggest the act, omission or defect which actually caused the fire. Again he must keep his mind open to possibilities which may not be immediately obvious, e.g. animals attacking and damaging cables or spreading burning materials.

c. Unknown causes

The number of fires where the source of ignition is reported as unknown has fallen in the last two years for which figures are available. This could be put down to the introduction of the new reporting system. But the sustained efforts of the Fire Service College and Brigades to train officers in the field of investigation appear also to be bearing fruit. The number still stands, however, at about 8% of the total. The officer in charge has got to avoid the temptation to record a cause as unknown when more painstaking efforts could make it possible to state a probable cause.

3 The process of investigation

All firemen should be constantly vigilant for any signs which might show how a fire started and how far and in what direction it spread. They should also notice any unusual circumstances. The officer in charge should bear in mind from the start that he will in due course have to assess the cause. Throughout the operation he should try constantly to note, at least mentally, any data which might be relevant. If appropriate and possible he should make sketches and take samples at an early stage.

a. Initial action

The process of investigation will start when the officer arrives at the fire. He will automatically note its extent and if he has arrived during its early stages the part of the building actually on fire. This is particularly important in cases where the fire subsequently spreads through the whole building and perhaps involves others before it is extinguished. The officer should beware however of assuming that the seat of the fire is necessarily where the most smoke is. He should nevertheless note the colour of the smoke and the smell of materials on fire because these may help to indicate the nature of what is burning. Special notice should be taken when they are not what might be expected. The officer should also notice the path of fire travel. This may be abnormal if liquid accelerants such as petrol or paraffin have been involved. All firemen should develop the habit of noticing the state of doors and windows on first arrival. At the end of an incident it may not be clear whether they were open at the start, broken open by firemen to gain entry, or opened later for ventilation.

b. The investigation proper

An officer may find it helpful to develop a routine for fire investigation and carry this out on clearly defined lines. He might bear in mind the following points:

(i) when the fire is out or under control, the officer should decide whether it is likely he can determine the cause reasonably accurately himself or whether he needs assistance. In the latter case he should summon the assistance without delay. Requests for forensic help should be made through the police;

(ii) any person summoned to help should have an opportunity to see the remains of the fire before possible evidence is disturbed. The officer in charge should therefore ensure that debris is disturbed as little as possible and that damping down and salvage work which might interfere with the evidence are restricted to the immediately essential until the investigation is complete;

(iii) the investigation will have various parts: a thorough investigation of the site; the questioning of witnesses, occupiers and any others who might be able to help with useful information; identification of burned material; and determination of the probable cause.

c. Concluding the investigation

The final stage will be completion of the fire report. In this the officer will only attribute the fire to what he considers its most probable cause. To emphasise what has been said previously, however, he must not, on those grounds, adopt a more casual approach than is warranted. In a very small number of cases the origin of a fire will remain in doubt. It would then be misleading and inadvisable to make any more positive statement, particularly where an insurance claim or court proceedings might follow. If there is a thorough investigation of the kind described, however, it should normally be possible to state a definite cause with reasonable confidence.

Where life has been lost in a fire the officer should recall that it will be for a coroner to pronounce on the cause of death. His comments on the fire report form should take this into account [see Chapter 13].

4 The interviewing of witnesses and others

a. General

In seeking to establish the cause of a fire the officer in charge must speak to as many people as possible who might be able to supply useful information. He should give particular attention to the person who discovered the fire or was last in that part of the premises, but should not overlook the possibility that useful details might be supplied from some unexpected quarter. It is good practice to record relevant points in a note-book. The officer must remember throughout that he has no right to demand answers to his questions.

b. The attitude of those questioned

The officer should take into account the likely state of mind of owners or occupiers after a fire. Whatever the circumstances, and however accidental the cause, many will show a natural desire to emphasise their own total innocence. Householders in particular will probably be very upset and worried. Employees may fear for their jobs, particularly if equipment has been neglected or misused. Employers may fear legal repercussions, especially if any of their work-force has been involved or there have been any illegal practices or breaches of Health and Safety at Work legislation. There may in all cases be concern over insurance. People may resent questioning at such a time particularly when they cannot see the immediate purpose of specific questions. The officer should therefore take into account the possibility that people may not give him all the information they have or may give misleading information. He should also not forget that the powers of observation and memory of untrained people are very limited. Even when they think they remember they often do not do so correctly. This problem is worsened by any distress, worry or other agitation they may be experiencing.

c. Methods of questioning

The officer may find it useful to plan his questions in general terms beforehand. Where he intends to question employees he should first seek the permission of management. He should question all the relevant people separately, starting with the junior and concentrating on the person who reported the fire or was last on the premises. His approach should be geared to producing the necessary co-operation in getting the information he needs. Generally speaking, it should be polite and friendly but persistent. With those not directly involved a straightforward, direct approach might be best. However, the officer should be prepared, particularly with householders and owners of premises, to explain why certain information is required and to talk over the matter as a joint problem where each can help the other. He should remove householders to a quiet atmosphere and get them to sit down, allowing time for them to settle and encouraging whatever might assist this. He himself can help by removing his helmet and talking informally rather than as though conducting a courtroom interrogation. With young children, of course, an even softer, more friendly approach will be needed to coax them to tell of events and they should always be interviewed in the presence of their parents or a guardian.

d. Information required

The officer will need to establish to whom he ought to direct his questions: employees, management, owners, neighbours, witnesses, the last person on the premises, the person reporting the fire, and any others. He should ensure he speaks with them all and he should not overlook relevant details which other firemen at the incident might have noticed. He should confirm the information he gets from one source with that he gets from all the others and not look at it in isolation. Where possible he should get particularly interesting data confirmed by others, though he must guard against leading them to give the answers he wants. If, however, during questioning, he becomes suspicious, he must stop, call the police, convey his suspicions to the scenes of crime officer, and pass over questioning to him.

The following are areas the officer might wish to cover and examples of the sort of question he might want answering:

(i) initial indication of the fire:
 (a) where was the fire first seen?

(b) when?
(c) where was the witness standing?
(d) was there smoke only, or also flames?
(e) were any doors open?
(f) were any windows broken or discoloured?
(g) was there any further development — explosions, collapse, fire spread — before the Brigade arrived?

(ii) situation immediately before the fire:
(a) who was last on the premises? At what time?
(b) what was the last thing done before the premises were vacated?
(c) were there any animals present?
(d) were any strangers seen in the vicinity?
(e) did anyone see, smell, or hear anything unusual?
(f) was any machinery left switched on?
(g) was any repair work, decorating or other non-everyday activity in progress?

(iii) general information about the premises:
(a) is there any machinery which might cause sparks?
(b) is there any evidence of equipment or installations not properly maintained, or does anyone know of any?
(c) are there any dangerous substances [explosives, highly flammable goods, etc.]?
(d) what are the normal procedures for waste disposal and other recurring tasks?
(e) is there any evidence of carelessness or neglect, or can anyone quote examples?
(f) have there been previous fires or electrical or other faults at the premises?
(g) were the services [electricity, gas, etc.] on or off?

This list is not exhaustive and the officer should adjust it according to circumstances. [Chapter 15 deals specifically with information suggesting arson as a possible cause.]

5 Investigations on the site

Clearly, the officer's own observations and the information he obtains from others will not, by themselves, be sufficient to enable him to determine the cause of a fire. Despite the difficulties caused by the amount of debris and fire damage, he must search for physical evidence on the site itself. This will entail constant vigilance throughout firefighting operations and an active search through the debris as soon as conditions allow, if possible, even before the fire is out.

a. Temperature reached

The behaviour in fire of materials commonly found in different premises can help in estimating the maximum temperature reached. Table 1 gives some relevant information:

Table 1

Substance	Approximate temperature °C	Condition
Polystyrene	120–140	Softening or collapsing
	250	Melting and flowing
Polyethylene	120	Shrivelling
	150	Softening and melting
Tin	235	Melting
Solder	250	Melting
Lead	300–350	Sharp edges being rounded, drops forming
	330	Melting
Zinc	400	Drops forming
Aluminium	400	Softening
	650	Melting
Structural steel	595	Losing strength and sagging
	1430	Melting
Glass	700–800	Softening, adherent
	850	Flowing easily
Bronze	790	Melting
Brass	800–1000	Melting
Silver	950	Melting
Gold	1065	Melting
Copper	1100	Melting
Cast iron	1100–1200	Melting
Nickel	1480	Melting

The fireman should however beware in his interpretation of the data, e.g. a higher temperature than that required for a particular occurrence might have been reached but not maintained long enough for the effect to be achieved.

b. Establishing the point of origin

The first requirement in assessing the cause of a fire will be to establish where it started. This will itself often give a strong indication of the cause. The observations of the first attendance and information obtained from witnesses might give an initial clue to the point of origin but the officer should not regard them as conclusive.

(1) Degree of burning

The officer will naturally look first for the area of most extensive burning. He must remember however that this is not necessarily where the fire started but may be due to the presence of more flammable materials or a greater supply of air in one place than in another. The fire may have started elsewhere and spread to that place. If, however, one part of a structure [e.g. a roof] is more severely damaged than others and these considerations do not apply, this usually does indicate that the fire lasted longer there and so points to the possible place of origin [see Plates 21 and 22]. If possible, the officer should look for the lowest point of burning in the area of supposed origin, remembering especially where liquids can penetrate below floorboards etc.

(2) Patterns of fire spread

As far as individual items [laths, beams, doors, partitions, etc.] are concerned, the direction from which the fire attacked them is generally indicated by the side which is most deeply charred. This is shown in Figs 14.1, 14.2 and 14.3. Fig. 14.1 also shows the arrow pattern often evident in the shape of the fire's path, particularly where the growth of a fire has been rapid. The laths are burnt progressively more widely the nearer they are to the seat of the fire. The deepest charring of timber usually follows the direction of fire spread, irrespective of the grain of the wood. In furniture burning from the inside causes the springs to soften and collapse. When padding is burnt from the surface the fire does not raise the temperature inside or burn long enough to cause collapse. Outside burning followed by cooling can however cause hardening of the springs.

(3) Smoke and fire staining

The *pattern* of smoke staining may well be different from the pattern of fire spread. Smoke is immediately and invariably carried upwards until it finds an open vent. It will mushroom out at the top of the building [see Chapter 10 on ventilation]. The issue of smoke from a particular window does not indicate that the fire is located there: smoke from a fire in the basement can issue from top floor windows if no lower vent is open. Fire however may be drawn sideways by draughts, open doors, or nearby combustible material.

The *amount* of smoke staining can however help in assessing the pattern of fire spread, particularly in the room of origin.

c. Establishing the material first ignited

Even when the area in which the fire started has been determined, it may not be clear where precisely the origin was. The officer

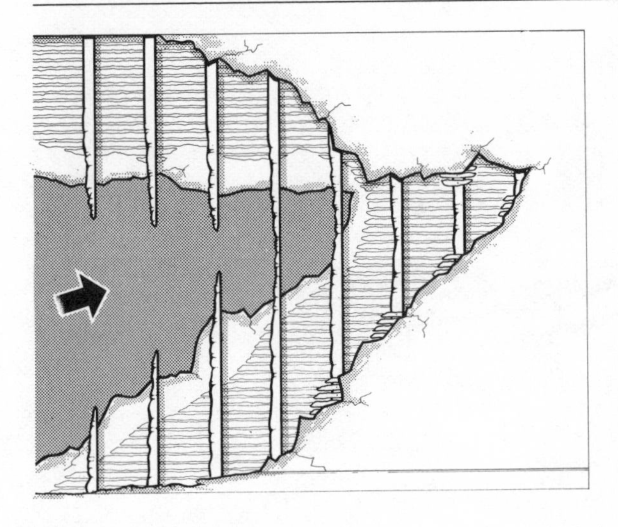

Fig. 14.1 Arrow pattern of fire spread: the more widely burnt laths are nearest the seat of the fire.

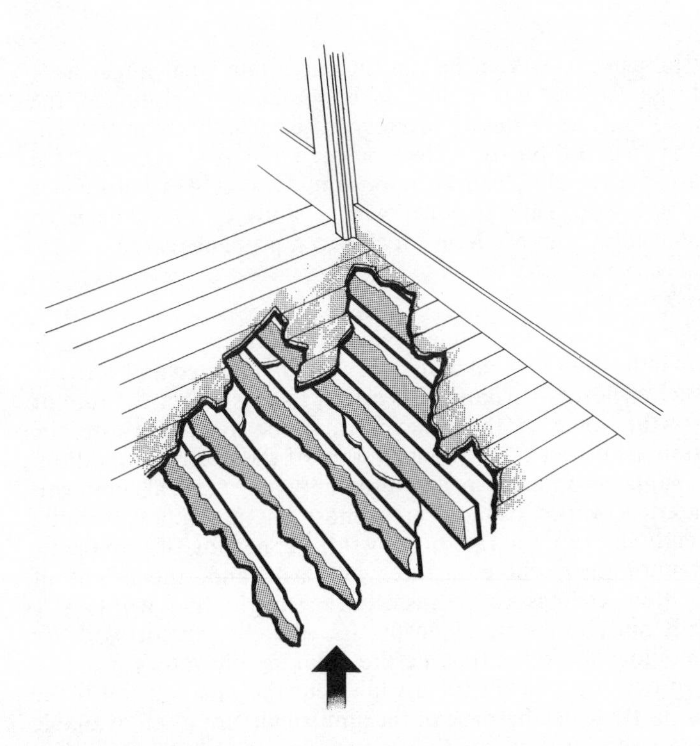

Fig. 14.2 Effect of a fire below.

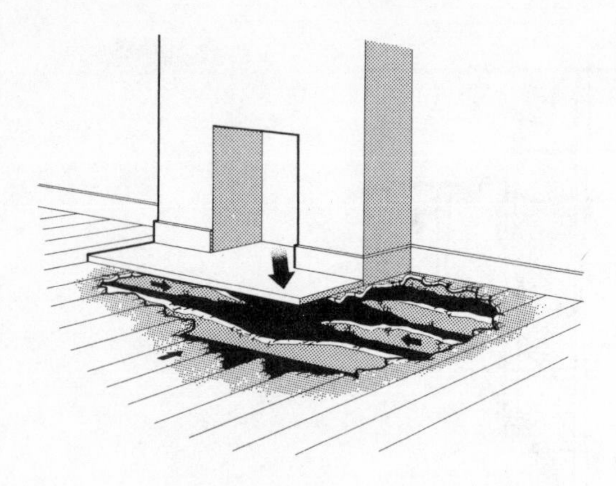

Fig. 14.3 Effect of a fire above.

must establish this so that he can then ascertain what might have caused the fire at this point. It is sometimes helpful to the investigation if the layout of a room can be partially reconstructed. With the help of the occupier, or even the first crew in, the furniture, or remains, can be re-positioned as it was before—or during—the fire. This, together with a study of the damage to particular areas, can often give a clue to a probable cause.

(1) Fire growth

Whether a fire develops quickly or slowly in its early stages is often an indication of what materials were first ignited and whether they were enclosed or compact. Various factors affect the rate of fire growth. Some of the principal are: the availability of air; insulation against heat loss; temperature of the source of ignition; mutual support of flames in close proximity [e.g. vertical combustible materials whose surfaces are almost but not quite touching will greatly increase the rate of growth]; the heating of flammable liquids until their whole surface will flash; and, the height of ceilings [low ceilings cause faster fire growth than high]. Fire growth is not consistent. Typically, for example, an enclosed fire may smoulder for some time before breaking out into a room; it will then develop quickly for a while, but the rate will fall if the room is partly sealed because of the limited amount of air available to support combustion; the failure of a door or window will then lead to a further rapid development.

(2) Indications of slow or quick growth

There are various indications of the rate of growth:

(i) glass [windows and mirrors]: when fire growth is rapid glass generally shows clean breaks following the line of the frame; when it is slow the glass does not break but appears crazed with little or no staining. The glass may then soften, possibly without breaking or falling if the heat builds up very slowly. If the glass is heavily stained without crazing it indicates a slow build up of heat with plenty of smoke. An officer should however remember that some glass is tinted during manufacture;

(ii) plaster: plaster and brickwork have different rates of expansion and this can cause plaster to fall from walls when they are heated by fire. If this occurs, there was probably a quick build up of heat. With a slow build up the plaster will probably remain in place. Ceiling plaster does not usually fall as a result of heating. An officer must take into consideration the impingement of jets on hot plaster, e.g. opposite the point of entry;

(iii) degree of burning: this relates mostly to the pattern of fire spread [see above]. However, where the degree of burning is not uniform, this usually indicates a slow rate of growth;

(iv) wallpaper: if a black coating, possibly with the pattern still visible, is left on the wall, fire growth was probably slow.

d. Establishing the time of ignition

The time of ignition can also be a clue to the cause of a fire. The time of the call to the Fire Brigade and information gathered during questioning are basic pointers to the time the fire started, although of course people may have been unobservant and a fire may have been smouldering or building up long before a call was made. Features such as the failure of a clock at a particular time can sometimes be further pointers.

(1) Timber

The charring of timber in a building which has been on fire can help indicate when the fire started. British Standard 5268 Part 4 Section 4.1 lays down rates for the charring of timber which vary from 30 mm. to 50 mm. per hour according to species. Rapid fire and very high temperatures do increase these burning rates however. Tests have shown that wood ignites in five minutes at 320°C., 30 minutes at 190°C. Soft woods are better insulators than hard woods.

6 Sources of ignition

a. The process of combustion

(1) General principles

The general subject of combustion is dealt with in the *Manual*, Book 1, Parts 1 and 2. For a fire to occur three requirements must be met: there must be a combustible substance, there must be oxygen [or another agent, see Book 1, Chapter 6] to support combustion, and there must be the attainment and maintenance of a certain minimum temperature. Much depends on the amount of heat energy rather than momentarily high temperatures and in this context insulation is very important.

Having established as much other information about the fire as he can the officer must now determine from where came the heat to cause the fire in the first place, in other words, the source of ignition. He may then be able to ascertain whether it was due to natural causes, accident, malfunction, carelessness, neglect, or deliberate act. In making statements about the cause the officer should be as specific as possible. If for example the supposed cause is the over-heating of a motor, he should suggest why it over-heated.

There are many possible sources of ignition and this Section can only suggest characteristics of some categories. Plates 23 and 24 illustrate some sources of ignition.

(2) Pyrophoric action

When a low heat is applied to a cellulosic material such as wood over a long period the material dries out and eventually the timber can decompose into pyrophoric carbon. 65°C. can be regarded as the maximum safe temperature for prolonged exposure. The pyrophoric carbon is capable of absorbing oxygen and self-heating when large quantities are involved and its ignition temperature is much lower than that of normal wood. This situation, which may take years to achieve, can be brought about by the close proximity of steam pipes, domestic pipes, and electric lamps.

(3) Smouldering

Decomposition can take place in solid material under heat but without flame. This process is known as smouldering. It can begin at temperatures as low as 200°C. for some substances such as wood and fabrics.

b. Electric wiring

Electricity is often wrongly blamed as the cause of fire. The officer should not therefore assume that electric cable has been the cause of fire simply because it has been burnt through. When electric wiring is responsible, it may be because of short circuits, partial shorts or over-heating [see *Manual*, Part 6b, Chapter 42]. Partially burnt insulation [other than plastic] may indicate either external or internal heating. When a short circuit causes a conduit pipe to be burnt from the inside fused metal may form lips on the edges. Internal heating may also cause swelling or bubbles due to vapours being formed inside the insulation. This loosens the wire within the sleeve, whereas external heat affects the outside first and causes the rubber sleeve to soften and stick to the wire.

The use of over-size wire to replace a broken fuse is one of the most common causes of electricity fires. Even nails have sometimes been used to replace fuse wire. It will often be revealing to examine the fuse bridge. A full short will burn the contacts in addition to melting the fuse wire and will blacken the fuse bridge. A normal overload will cause the fuse to melt without blackening. A blackened fuse bridge may of course be the result of earlier short-circuits. An arc or short can result in a temperature of up to 4000°C. and copper wire will melt at about 1100°C.

c. Electrical apparatus

(1) General

Faulty apparatus causes more fires than defective wiring. When carrying out an investigation the officer should check for switches left on. He should remember that the up or down position of a switch does not necessarily indicate this. Switches are often fitted upside down. Also, if the switch is incorrectly wired, the apparatus can remain live even when switched off. A fire can then result from the accidental earthing of the appliance. Bad connections can also cause fires and defective thermostatic controls can lead to apparatus remaining on and over-heating. How apparatus was used can also be significant. For example, clothes may have been put to dry too close to a heater for too long a period.

(2) Lamps

Lamps of up to 60 or 75 watts will normally just burn clear if in contact with thin material and not cause a fire. However, even a small wattage lamp can cause a fire if so enveloped that heat can build up. Although the working temperature of a lamp varies from 110°C. for older types to 130°C. for newer, mushroom, types, a temperature of 600°C. has been produced in the laboratory by wrapping up a lighted bulb. If an electric lamp has started a fire the glass may be heavily stained, distorted and have ash stuck to it.

(3) Irons

Thermostatically controlled irons have a maximum temperature of about 230°C. and are unlikely to cause a fire in less than ten hours unless covered. An iron will usually take three hours to burn through the common type of ironing board.

(4) Electric blankets and carpets

Most electric blanket fires are due to broken elements or to over-heating, especially if one part of the blanket is covered by others. Broken elements are often caused by folding the blanket. Electrically heated carpets can self-ignite if covered by foam rubber, as for example when cushions are placed on them.

d. Electric motors

Over-heating of electric motors will generally melt the coatings of the windings and the heating will be apparent for some considerable time afterwards. When the outside of a motor is hotter than other nearby metal this indicates that the heat has come from inside the motor and confirms over-loading. Over-heating of the commutator often throws out solder. Friction damage to belts driven by electric motors indicates an overload, as does seizure of a motor shaft to the bronze bearings, and internal burning of the motor. Over-loading usually occurs at about 980°C. External fires involving belting will damage it between the pulleys when the belt is static but cause little or no damage at the pulleys.

e. Cigarettes

Discarded cigarette ends only cause fires in favourable conditions and except in extremely unusual circumstances the fires take a long time to develop. While the temperature of a burning cigarette is quite high [300°C.] the heat energy is low. The temperature can be increased to about 510°C. with a good draught and insulation. If a discarded cigarette falls on almost any combustible material through which heat can dissipate, it will burn out. Flaming will generally only occur if there is good insulation, as for example, down the side of an armchair.

f. Spontaneous combustion

The subject of spontaneous combustion is dealt with in the *Manual*, Book 1, Chapter 6 and pyrophoric action, which can be regarded as a special sub-category, has been dealt with above. When considering spontaneous combustion as a possible cause the officer must ensure that the conditions are appropriate. It occurs most commonly in haystacks, coal heaps and oil-impregnated material. The signs are characteristic: heavy internal charring at the point of ignition; fairly dense material burnt through for several tens of millimetres; a flue made by the heat while burning to the outside edge; and acrid or aromatic odours.

g. Explosions

Explosions are more often caused by fire than they are themselves the cause of fire, but this can occur. In general, if a gas lighter than air explodes it will burn or blow out walls at the top; if a gas is heavier than air it will affect the walls at the bottom and cause them to collapse.

7 Identifying burnt material

If is often impossible to identify, by normal means, debris and remains of material that has been burnt, especially after an extensive fire. Often only minute quantities of the substance in question are available. When conclusions depend on accurate identification scientific advice may be invaluable.

The officer may, in conjunction with the scenes of crime officer (S.O.C.O.), then find it useful to call on the resources of the Forensic Science Laboratories. These are devoted mainly to work for the police but may also be available to Fire Brigade officers to assist in the analysis of samples or to arrange for scientists to attend at fires. An officer wanting forensic help should make his request through the police scenes of crimes officer.

Forensic scientists are specially qualified and have equipment for various types of analysis: chemical analysis, spectrography, infra-red and ultra-violet spectrophotometry and gas chromatography. They can therefore make a conclusive comparison between, for example, minute traces of unburnt petrol residues. However, while they are capable of this accurate identification of minute traces, the officer should select his samples carefully and give the scientists a clear indication of what to look for. To submit haphazard samples in the vague hope that forensic investigation might reveal useful information could lead to much fruitless work.

Chapter 15
Arson

1 Definition

In general terms arson is the deliberate and malicious destruction or damaging of property by fire. The precise criminal offence is set out in section 1 of the *Criminal Damage Act 1971*, as follows:

'1. A person who without lawful excuse destroys or damages any property belonging to another intending to destroy or damage any such property or being reckless as to whether any such property would be destroyed or damaged shall be guilty of an offence.

2. A person who without lawful excuse destroys or damages any property, whether belonging to himself or another —

   a. intending to destroy or damage any property or being reckless as to whether any property would be destroyed or damaged, and

   b. intending by the destruction or damage to endanger the life of another or being reckless as to whether the life of another would be thereby endangered;

   shall be guilty of an offence.

3. An offence committed under this section by destroying or damaging property by fire shall be charged as arson'.

A person guilty of arson is, on conviction on indictment, liable to imprisonment for life.

2 Prevalence

In 1969, *Fire Statistics, United Kingdom* recorded fewer than 4000 fires under the heading doubtful or malicious [the category which includes arson]. In the next four years this figure doubled and by 1979 it stood at nearly 9,500, a rise of 1,500 on the previous year and the highest ever recorded. Even so, it probably under-represents the true number of fires due to arson. Of the fires recorded in 1979 as malicious or doubtful, roughly a third were at dwellings, the remaining two thirds at other occupied buildings. There were 81 fatal and 731 other casualties. The financial cost ran into millions of pounds. It is easy therefore to see that arson is a serious crime. If those responsible are to be caught by police and the crime successfully fought, it is important to establish when the probable cause of a fire is arson.

3 Motives

Many different people set fire to property for many different reasons. It is impossible to describe a typical malicious fire or a typical arsonist. There are however certain broad categories of motive, of which it may be helpful to be aware.

a. Mental abnormality

A number of people are driven to set fires by their mental condition [although this does not necessarily mean they are of a low I.Q. or otherwise mentally disturbed]. In some cases the motivation is sexual: the people concerned derive gratification from the sight of flames or from such sights as a fireman directing a jet. In others, they may have an obsession with fire itself or with the destruction of certain buildings, such as churches, or certain people. They may have delusions of persecution and set fires to hit back or in self-defence, or they may have delusions of grandeur and set fires to demonstrate their power.

b. Vandalism and boredom

Vandals, who might on other occasions use other methods, may use fire merely as a convenient tool with which to damage property. Boredom may be a contributory factor in fire-raising, to create excitement.

c. Ideology

Racial, religious and political motives may inspire arson, either as a direct attack on an oppositon group, or as a threat, or to gain publicity. The fire itself may be a weapon or may result from some other form of attack, such as a bomb. Individuals and groups responsible for such attacks are less likely than others to attempt to disguise the deliberate nature of the fire's origin and indeed may often advertise it and their own role.

d. Self-glorification

A person may start fires to gain some sort of distinction by being the one to discover and start fighting them. Such fires are generally small, in intention, and not aimed at causing serious damage or hurt.

e. Revenge

A number of malicious fires are due to the arsonist's having a grievance against the owner of the property and wishing to get revenge. Disputes between sexual partners are an obvious example. Arson may also result from events at work where, for example, an employee may feel unfairly treated, may have been passed over for promotion, or may have been dismissed. An evicted tenant may set fire to rented property.

f. Concealment

A person may set fire to a property to destroy evidence of another crime such as murder or theft, or to destroy records containing disadvantageous information. Other circumstances in which damage or destruction by fire is not the prime aim are when it accompanies suicide.

g. Financial gain

(1) Fraud

People may set fire to their own property in the hope of financial gain, usually by defrauding an insurance company. On the private level, people may find their property depreciating more rapidly than they expected, they may find themselves unable to afford necessary repairs or keep up payments to which they are committed, they may find themselves unable to dispose of a property as quickly as they need or at the price they want, they may hope to acquire a replacement better than the original. Businesses may find that trade is poor, that their stock is out of date or cannot find buyers, that they are unable to fulfil contracts or meet deadlines after which penalty clauses operate, that they cannot afford structural or other changes to meet fire and safety requirements. Their aim may be a straightforward fraud, for example to destroy low quality goods but claim recompense for goods of high value.

(2) Attacking competition

A fire may be the means of shutting down or at least adversely affecting the performance of a successful competitor.

(3) Extortion

Criminals may start a fire at business premises as a warning either to the proprietors of that business or to other businesses in the area to pay money demanded or suffer the consequences.

4 Indicators of arson

Since there is no such thing as a typical arson fire, because they may be started in many different ways, the detection of arson is more than usually difficult. There is an obvious temptation to record the cause of fire as unknown, and even when a cause is assigned, it may not reflect the whole truth: a malfunction of electrical equipment, for example, may be deliberately engendered rather than accidental. There are however certain features for which the fireman should look at an incident.

a. General

First, there are a number of general indicators which might suggest, some very strongly, that arson is the cause of a fire [see Plates 25–29]. Their absence does not however imply that arson can be ruled out. It is quite possible, for instance, for an arsonist to enter premises without breaking in and start a fire using just materials that are naturally present. These indicators are as follows:

(i) the remains of a timing device, used to start the fire after the arsonist had left;

(ii) alarms turned off or made inoperative;

(iii) signs of forced entry, or doors or windows unexpectedly open, possibly in a part of the premises unaffected by the fire [less likely when the fire was started by an occupier];

(iv) people behaving suspiciously in the area. This can include those entitled to be there if they are present at an unusual hour;

(v) apparent attempts to conceal the fire or encourage its growth and hinder its extinguishment, e.g. items moved to block windows, fire doors left open;

(vi) signs of the use of an accelerant;

(vii) the presence of unusual or unexpected material, or material which is in itself unremarkable but is in an unexpected place;

(viii) unusual sounds, such as explosions, and unusual or unexpected smells and colours;

(ix) separate seats of fire in the same premises;

(x) an unlikely location for the seat or seats of the fire, an unlikely pattern of fire spread, or an unlikely rate of growth.

b. Specific to certain motives

It will sometimes be clearly apparent that a fire could have one of the motives listed in Section 3 above. Some features which the fireman might notice at the scene could point particularly to one or another.

(1) Mental abnormality

The presence without good explanation of the same person at a number of fires, unusual excitement in an onlooker, and numerous fires over a short period, particularly if similar, are all significant.

(2) Self glorification

It may be significant if the same person reports or is first on the scene at a number of small fires. This is particularly so if there are unusual coincidences, such as the mere fact of a person being in just the right place at just the right time.

(3) Revenge

A fire started for revenge may be accompanied by non-fire damage to property at the same location.

(4) Concealment

Forced drawers, missing valuables, destroyed records and wounds on bodies that are found could all indicate that the fire was started to hide another crime.

(5) Financial gain

It might be significant if the fire starts at a convenient time, for example when the occupier of the premises would know that a detection or firefighting system was not working or that a night-watchman would be absent. It is also suspicious if items of particularly monetary or sentimental value happen to have been removed just before the fire. Statements from the occupier which do not accord with firemen's observations [for example on the value of goods], the glibness or clumsiness of such statements and the occupier's demeanour may be further indicators.

5 Action by the Fire Brigade

a. General

In conducting investigations the Fire Brigade officer responsible should always bear in mind the possibility of arson. When this arises he should notify the police of his suspicions and arrange for them to attend if they are not already present. The general procedure for fire investigation is laid down in the preceding Chapter and the officer should follow this as far as possible. It will be particularly important to restrict salvage work to the essential and avoid undue disturbance of debris: items found at the scene which could provide useful information must be carefully preserved in position. The officer in charge may need to delegate a fireman to watch that nothing is removed, added or disturbed. He should try to ensure that any suspicion of arson remains confidential to the Brigade, the Salvage Corps if in attendance, and the police. Firemen should not make such suspicions public. Comments on the fire report form should also take into account continuing police investigations and the possibility of future court proceedings: the issue should not be prejudged.

b. Working with the police

As already pointed out, an officer in charge should inform the police as soon as he has reason to suspect arson. The criminal investigation will then be a matter for the police. The advice the officer can give the police on the basis of his greater knowledge and experience of fire can be very helpful. He should give any relevant information he can clearly and concisely. He should remain as freely available to police as he can at the scene and bear in mind that they may need to consult him again or obtain further specialist advice later.

c. Photographs and notes

(1) Photographs

If a Fire Brigade photographer is present at the early stages of an incident he may be able to take photographs of great subsequent value to the police. These might show, for example, the early extent of a fire, the pattern of fire spread, the contents of premises and their relative positions, doors and windows open or closed, and anything appearing specifically to suggest the possibility of arson. Such photographs are particularly important where these indicators may later become obscured. However, photographs which might have to be used in court must have nothing added; there must, for example, be no emphasis given to a particular feature by including someone pointing to it or by drawing a chalk line round it first.

(2) Notes

Court proceedings and the giving of evidence are dealt with in Chapter 13. The officer concerned should bear in mind that it may be a very long time before an arson case is heard. He should therefore make very careful notes with sketches if possible, *at the time*. Each page should be signed, numbered and dated.

Glossary

This glossary consolidates, summarises, and in places expands on information given in the text. Its purpose is four-fold:

(i) to explain expressions which are possibly unfamiliar;

(ii) to explain familiar expressions used in an unfamiliar way;

(iii) to give precise definitions to expressions sometimes used more generally;

(iv) to spell out abbreviations.

A.D.R.
Accord Dangereuse Routier: European Agreement on the Carriage of Goods by Road.

"A" post [and B, C, D, and E posts]
Vertical post in the bodywork of a car. The A post is nearest the front, the others successively further away.

Arrow pattern
Standard pattern of burnt material, showing the direction of fire travel. The base of the arrow is nearest the seat of the fire.

Arson
Malicious or reckless destruction or damaging of property by fire.

Asphyxia
Suffocation.

Australian lift
Method of lifting a person by putting shoulders under his arms.

B.A.
Breathing apparatus.

Barring gear
Means of hand-winding some high-speed gearless lifts, usually by employing a tommy bar to rotate a nut which operates a threaded rod connected from the motor bed plate to the brake drum.

Blind well
Stretch of lift well without landing doors, found where the lift does not serve all floors.

Bull's eye
Very small core of burning material often found in woodwork when the main fire has been extinguished.

C.A.B.A.
Compressed air breathing apparatus.

Carry chair
Type of light support chair into which a patient can be strapped for removal.

C.E.F.I.C.
Centre Européen des Federations de l'Industrie Chimique: European Centre of Chemical Industry Federations.

Cellulosic
Composed of or containing cellulose, the component of cell walls in plants.

Cervical
Of the neck.

Chance
Type of folding stretcher with a tubular jointed frame, folding legs and a special sling.

Chemsafe
Chemical Industries' Scheme for Assistance in Freight Emergencies: scheme amongst members of the Chemical Industries' Association to ensure the provision of adequate information in the event of an emergency involving chemicals in transit.

C.I.M.
Convention Internationale Concernant le Transport des Marchandises par Chemins de Fer: International Convention Concerning the Transport of Goods by Rail.

Compression
Pressure on the brain.

Concussion
Temporary loss of consciousness.

Conjunctiva
Mucous membrane connecting inner eyelid and eyeball.

Contusion
Tearing of the brain substances.

Crownbars
Main suspension channels of a lift car.

Cyanosed
Made blue through lack of oxygen.

Davey
Type of fixed rescue apparatus.

Decontamination
Process of removing dangerous substances from a person's body or clothing.

Dolly
Bag filled with sand or sawdust and used to dam or divert water.

E.E.C.
European Economic Community [Common Market].

Emergency action code
Code advising firemen how to deal with a chemical incident. It appears in the hazard warning panel [see below] and consists of a number plus one or two letters.

Entonox
Manufacturer's brand name for a mixture of equal amounts of oxygen and nitrous oxide used in pain relief.

Escape, secondary means of
Means of exit from a building other than those, e.g. doors, specifically intended as such.

Femur
Bone of the upper leg.

Fireman's lift
Method of picking up and carrying a person across the shoulders as laid down by the *Fire Service Drill Book*.

Flash-over
Stage in the development of a contained fire at which fire spreads rapidly to give large merged flames throughout the space.

Fracture
Closed [simple]: one to which no open wound leads;
Complicated: one with which another injury is directly associated;
Compound: one to which an open wound leads or which causes bones to protrude from the skin.

Gas chromatography
Means of analysis by individually separating out gases that are present or may be released: they are recorded in different colours.

Governor
Control device on machinery, used on some lifts for safety purposes, to stop the car when it exceeds a pre-determined speed.

Grid
National network of electricity supply.

Hare
Type of traction splint.

Hazard warning panel; hazard warning diamond
Panel required by law to be displayed on a vehicle carrying dangerous chemicals. It includes a hazard warning diamond identifying the nature of the principal hazard, an emergency action code [see above], a substance identification number [see below], and an indication of a source of further information.

Hazchem
Name first used for the emergency action code [see above].

Health and Safety
The *Health and Safety at Work etc. Act 1974*, and legislation under it, aimed primarily at securing the health, safety and welfare of persons at work and at protecting others from risks brought about by work activities.

Holding area
Area to which personnel and appliances attending an incident can report and where they can be kept as a reserve or relief, out of the immediate scene of operations.

Hopper
Container into which water can drain from above and be directed out of the building by means of the hose attached.

H.P.
Hydraulic platform.

Hydrocarbons
Various compounds of hydrogen and carbon, including petrol.

Karabiner
Coupling device consisting of a metal ring fitted with a gate against accidental opening.

Kemler code
Two or three figure code indicating the hazards presented by a dangerous substance. The code is laid down in international conventions and appropriate vehicles abiding by these conventions do not also have to display a hazard warning panel [see above].

Kinetic
To do with movement.

Lanyard
Type of short rope or line used for securing an item.

Lumbar
Of ther lower back.

M.A.C.C.
Military Aid to the Civil Community: arrangement under which, if requested by a competent authority, the armed forces can assist civilian emergency services in dealing with an incident.

Major disaster
Incident which causes or threatens multiple deaths and injuries, or severe disruption, and is beyond the normal capacities of the emergency services.

Mushrooming
Action of smoke in spreading horizontally when it can rise no further because of an obstruction.

N.C.E.C.
National Chemical Emergencies Centre.

Neil Robertson
Type of stretcher which wraps round the casualty.

Organic peroxide
Compound substance formed essentially of carbon and hydrogen and containing a high level of oxygen, which promotes combustion.

O.S.D.
Over-all stopping distance: the distance covered by a vehicle from the time its driver first sees a cause to stop to the time the vehicle is motionless.

Paraguard
Type of folding stretcher with a tubular frame.

Paternoster
Type of lift in which a number of cars are arranged on an endless chain, some cars moving up whilst others are moving down.

Pathogens
Organisms causing disease classified in four categories: A, B1, B2, and C.

Pattern bruising
Bruising which reflects the pattern of material, e.g. clothing caught between a person's body and the source of pressure.

P.D.S.A.
People's Dispensary for Sick Animals.

Pickets
Vertical bars in a lift gate.

Plasma
Watery fluid containing salts, proteins and other compounds in which blood cells float.

Polyethylene
Polythene. A thermoplastic polymer of ethene used for making bags, cling-wrappings, bottles, buckets, etc.

Polystyrene
Styrene resin. A compound formed by the polymerisation of styrene, used for food containers, light shades, handles, curtain hooks, radio casings, ceiling tiles, etc.

Procurator Fiscal
Scottish legal official one of whose duties is to investigate certain categories of deaths and fires in the district to which he is appointed.

Pyrophoric carbon
Cellulosic material which has been exposed to a low heat over a long period, is capable of absorbing oxygen and self-heating, and has a much lower than normal ignition temperature.

Recovery position
Threequarter prone position in which an unconscious person can be laid to ensure his safety from choking, etc.

Rescue sheets
Special sheets fitted to some hospital beds and so designed that a patient can be easily moved from the bed and out of the room whilst wrapped in one.

Rescumatic
Type of fixed safety device.

R.I.D.
Règlement International Concernant le Transport des Marchandises Dangereuses: International Ruling Concerning the Transport of Dangerous Goods.

Roller shoes
Part of the type of guiding mechanism common on modern high speed lifts.

R.S.P.C.A.
Royal Society for the Prevention of Cruelty to Animals.

R.T.A.
Road traffic accident.

Safety gear
Various devices fitted to all lifts to stop their descent in the event of a malfunction.

Salvage
Operations to minimise the loss and damage caused by firefighting operations

Salvage Corps
Specialist bodies in Glasgow, Liverpool and London organised by the insurance companies and devoted to salvage work.

Salvage sheets
Oblong, waterproofed sheets with eyelets at their corners and along each side, used for protecting goods, etc., and for holding or diverting water.

Salvage tender
Appliance specially equipped with gear for use in salvage work.

Section 1.1(d) inspections
Inspections carried out under s.1.1(d) of the *Fire Services Act 1947* in order to obtain information for firefighting purposes on the character of buildings in an area, means of access, etc.

Sewer gas
Toxic mixture of methane and sulphuretted hydrogen.

Sherman
Splint composed of a combined board and fabric corset.

Shock
Depressed condition of the body resulting from an insufficient supply of blood to the brain and consequent oxygen deficiency.

Shut in
Used to refer to people unable to leave a lift car because of a malfunction. To be distinguished from 'trapped in' [see below].

Sisalcraft
Type of fibre used to provide a covering to damaged property.

Smoke
Mixture of fine particles, droplets of water etc., and products given off by the materials involved in a fire.

Smouldering
Decomposition of solid material under heat but without flame.

Special Safety Organisation
R.A.F. body responsible for dealing with incidents involving radioactive substances in use for military purposes.

Special service
Any operation, e.g. rescues not involving a fire, which a Brigade performs voluntarily in view of its expertise and equipment but is under no statutory obligation to carry out, and for which it may require payment.

Spectrography
Photography of the spectrum of a substance.

Spectrophotometry
Measurement of the intensity of light of different wavelengths in a spectrum.

Spectrum
Image formed by rays of light, other radiation, or sound, in which the parts are arranged by wavelength. A substance has its own characteristic spectrum when emitting or absorbing radiation.

Substance identification number
Number assigned to a hazardous substance by the Health and

Safety Commission; the same as the U.N. number [see below] where the substance concerned has one.

Tauranga Thomas
Type of traction splint.

T.L.
Turntable ladder.

Top man
Sewerage worker who remains on the surface whilst another is in the sewer.

Trac 3
Type of traction splint.

Traffitape
Narrow fluorescent orange tape used to mark off an area.

Trapped in
Used to refer to someone caught in lift machinery. To be distinguished from 'shut in' [see above].

Tremcards
Cards prepared by C.E.F.I.C. [see above] which each give information on a particular dangerous substance and are carried in vehicles conveying those substances.

Two [three, or four] handed seats
Methods by which firemen can carry a patient, using two, three or four hands and no equipment.

Tynemouth
Type of fibreglass spinal splint.

U.K.T.H.I.S.
United Kingdom Transport Hazard Information System. System under which vehicles carrying dangerous substances are labelled with a hazard warning panel [see above].

U.N. number
The number assigned by the U.N. Committee of Experts on the Transport of Dangerous Goods to each of the substances it lists as dangerous.

Urethra
Duct by which urine is expelled from the body.

Utility services
Basic services provided to the public at large, principally electricity, gas and water.

Ventilation
Inducing heat, smoke, etc. to leave a building on fire.

Wall climber
Type of lift where the car is not encased in a well but moves up and down a wall.

W.R.V.S.
Women's Royal Voluntary Service.

Index

Manual of Firemanship
Structure and publishing history

The *Manual of Firemanship* was first published in a series of nine 'Parts' (1–5, 6a, 6b, 6c, and 7) between 1943 and 1962.

In 1974 it was decided that these nine Parts should be gradually replaced by 18 'Books' and a revised format for the *Manual* was drawn up. The new Books were to up-date the information given and arrange the subjects covered in more compact and coherent groups, each group occupying one of the new Books. The following pages show the original plan, *as amended to date.* Book 12 is the tenth of these Books to be published.

Since 1974 there have been many developments in Fire Brigade practice and equipment and in the problems which firemen may have to face. To remain an authoritative and up-to-date survey of the science of firefighting the *Manual* must take these developments into account. Not all the necessary changes can be accommodated within the format announced in 1974. The reader should therefore be aware that the structure of unpublished Books of the *Manual* as set out on the following pages is subject to change. Such changes will be publicised as far in advance as possible.

The next Book planned for publication is Book 5, 'Fire Brigade ladders'. This should appear in the form described.

Book 1 Elements of combustion and extinction (published in 1974)

Part	*Formerly* Part	Chapter
1 Physics of combustion	1	1
2 Chemistry of combustion	1	1
3 Methods of extinguishing fire	1	2
	and	
	6a	32 (III)

Book 2 Fire Brigade equipment (published in 1974)

Part	*Formerly* Part	Chapter
1 Hose	1	4
2 Hose fittings	1	5
3 Ropes and lines, knots, slings, etc.	1	7
	and	
	6a	39
4 Small gear	1	13

Book 3 Fire extinguishing equipment (published in 1976)

Part	Formerly Part	Chapter
1 Hand and stirrup pumps	1	8
2 Portable chemical extinguishers	1	9
3 Foam and foam making equipment	1	10

Book 4 Pumps and special appliances (not yet published)

Part	*Information available in* Part	Chapter	Last edition
1 Pumping appliances	2	1	1973
2 Practical pump operation	2	2	1973
3 Special appliances	2	6	1973

Book 5 Fire Brigade ladders (not yet published)

Part	*Information available in* Part	Chapter	Last edition
1 Extension ladders, hook ladders and roof ladders	1	6	1963
2 Escapes	2	3	1973
3 Turntable ladders	2	4	1973
4 Hydraulic platforms	2	5	1973

Book 6 Breathing apparatus and resuscitation (published in 1974)

Part	Formerly Part	Chapter
1 Breathing apparatus	1	11
2 Operational procedure	6a	32 (V)
3 Resuscitation	1	12

Book 7 Hydraulics and water supplies (published in 1975)

Part	Formerly Part	Chapter
1 Hydraulics	3	19
2 Hydrants and water supplies	3	20
3 Water relaying	3	21
Appendices	3	

Book 8 Building construction and structural fire protection (published in 1975)

Part	Formerly Part	Chapter
1 Materials	4	23
2 Elements of structure	4	23
3 Building design	4	23

Book 9 Fire protection of buildings (published in 1977)

Part	Formerly Part	Chapter
1 Fire extinguishing systems	4	24/26
2 Fire alarm systems	5	28
3 Fire venting systems	4	23

Book 10 Fire Brigade communications (published in 1978)

Part	*Formerly* Part	Chapter
1 The public telephone system and its relationship to the Fire Service	5	27
2 Mobilising arrangements	5	29
3 Call-out and remote control systems	5	30
4 Radio	5	31
5 Automatic fire alarm signalling systems	5	28

Book 11 Practical firemanship I (published in 1981)

Part	*Formerly* Part	Chapter
1 Practical firefighting	6a	32
2 Methods of entry into buildings	6a	35
3 Control at a fire	6a	33

Book 12 Practical firemanship II (published in 1983)

Part	*Formerly* Part	Chapter
1 Fire Service rescues	6a	36
2 Decontamination	—	—
3 Ventilation at fires	6a	37
4 Salvage	6a	38
5 After the incident	6a	34

Book 13 Fireboats and ship fires (not yet published)

Part	*Information available in* Part	Chapter	Last edition
1 Fireboats and their equipment	7	1	1972
2 Seamanship	7	2	1972
3 Firemanship	7	2	1972
4 Fire in ships	7	3	1972

Book 14 Special fires I (not yet published)

Part	*Information available in* Part	Chapter	Last edition
1 Fires in animal and vegetable oils	6c	45(8)	1970
2 Fires in fats and waxes	6c	45(3)	1970
3 Fires in resins and gums	6c	45(13)	1970
4 Fires in grain, hops, etc.	6c	45(6)	1970
5 Fires in fibrous materials	6c	45(4)	1970
6 Fires in sugar	6c	45(15)	1970
7 Fires in paint and varnishes	6c	45(9)	1970

Book 15 Special fires II (not yet published)

Part	*Information available in* Part	Chapter	Last edition
1 Fires in dusts	6c	45(1)	1970
2 Fires in explosives	6c	45(2)	1970
3 Fires in metals	6c	45(7)	1970
4 Fires in plastics	6c	45(10)	1970
5 Fires involving radioactive materials	6c	45(11)	1970
	and		
	6a	33(VI)	1971
6 Fires in refrigeration plant	6c	45(12)	1970
7 Fires in rubber	6c	45(14)	1970

Book 16 Special fires III (not yet published)

Part	*Information available in* Part	Chapter	Last edition
1 Fires in rural areas	6b	1	1973
2 Fires in electricity undertakings	6b	3	1973
3 Fires in aircraft	6b	4	1973

Book 17 Special fires IV (not yet published)

Part	*Information available in* Part	Chapter	Last edition
1 Fires in fuels	6c	45(5)	1970
2 Fires in oil refineries	6b	5	1973
3 Fires in gasworks	6b	2	1973

Book 18 Dangerous substances (not yet published)

	Information available in Part	Chapter	Last edition
Alphabetical list of dangerous substances	6c	45(16)	1970

Printed in the UK for HMSO
Dd718620 2/83 (2537)